FAO SPECIES CATALOGUE

Vol.1 - SHRIMPS AND PRAWNS OF THE WORLD

An Annotated Catalogue of Species
of Interest to Fisheries

Prepared by

L.B. Holthuis
Rijksmuseum van Natuurlijke Historie
Leiden, The Netherlands

FOOD AND AGRICULTURE ORGANIZATION OF THE UNITED NATIONS
Rome, 1980

M-42

ISBN 92-5-100896-5

PREPARATION OF THIS DOCUMENT

The present publication is intended to provide as complete an enumeration as possible of the species of *Decapoda Natantia* (shrimps and prawns) that are of interest to fisheries. It actually is the third edition of a list, the first draft of which was prepared by Mr. H. Rosa, Jr. and circulated in April 1964 as part of the paper "Note on the FAO Scientific Meeting on the Biology of Shrimps and Prawns with a preliminary List of their Species of Economic Value and Information on their Distribution" which formed *FAO Fish.Tech.Pap.*, (14). The second draft was published in 1965 by L.B. Holthuis and H. Rosa, Jr. under the title "List of Species of Shrimps and Prawns of Economic Value" as *FAO Fish.Tech.Pap.*, (52). During the 1967 FAO World Scientific Conference on the Biology of Shrimps and Prawns held in Mexico City, the present author was charged with the revision and expansion of this list. The present publication is now presented in fulfillment of that request.

The actual catalogue in its present form was completed by the author in 1978. The editorial work as well as the preparation of the additional section "List of Species by Major Marine Fishing Areas" and the indices of Latin and vernacular species names were carried out in the Fishery Resources and Environment Division of FAO, under the supervision of W. Fischer.

Distribution:

Author
FAO Fisheries Department
FAO Regional Fisheries Officers
Regional Fisheries Councils and Commissions
Selector SM
Selector SI

For bibliographic purposes this document should be cited as follows:

Holthuis, L.B., FAO species catalogue. Vol.1.
1980   Shrimps and prawns of the world. An annotated catalogue of species of interest to fisheries. FAO Fish.Synop., (125)Vol.1:261 p.

CONTENTS

1. INTRODUCTION

This catalogue includes: (i) all species known to be used for human consumption, (ii) species known to be sold for bait and as sub-products, (iii) species not commercially exploited at present but considered by experts to be of potential commercial value. The last category includes deep-sea forms which during exploratory fishing cruises found to be sufficiently abundant, large enough in size, and sufficiently accessible to fishing gear so that a fishery for them might be profitable. Edible species found in markets as an admixture to the main catch are included, even if they only make up a negligible percentage of the catch.

The present catalogue is largely based on data obtained from the literature. Sometimes it has proved very difficult to evaluate the reliability of published data. It is quite understandable that authors working far away from good library facilities have difficulties in correctly identifying the species they encounter in the field. Moreover, the discovery of new species, the more correct delimitation of known species, or even the introduction of nomenclatoral changes, may cause confusion and lead to the use of scientific names that are incorrect by modern standards, or apply to more than one species. For instance, the name *Metapenaeus mastersii* has been used for four different species, and without additional information (i.e. the locality in this case) it is impossible to decide which of the species is actually meant; *Penaeus merguinsis* has sometimes been mixed up with *P. indicus*, while the names *Penaeus monodon* and *P. semisulcatus* have been interchanged at one period. Although great care was exercised in evaluating the published information used in the catalogue, some misjudgements and incorrect interpretations have undoubtedly occurred.

Another difficulty is that in taxonomic literature (with which I am best acquainted) information on economic importance of species is rather scarce and of a very general nature. Relevant fisheries literature, being less familiar to me, was often difficult to locate, and notwithstanding the great help I received from Dr. W. Fischer and other officials of FAO in obtaining such literature, I may have overlooked important information.

Due to the fact that the preparation of the present catalogue has taken such a long time, some of the information included in it may be outdated, especially when taking into account the very rapid development of shrimp stock appraisal and exploitation in various world areas in the course of the last few decades.

Apart from published data, it was possible to obtain valuable direct information from field workers. To this connection, several FAO fishery project officers, as well as fishery workers from various nations, contributed greatly by filling out and returning questionnaires prepared and distributed by FAO concerning shrimp species of particular areas. These field workers indicated the literature used in the identification of the species and in many instances they also sent me specimens, which permitted confirmation of their identity.

The present catalogue is arranged systematically. The highest category dealt with is the suborder Natantia of the order Crustacea Decapoda to which all shrimps and prawns belong. The heading for each family or species is followed by a reference to the original publication of the family or species name. In the case of categories higher than families (suborders, infraorders and suprafamilies) the heading is followed by a citation of the author who first defined the limits of the group as now accepted. The papers indicated in these references, as well as those of authors given in the synonymies, are not necessarily listed in the bibliography.

The information pertaining to each species is arranged by paragraphs, as follows:
(1) synonymy, (2) vernacular names, (3) literature, (4) distribution, (5) habitat, (6) size,
(7) interest to fisheries, and (8) remarks.

(1) <u>Synonymy</u>: only true synonyms of the valid species name are listed. In a few
cases - where pertinent - incorrect identifications are mentioned, but always indicated
as such; for example, the specific name *mastersii* in the combination *Penaeus mastersii*
Haswell is a synonym of *Metapenaeus ensis* (De Hann), and is listed in the synonymy there;
but the name *mastersii* has also been - incorrectly - used for Malayan specimens of *M.
moyebi*, for western Australian specimens of *M. dalli*, and for eastern Australian specimens
of *M. bennettae*. The name *mastersii* is therefore not given as a synonym of *M. moyebi*, *M.
dalli* and *M. bennettae* as it has been used for these species only because of incorrect
identifications. In such cases, however, usually a short note is added after the list
of synonyms, explaining such incorrect identifications that have been widely used.

(2) <u>Vernacular Species Names</u>:

2.1 FAO Names: English, French and Spanish names for each species, to be used pri-
marily within FAO, were selected on the basis of the following criteria: (i) each name
must apply to one species only, in a worldwide context; (ii) the name must conform to
FAO spelling nomenclature; (iii) the name should not lead to confusion with crustaceans
other than shrimps (i.e. the name langostino used for some shrimps in Spain and Venezuela
was avoided because it also applies to certain lobster and galatheid species). Wherever
possible, the denominations selected were based on vernacular names (or parts of names)
already in existence within the areas where the species is fished. FAO names are of
course not intended to replace local species names, but they are considered necessary
to overcome the considerable confusion caused by the use of a single name for many different species, or several names for one species.

2.2 Local Names: these are the names used locally for the species. The country (or
countries) where a name is in use, is (are) cited in parentheses; the language of the
denomination is only given where this is thought to be of particular interest (e.g. when
more than one language is spoken in the country)..The catalogue was compiled from many
sources, but it is doubtless incomplete and may include some artificial denominations,
although these were omitted as far as possible. Where a large number of local names
are used for one species in a restricted area, only those better known are included,
but in such cases reference is made to relevant literature for the others. When more
than one name is used within a country, the official name, or in its absence, the best
known, is cited first.

(3) Literature: reference is made to those papers treating the species extensively
(e.g. Species Synonyms of FAO, CSIRO, etc.) or given a helpful account of it.

(4) Distribution: the entire known geographic range of the species is given, including
areas where it is of no commercial value.

(5) Habitat: the known depth range of the species, and information on types of sub-
strate, salinity and temperature of its habitat are given here. In most instances, this
information is rather incomplete.

(6) Size: the known total length, as well as the known carapace length of both males
and females are provided where possible. Total length is measured from the tip of the rostrum to the extremity of the telson, but due to the curvature of the body this measurement
usually is not very accurate. The carapace length generally includes the rostrum, but very
often the actual extent of this length (whether measured from the tip of the rostrum or from
the posterior margin of the orbit to the posterior margin of the carapace) is not indicated

in the literature. Where total and carapace lengths are both given, the respective figures
do not necessarily pertain to the same specimens but may have been obtained from different
sources. As often the available information on the size attained by some species is very
meagre, the maximum size cited here may be well below the actual maximum size.

(7) Interest to Fisheries: this paragraph gives an account of the areas where the
species is fished and of the nature of the fishery; its importance is either estimated
(minor, moderate, major, or potential) or actual figures of annual landings are provided.
Data on utilization (fresh, dried, cooked, frozen, canned, etc.) are also given where
available. Here too, the quality and quantity of the available information vary con-
siderably with the species.

(8) Remarks: important information concerning the species and not fitting in any of
the previous paragraphs is given here. For instance, in some cases the scientific name
used in the present catalogue, although nomenclaturally correct, is not the best known.
The reasons for such changes (e.g. *Metapenaeus burkenroadi* Kubo, 1954 to *M. moyebi*
(Kishinouye, 1896); *Penaeus orientalis* Kishinouye, 1918 to *P. chinensis* (Osbeck, 1765);
Trachypenaeus faoea Loesch & Avila, 1969 to *T. faoea* Obarrio, 1954) are also given in
this paragraph.

Because of the existing confusion in the use of the names "shrimp" and "prawn", it
seems useful to draw some attention to this problem. It is impossible to give a short
definition of either name, as in different regions these terms are used for different
animals or animal groups, and even within a single region the usage is not consistent.
Both terms of course have originated in Great Britain. There "shrimp" stands for members
of the family Crangonidae (*Crangon crangon* being the "Common Shrimp"), while the term
"prawn" is used for species of Palaemonidae (*Palaemon serratus* being the "Common Prawn").
But also Crustacea not belonging to these two families are often indicated as shrimps and
prawns, and here the difficulty starts. The term prawn is then usually employed for the
larger forms (often those that are more laterally compressed and have a well-developed
rostrum), so *Pandalus montagui* Leach is known as "Aesop Prawn" and even *Nephrops norvegicus*
(L.) is sometimes indicated as "Dublin Bay Prawn". The term "shrimp" is commonly used for
the smaller forms (often dorsoventrally depressed and with a poorly developed rostrum):
the name "Opossum shrimps" is given to the Mysidacea, "Skeleton shrimps" to the Caprellidae
while for instance Gordon (1958, Nature (Lond.), 182:1186) referred to *Thermosbaena* as "a
thermophilous shrimp from Tunisia". Even in England the use of the two terms is not consistent, so *Pandalus montagui* is not only referred to as "Aesop Prawn", but sometimes also
as "Aesop Shrimp" or "Pink Shrimp", while the mysid *Praunus flexuosus* (O.F. Müller) [the
generic name *Praunus* Leach, 1814, itself is a latinization of the word "prawn"], is known
noth as "Chameleon Shrimp" (e.g. Eales, 1950, Littoral Fauna of Great Britain, ed. 2, p. 122)
and "Chameleon Prawn" (e.g. Ingle, 1969, A Guide to the Sea Shore, p. 95).

Summarizing, we may say that in Great Britain the term "shrimp" is the more general of
the two, and is the only term used for Crangonidae and most smaller species. "Prawn" is the
more special of the two names, it being used solely for Palaemonidae and larger forms, never
for the very small ones.

In North America the name "prawn" is practically obsolete and is almost entirely replaced by the word "shrimp", even the species of Palaemonidae, like those of *Palaemonetes*
("Grass Shrimps") and *Macrobrachium* ("River Shrimps"), are usually indicated as shrimps.
If the name prawn is used at all here, this seems to be done only for the smaller Palae-
monids and Atyids, which, e.g. in Pennak's (1953, p, 451) "Freshwater Invertebrates of the
United States", are indicated as "Freshwater prawns". Where in England the word "prawn"
denotes the larger Natantia (the English Oxford dictionary defines prawn as "a marine
crustacean-like large shrimp"); in America, if used, it refers to the small species (the
American Webster dictionary gives as definition of prawn "a small crustaceous animal of the
shrimp family"). Although in both Britain and North America, shrimp is the more general
term (in America far more strongly so than in Britain), the usage of the term "prawn" is
almost the direct opposite in the two regions, denoting in Britain the larger palaemon-
like animals, in America the smaller ones.

In South Africa the larger Natantia, starting with *Macrobrachium* and including the Penaeidae are called "prawns", the smaller forms (including *Palaemon* species) are indicated as shrimps. This seems to be more or less also the situation in former British colonies in Asia, where the species of *Macrobrachium* and the Penaeidae are called prawns, and smaller species like *Caridina* and *Acetes* shrimps. A sharp division cannot be made here either, so Chuang (1961, on Malayan Shores, p. 181, pl. 80) used the names "Snapping-prawn" and "Pistol-prawn" for Alpheids.

In Australia and New Zealand the Crangonidae are called shrimps, the Palaemonidae (even the small species) and Penaeidae, prawns. Hale (1927, The Crustaceans of South Australia) listed furthermore the Processidae and Atyidae as shrimps, the Hippolytidae, Alpheidae, Pandalidae and Campylonotidae as prawns. However, several other Australian authors use the name Pistol shrimp for Alpheidae, while also the more prawn-shaped *Stenopus hispidus* is given the name Banded shrimp.

All in all the situation is quite confused, and nowhere a sharp distinction seems to be made between shrimps and prawns. In general one can say that the larger Palaemonidae and Penaeidae (thus the species that are commercially most attractive) are called shrimps in America, and prawns in most of the rest of the English-speaking world. The word shrimp being used almost everywhere for the Crangonidae and other small forms, but many exceptions occur here.

In French, the general term "crevette" is quite generally used for both shrimps and prawns and fortunately causes no problems. In Spanish, the general term for shrimps and prawns is "camaron" (camarão in Portuguese). The word "gamba" is less generally used; in fact it is applied only to a few species. The most confusing Spanish term is "langostino". In Spain, "langostino" is the official name for *Penaeus kerathurus*, in Argentina it is applied to *Pleoticus mülleri*, in Cuba to *Machrobrachium* species, and in Venezuela to various of the larger species of shrimps. Moreover, the term "langontino" is used in Chile for two species of galatheid crustacea (*Cervimunida johni* Porter and *Pleuroncodes monodon* H. Milne Edwards). The similar French word "Langoustine" stands for *Nephrops norvegicus* (L.).

ACKNOWLEDGEMENTS

It is great pleasure to thank here the following persons who sent in completed FAO questionnaires and so greatly facilitated my work and made it more reliable; Dr. Nasima M. Tirmizi (Pakistan), Messrs. Harold A. Brusher (Kenya), H.F.B. Champion (S. Acrica), Juan Luis Cifuentes L. (Mexico), Petrônio Alves (Coélho (Brazil), Dan Gotshall (California, U.S.A.), Mario Siri (Uruguay), Hubert J. Aquires (for Colombia), and Julio Vidal J. (for Chile). A word of special gratitude is due to Mr. H. Rosa, Jr., who started the present project and did all the difficult initial spade work for it.   Also, I am most grateful to Dr. M.N. Mistakidis, Scientific Secretary of the FAO World Scientific Conference on the Biology and Culture of Shrimps and Prawns, for his help and encouragement offered notwithstanding the very limited time available to him.   This list would never have been published if it were not for Dr. Walter Fischer of FAO, who during two weeks stay at FAO in Rome made extensive published and unpublished information available to me, discussed with me the definite format of the list, and finally saw to it that it was published.

Drs. Isabel Pérez Farfante, Fenner A. Chace, Jr., and Raymond B. Manning (all of Washington, D.C.) read an early draft of the manuscript and gave very valuable suggestions, corrections and additions, for which I am deeply grateful.

2. SYSTEMATIC CATALOGUE OF SPECIES

SUBORDER (DECAPODA) NATANTIA Boas, 1880

Natantia - Boas, 1880, K.Dan.Vidensk.Selsk.Skr., (6)!(2):28,155,164

All shrimps and prawns considered here belong to the suborder Natantia of the Crustacean order Decapoda. This suborder is divided into three infraorders: Penaeidea, Caridea and Stenopodidea. The first two of these are the largest and contain all the commercial species; the Stenopodidea is the smallest group and, being of no commercial importance, is not further considered here.

INFRAORDER PENAEIDEA Rafinesque, 1815

Penaeidea - Bate, 1888, Rep.Voyage Challenger, (Zool.), 24:220

The Penaeidea are divided into two superfamilies Penaeoidea and Sergestoidea, which formerly were only assigned the rank of families. Both superfamilies contain commercially important species.

SUPERFAMILY PENAEOIDEA Rafinesque, 1815

Penaeoidea - Glaessner, 1969, Moore's Treatise Invertebr.Paleontol., R4 (2):447

This superfamily consists of four families: Solenoceridae, Aristaeidae, Penaeidae and Sicyoniidae. A key to the most important species of the present superfamily is provided by Anderson & Lindner (1945), who more extensively deal with American species. Furthermore there are several regional treatises dealing with the species of this superfamily, such as those by Yoshida, 1941 (Korea), Kubo, 1949 (Japan), Liu, 1955 (N. China), Cheung, 1960 (Hong Kong), Dall, 1957 (Australia), Racek & Dall, 1965 (Australia and Indonesia), Hall, 1962 (Malaya), Ahmad, 1957 (Bangladesh), De Bruin, 1965 (Sri Lanka), Jones, 1967, Kurian & Sebastian, 1976 (India), Tirmizi, 1969, Tirmizi & Bashir, 1973 (Pakistan), Crosnier, 1965 (Madagascar), Hall, 1966 (E. Africa), Barnard, 1950 (South Africa), Monod, 1967, Crosnier & de Bondy, 1967 (W. Africa), Zariquiey Alvarez, 1968 (Atlantic coast of Europe and W. Mediterranean), Holthuis & Gottlieb, 1958 (E. Mediterranean), Williams, 1965 (North and South Carolina, U.S.A.), Joyce, 1965 (Florida, U.S.A.), Voss, 1955 (Western N. Atlantic and Gulf of Mexico), Davant, 1963 (Venezuela), Holthuis, 1959 (Surinam), Fausto Filho, 1968 (North and Northeast Brazil), Neiva & Mistakidis, 1966 (Central and South Brazil), Boschi, 1963 (Atlantic South America), Loesch & Avila, 1964 (Ecuador), Burkenroad, 1938 (Baja California).

FAMILY SOLENOCERIDAE Wood-Mason, 1891

Solenocerina - Wood-Mason, 1891, Ann.Mag.Nat.Hist., (6)8:275

Five genera of Solenoceridae are of interest to fishery. A revision of the family was published by Pérez-Farfante (1977).

Hadropenaeus lucasii (Bate, 1881)   SOLENO Hadr 1

Solenocera lucasii Bate, 1881, Ann.Mag.Nat.Hist., (5)8:185

Synonymy: *Philonicus lucasii* - Bate, 1888; *Pleoticus lucasii* - Bate, 1888; *? Haliporus malhaensis* Borradaile, 1910; *Hymenopenaeus lucasii* - Burkenroad, 1936.

FAO Names: Trident shrimp (En), Salicoque trident (Fr), Camarón tridente (Sp).

Literature: Pérez-Farfante, 1977:327, Figs. 9,16,44C,53-55.

Distribution: Indo-West Pacific: Madagascar to Japan, Indonesia and Hawaii.

Habitat: Depth 180 to 500 m. Marine.

Size: Maximum total length 72.5 mm (♂), 100 mm (♀); maximum carapace length 18.5 mm (♂), 25.5 mm (♀) (Pérez-Farfante, 1977:329). Crosnier & Jouannic (1973:11) stated that the size "ne semble guère dépasser 12 cm".

Interest to Fishery: Potential. Crosnier & Jouannic (1973:11) listed the species as "éventuellement commercialisable" on the continental shelf of Madagascar.

| *Haliporoides diomedeae* (Faxon, 1893) | SOLENO Hali 1 |

Peneopsis diomedeae Faxon, 1893, Bull.Mus.Comp.Zool.Harv.Coll., 24:212

Synonymy: *Faxonia diomedeae* - Bouvier, 1905; *Haliporus diomedeus* - Bouvier, 1906; *Haliporus diomedeae* - De Man, 1911; *Hymenopenaeus diomedeae* - Burkenroad, 1936.

FAO Names: Chilean knife shrimp (En), Salicoque couteau (du Chili) (Fr), Camarón cuchilla (Sp).

Local Names: Gamba roja (Peru), Gamba, Camarón de mar, Camarón de profundidad (Chile).

Literature: Pérez-Farfante, 1977:290, Figs 9,20,24-28

Distribution: Eastern Pacific: from Panama (7°31'30"N) to Chile (36°26'S).

Habitat: Depth 300 to 1 360 m. Bottom mud. Marine.

Size: Maximum total length 215 mm (♀); maximum carapace length 101 mm.

Interest to Fishery: Potential. When the difficulties involved in the capture of a deep-sea species like this are resolved, *H. diomedeae* may become of economic value and investigations to this end are being undertaken.

| *Haliporoides sibogae* (De Man, 1907) | SOLENO Hali 2 |

Haliporus sibogae De Man, 1907, Notes Leyden Mus., 29:138

Synonymy: *Hymenopenaeus sibogae* - Burkenroad, 1936; *Parahaliporus sibogae* - Kubo, 1949.

FAO Names: Jack-knife shrimp (En), Salicoque canif (Fr), Camarón cortapluma (Sp).

Local Names: Jack-knife prawn (New Zealand).

Distribution: Indo-West Pacific: Madagascar; Japan; South China Sea; Malay Archipelago; Australia; New Zealand.

Habitat: Depth 100 to 1 460 m, usually between 350 and 600 m. Marine.

Size: Maximum total length 165 mm (♂), 200 mm (♀).

Interest to Fishery: Crosnier & Jouannic (1973:11) listed the species as being "éventuellement commercialisable" on the Madagascar continental shelf. It is listed by Yasuda (1957:30) as of importance in the fishery in the Inland Sea of Japan. Richardson & Yaldwyn (1958:24) indicated the species as "commercially usable" in New Zealand waters.

Haliporoides triarthrus Stebbing, 1914   SOLENO Hali 3

Haliporoides triarthrus Stebbing, 1914, <u>Ann.S.Afr.Mus.</u>, 15:21

Synonymy: *Hymenopenaeus triarthrus* - Burkenroad, 1936.

FAO Names: Knife shrimp (En), Salicoque navaja (Fr), Camarón navaja (Sp).

Local Names: Knife prawn (S. Africa), Pink prawn (S.E. Africa).

Distribution: Indo-West Pacific: South and Southeast Africa.

Habitat: Depth 360 to 460 m. Bottom soft mud. Marine.

Size: Maximum total length 150 mm; carapace length approximately 50 mm.

Interest to Fishery: Of major commercial importance both in South Africa and Mozambique. Landed at Durban and in Mozambique. Used fresh, and sold mainly peeled and headed.

Hymenopenaeus aequalis (Bate, 1888)   SOLENO Hymeno 1

Haliporus aequalis Bate, 1888, <u>Rep.Voyage Challenger, (Zool.)</u>, 24:285

FAO Names: Veiled shrimp (En), Salicoque voilée (Fr), Camarón de velete (Sp).

Literature: Kubo, 1949:219, figures.

Distribution: Indo-West Pacific: east coast of Africa to Japan and Indonesia.

Habitat: Depth 200 to 1 362 m. Marine.

Size: Total length about 90 mm; carapace length 11 to 15 mm.

Interest to Fishery: Probably none. Listed by Kurian & Sebastian (1976:95) among the commercially important prawns of India, but with the annotation that "stray catches only" have been obtained, probably during exploratory cruises.

Pleoticus muelleri (Bate, 1888)   SOLENO Pleot 2

Philonicus mülleri Bate, 1888, <u>Rep.Voyage Challenger, (Zool.)</u>, 24:275

Synonymy: *Parartemesia carinata* Bouvier, 1905; *Haliporus carinatus* - Bouvier, 1906; *Haliporus mülleri* - Bouvier, 1908; *Hymenopenaeus mülleri* - Burkenroad, 1936.

FAO Names: Argentine red shrimp (En), Salicoque rouge d'Argentine (Fr), Camarón langostin argentino (Sp).

Local Names: Langostino, Langostín (Argentina, Uruguay), Lagostinho da Argentina, Camarão de Santana, Camarão vermelho, Camarão ferro, Camarão barbado (Brazil).

Literature: Pérez-Farfante, 1977:309, Figs. 9,34,37-42.

Distribution: Southwestern Atlantic: southern Brazil (south of 20°S); Uruguay; Argentina (as far south as 48°S); most frequent in Argentina, the greatest concentration being between 41° and 44°S.

Habitat: Depth 2 to 100 m, most frequent between 5 and 25 m. Bottom mud, or mud and sand. Temperature 9° to 23°C. Salinity 33.27 to 33.94°/∘∘ Cl.

Size: Maximum total length 190 mm, average total length around 100 mm; maximum carapace length 37.5 mm (♂), 58 mm (♀).

Interest to Fishery: In Argentina the species is the commercially most important crustacean. The annual catch (in metric tons) in Argentina was 100 (in 1973), 100 (in 1974), 180 (in 1975), and 151 (in 1976). In Uruguay and Brazil the species is of minor importance. In Argentina it is sold fresh, frozen and canned; in that country experiments have been undertaken for the aquaculture of this species.

| *Pleoticus robustus* (Smith, 1885) | SOLENO Pleot 1 |

Hymenopenaeus robustus Smith, 1885, Proc.U.S.Natl.Mus., 8:180

Synonymy: *Peneopsis ocularis* Faxon, 1896; *Faxonia ocularis* - Bouvier, 1905; *Haliporus robustus* Bouvier, 1906.

FAO Names: Royal red shrimp (En), Salicoque royale rouge (Fr), Camarón rojo real (Sp).

Local Names: Royal red shrimp (U.S.A.), Camarón rojo gigante (Mexico), Camarón real rojo (Cuba), Langostino rojo (Venezuela).

Literature: Pérez-Farfante, 1977:297, Figs. 9,29-36.

Distribution: Western Atlantic: upper part of the continental slope off the east coast of America from south of Martha's Vineyard (Massachusetts, U.S.A.) to French Guiana.

Habitat: Depth 245 to 730 m. Bottom mud, sandy mud or silt. Temperature 7° to 13°C. Marine.

Size: Maximum total length 180 mm ($\male$), 225 mm ($\female$), average total length about 130 mm (Klima, 1969); maximum carapace length 42 mm ($\male$), 61.5 mm ($\female$) (Pérez-Farfante, 1977:304). It is estimated that there are on the average 26 to 30 shrimps to the pound (Bates, 1957:11).

Interest to Fishery: After a long period of exploratory investigations (since about 1950) it was found that commercial exploitation for *P. robustus* at suitable grounds in the northeastern Gulf of Mexico, southwest of Dry Tortugas, and off northeastern Florida was possible; since 1962 commercial fishery is, be it intermittently, carried out in the latter region. Grounds southeast of the Mississippi River delta and off the Dry Tortugas are being exploited at present. The species has also been taken by trawlers off the coast of Venezuela (Davant, 1963:361). The shrimps are sold whole and peeled, either fresh or precooked breaded frozen. The annual catch of the species (in metric tons) in the U.S.A. was 300 (1973), 181 (in 1974), 122 (in 1975) and 136 (in 1976).

| *Solenocera africana* Stebbing, 1917 | SOLENO Soleno 2 |

Solenocera africanus Stebbing, 1917, Ann.S.Afr.Mus., 17:32

Synonymy: *Solenocera membranacea capensis* Heegaard, 1966. The species has often been synonymized with *Solenocera membranacea* (Risso), but was shown to be distinct by Crosnier & Forest (1973).

Literature: Crosnier & Forest (1973:270, Fig. 90,91a-c).

FAO Names: African mud shrimp (En), Solenocère d'Afrique (Fr), Camarón fanguero africano (Sp).

Distribution: Eastern Atlantic: West Africa from Mauritania to South Africa.

Habitat: Depth 50 to 450 m (juveniles usually in the shallower waters (50 to 100 m), the adults at greater depths). Bottom sandy mud.

Size: Maximum total length 138 mm.

Interest to Fishery: Minor. The species is taken together with *Parapenaeus longirostris*, but is hardly of commercial importance.

| *Solenocera agassizii* Faxon, 1893 | SOLENO Soleno 3 |

Solenocera agassizii Faxon, 1893, <u>Bull.Mus.Comp.Zool.Harv.Coll.</u>, 24:211

FAO Names: Kolibri shrimp (En), Salicoque colibri (Fr), Camarón chupaflor (Sp).

Local Names: Camarón fidel (Costa Rica, Panama), Chupaflor (Colombia), Camarón rojo (Ecuador), Camarón rosado (Peru). These names are also used for other, similar species.

Literature: Faxon, 1895:183, Pl. 47, Fig. 2.

Distribution: Eastern Pacific: Costa Rica to Ecuador and probably also northern Peru.

Habitat: Depth 280 to 384 m. Marine.

Size: Total length 149 mm ($\female$); carapace length 54 mm.

Interest to Fishery: The species is commercially exploited off Costa Rica and Panama (Pérez-Farfante, in Litt.; see also Vidal & Rosetti, 1971); commercial interesting quantities seem also to occur off Nicaragua.

| *Solenocera choprai* Nataraj, 1945 | SOLENO Soleno 4 |

Solenocera choprai Nataraj, 1945, <u>J.Asiat.Soc.Bengal(Sci.)</u>, 11(2):91

Synonymy: *? Solenocera alticarinata* Kubo, 1949.

FAO Names: Ridgeback shrimp (En), Salicoque balafrée (Fr), Camarón costurón (Sp).

Local Names: Red prawn (Hong Kong; also used for other species of the genus).

Literature: Tirmizi & Bashir, 1973:2, Figs. 2-7.

Distribution: Indo-West Pacific: Pakistan; India. If *S. alticarinata* is synonymous, then the range of the species extends westward as far as the Red Sea and eastward to Japan and the South China Sea.

Habitat: Depth 102 to 106 m. Marine.

Size: Tirmizi & Bashir (1973) listed females with total length 75 to 92 mm and carapace length 22 to 28.5 mm. Kurian & Sebastian (1976:101) gave the maximum size as 130 mm.

Interest to Fishery: Slight. Kurian & Sebastian (1976:101) listed the species among the Indian prawns of commercial importance, but indicated that specimens were only obtained in stray catches in the Arabian Sea. Although Tirmizi & Bashir (1973:1) mentioned that their Penaeid material was "mostly obtained from the Fish Market of Karachi", this is not specifically stated for the present species.

Remarks: *Solenocera alticarinata* Kubo is considered by Tirmizi & Bashir (1973) a synonym of *S. choprai*, but Starobogatov (1972:361-363,382) treated the two as different species. Burkenroad (1959:71) assigned Red Sea specimens of *S. alticarinata* to *S. koelbeli*. The taxonomic situation of these and related species is quite confused, and a revision of the group is most desirable.

| *Solenocera crassicornis* (H. Milne-Edwards, 1837) | SOLENO Soleno 5 |

Penaeus crassicornis H. Milne-Edwards, 1837, <u>Hist.Nat.Crust.</u>, 2:418

Synonymy: *Solenocera sinensis* Yu, 1937; *Solenocera indicus* Nataraj, 1945; *Solenocera subnuda* Kubo, 1949; *Solenocera kuboi* Hall, 1956.

FAO Names: Coastal mud shrimp (En), Salicoque des vases côtières (Fr), Camarón fanguero de orilla (Sp).

Local Names: Red prawn (Hong Kong; also used for other species of the genus), Udang merah, Udang krosok (Indonesia).

Literature: Kubo, 1949:255, Figures (as *S. subnuda*); Kunju, 1970:1317-1333, Figs. 1-3; Tirmizi & Bashir, 1973:11, Fig. 10 (as *S. indica*).

Distribution: Indo-West Pacific: Pakistan and India to the Malay Archipelago, China and Japan.

Habitat: Depth 40 m or less. Bottom mud. Marine.

Size: Maximum total length 80 mm ($\male$), 140 mm ($\female$).

Interest to Fishery: The species is fished for in India: near Bombay (Kunju, 1967:1393; Mohamed, 1967:1416; Kurian & Sebastian, 1976:101), and to a lesser extent along the Visakhapatnam coasts. Ahmad (1957:15) mentioned it among the commercial species of Bangladesh. It is reported also as fished for around Hong Kong and in Indonesia; the fishery there, however, is not of great importance. Sold fresh.

Solenocera florea Burkenroad, 1938	SOLENO Soleno 6

Solenocera florea Burkenroad, 1938, Zoologica (New York), 23:64

FAO Names: Flower shrimp (En), Salicoque fleur (Fr), Camarón picaflor (Sp).

Local Names: Camarón fidel (Costa Rica, Panama), Chupaflor (Colombia), Camarón rojo (Ecuador), Camarón rosado, Camarón peneido (Peru).

Distribution: Eastern Pacific: Costa Ríca to northern Peru.

Habitat: Depth 35 to 60 m. Marine.

Size: Maximum total length 68 mm ($\male$), 77 mm ($\female$); maximum carapace length 17.2 mm ($\male$), 22.8 mm ($\female$).

Interest to Fishery: The species if commercially exploited off Costa Rica and Panama (Pérez-Farfante, in Litt.). In Ecuador small quantities of the species are obtained commercially (Cobo & Loesch, 1966:4).

Solenocera geijskesi Holthuis, 1959	SOLENO Soleno 7

Solenocera geijskesi Holthuis, 1959, Zool.Verh.Leiden, 44:56

FAO Names: Guiana mud shrimp (En), Salicoque guyanaise (Fr), Camarón guayanés (Sp).

Literature: Pérez-Farfante & Bullis, 1973:26, Figs. 15-18.

Distribution: Western Atlantic: Surinam; French Guiana; northern Brazil.

Habitat: Depth 18 to 70 m. Bottom mud and sand. Marine.

Size: Maximum total length 40 mm; maximum carapace length 17 mm.

Interest to Fishery: Of secondary commercial importance off the mouth of the Amazon and Tocantins Rivers, and off Maranhão (Turiaçu and São Luis). Eaten fresh and used in regional dishes.

Solenocera hextii Wood-Mason & Alcock, 1891	SOLENO Soleno 8

Solenocera hextii Wood-Mason & Alcock, 1891, Ann.Mag.Nat.Hist., (6)7:188

FAO Names: Deep-sea mud shrimp (En), Salicoque des vases profondes (Fr), Camarón fanguero de altura (Sp).

Literature: Tirmizi & Bashir, 1973:7, Figs. 8,9.

Distribution: Indo-West Pacific: Gulf of Aden to Bay of Bengal.

Habitat: Depth 120 to 505 m. Marine.

Size: Total length 55 mm (♂), 109 to 138 mm (♀) (George, 1966:338). Tirmizi & Bashir (1973) gave as total length 32 to 35 mm and as carapace length 10 to 20 mm.

Interest to Fishery: Potential. Kurian & Sebastian (1976:101) listed the species among the Indian prawns of commercial importance, but stated that "deep-water explorations at 150 to 200 fathoms [= 274 to 366 m] have caught [the species] in varying numbers, but never in large quantities. The large size is attractive to commerce".

| *Solenocera koelbeli* De Man, 1911 | SOLENO Soleno 9 |

Solenocera koelbeli De Man, 1911, Siboga Exped.Mon., 39(a):7,45,48,50,51

Synonymy: *Solenocera depressa* Kubo, 1949.

FAO Names: Chinese mud shrimp (En), Salicoque chinoise de vase (Fr), Camarón fanguero chino (Sp).

Local Names: Hung ha, Red prawn (Hong Kong; the names used also for other species of the genus).

Literature: Kubo, 1949:237, Figures (as *S. depressa*).

Distribution: Indo-West Pacific: Korea, Japan and Hong Kong to the Gulf of Tonkin. Also reported from the Arafura Sea, Indonesia (Purwito, 1972:651).

Habitat: Depth 50 to 152 m. Marine.

Size: Total length 57.5 to 88 mm (♂), 55 to 76 mm (♀); carapace length 16 mm (♂), 16 to 22 mm (♀).

Interest to Fishery: Mentioned by Yoshida (1941:17), under the name *S. distincta* (De Haan), as economically important in Korea. Motoh (1977:3) listed this species, as *S. depressa* in his list of "shrimps with commercial value" and reported it from Hong Kong on the authority of Cheung (1960). Cheung, however, did not make any mention that the species is of commercial importance. Muthu (1971: 145) reported material of what he considered *S. melantho* De Man, 1907, from commercial catches made off the east coast of India (Visakhapatnam and Kakinada); he synonymized De Man's species with *S. depressa*. If Muthu's interpretation is correct, the name *S. melantho* De Man, 1907, takes precedence over *S. koelbeli* De Man, 1911.

| *Solenocera membranacea* (Risso, 1816) | SOLENO Soleno 1 |

Peneus membranaceus Risso, 1816, Hist.Nat.Crust.Nice, 3:98

Synonymy: *Peneus siphonoceros* Philippi, 1840; *Solenocera philippii* Lucas, 1849; *Solenocera siphonocera* - Caullery, 1896.

FAO Names: Atlantic mud shrimp (En), Salicoque des vases (de l'Atlantique) (Fr), Gamba de fango (del Atlántico) (Sp).

Distribution: Eastern Atlantic: from Ireland to West Africa; entire Méditerranean.

Habitat: Depth 20 to 700 m, most common between 50 and 450 m. Bottom mud. Marine.

Size: Maximum total length 112 mm.

- 8 -

Interest to Fishery: In the Gulf of Genoa, Italy, the species is fished by "piropescherecci" at
a depth of 150 to 400 m (Brian, 1941:9). In Tunisian waters it is "pêchée en assez petites quantités"
by trawlers (Heldt, 1938:42). Zariquiey Alvarez (1968:50) indicated that the species "se captura en
abundancia para su consumo" in Spanish Mediterranean waters. Still the species seems to be of much
less importance that the other Mediterranean penaeids listed here. On the West African coast the
species is taken with *Parapenaeus longirostris*, but is hardly of commercial importance there; the
West African material may belong to *S. africana* Stebbing, 1917, a species often confused with
S. membranacea.

| *Solenocera pectinata* (Bate, 1888) | SOLENO Soleno 10 |

Philonicus pectinatus Bate, 1888, Rep.Voyage Challenger, (Zool.), 24:279

Synonymy: *Philonicus cervicalis* Zehntner, 1894; *? Solenocera pectinulata* Kubo, 1949.

FAO Names: Comb shrimp (En), Salicoque peigne (Fr), Camarón peine (Sp).

Literature: De Man, 1911:7,45; De Man, 1913, Pl. 4, Fig. 11; De Man, 1922:4, Pl. 1, Fig. 2.

Distribution: Indo-West Pacific: from East Africa and the Arabian Sea to the Malay Archipelago
and the South China Sea, perhaps as far as Japan.

Habitat: Depth 15 to 118 m. Bottom mud, sand or coral. Marine.

Size: Total length 26 to 50 mm (♂), 26 to 54 mm (♀); maximum carapace length almost 16 mm.
Kurian & Sebastian (1976:101) gave the maximum length as 75 mm.

Interest to Fishery: Minor or nil. Kurian & Sebastian (1976:101) listed the species among the
Indian prawns of commercial importance, obtained at the southwest coast of India, but they stated
that the species is only found in small numbers and that the small size of the specimens make them
commercially unattractive. Muthu (1971:146) reported the species from commercial catches landed at
Visakhapatnam and Kakinada (east coast of India).

| FAMILY ARISTAEIDAE Wood-Mason, 1891 |

Aristaeina - Wood-Mason, 1891, Ann.Mag.Nat.Hist., (6)8:278

This family contains three genera of commercially important shrimps: *Aristaeomorpha, Aristeus* and
Plesiopenaeus, all of which occur in deep waters.

| *Aristaeomorpha foliacea* (Risso, 1827) | ARIST Aris 1 |

Peneus foliaceus Risso, 1827, Hist.Nat.Eur.Mérid., 5:69

Synonymy: *Penaeus meridionalis* Hope, 1851 (nomen nudum); *Aristeus foliaceus* - Smith, 1885;
? Aristeus rostridentatus Bate, 1888; *Penaeopsis foliaceus* - Ortmann, 1890; *Aristaeomorpha
giglioliana* Wood-Mason, 1892; *Plesiopenaeus foliaceus* - Faxon, 1895; *Aristaeomorpha mediterranea*
Adensamer, 1898; *? Aristeus japonicus* Yokoya, 1933. Several records of *Aristaeomorpha rostridentata*
from the Indo-West Pacific do not pertain to the present species but to *A. woodmasoni* (see there).

FAO Names: Giant red shrimp (En), Gambon rouge (Fr), Gamba española (Sp).

Local Names: Langostino moruño (official Spanish name), Gamba roja, Chorizo (Spain), Crevette
rouge, Grande crevette rouge (France), Gambaru de fundu (Monaco), Ammiru cani, U patri di ammiru,
Ammiru turcu (Sicily, Italy), Gambero rosso (Italy), Garída (Greece), Ariston adom (Israel), Rote
Garnele (Germany; vid. Luther & Fiedler, 1967:121); Langostino rojo (Venezuela), Royal red prawn
(New Zealand).

Distribution: Eastern Atlantic: Bay of Biscay to N.W. Africa and the entire Mediterranean.
Western Atlantic: South of Massachusetts to the Straits of Florida, Gulf of Mexico, Caribbean Sea,
and Atlantic Ocean off Venezuela. Indo-West Pacific: East Africa to Japan, New Zealand and Fiji.
The Indo-West Pacific records may pertain to a distinct species, *A. rostridentata* (Bate, 1888), which
is usually identified with *A. foliacea*; however, some records of *A. rostridentata* do pertain to the
related *A. woodmasoni* Calman (see there).

Habitat: Depth 250 to 1 300 m. Bottom mud. Marine.

Size: Maximum total length 170 mm (♂), 225 mm (♀).

Interest to Fishery: Mostly fished for at depths between 250 and 700 m, the species is obtained
by commercial deep-sea trawlers off the Mediterranean coasts of Spain, France, Italy, Algeria and
Israel. Off Venezuela the species is considered to be of "valor comercial ......innegable"
(Davant, 1963:38). Longhurst (1970:299) mentioned that *A. foliacea* is landed at Durban, South Africa,
without indicating the commercial importance of the species there. Crosnier & Jouannic (1973:12)
considered the species "éventuellement commercialisable" on the continental shelf of Madagascar.
Richardson & Yaldwyn (1958:25) indicated *A. foliacea* as "commercially usable" in New Zealand waters
(see also Anon., 1964:5,9, Fig. 3); in 1972 one trawler was in operation off N.E. New Zealand fishing
for this species. *A. foliacea* is sold fresh or frozen.

Remarks: As already pointed out above the Indo-West Pacific records of the present species
pertain to a form described originally as *A. rostridentata*, which is usually synonymized with
A. foliacea, but the status of which is not yet perfectly clear. Next to *A. rostridentata*
(= ? *A. foliacea*) a second species occurs in the Indo-West Pacific region; this species *A. woodmasoni*,
which is definitely different from *A. foliacea*, has been incorrectly reported upon by some authors as
A. rostridentata (see below).

Aristaeomorpha woodmasoni Calman, 1925	ARIST Aris 2

Aristaeomorpha wood-masoni Calman, 1925, Rep.Fish.Mar.Biol.Surv.Union S.Afr., 4:8

FAO Names: Indian red shrimp (En), Gambon indien (Fr), Gamba roja india (Sp).

Literature: Alcock, 1901:39 (as *Aristaeus (Aristaeomorpha) rostridentatus* Bate); Kemp &
Sewell, 1912:17, Pl. 1, Fig. 6 (as *A. rostridentata*).

Distribution: Indo-West Pacific: Arabian Sea; Bay of Bengal; Andaman Sea.

Habitat: Depth 330 to 500 m. Marine.

Size: Maximum total length 153 mm.

Interest to Fishery: Minor. Listed by Kurian & Sebastian (1976:95) as commercially important in
India; but they remarked "obtained only in small numbers".

Remarks: This species has often, especially before 1925, been incorrectly indicated with the
name *Aristaeomorpha rostridentata* (Bate). The latter species, which was originally described from the
Indo-West Pacific region, is usually synonymized with *A. foliacea* (see there).

Aristeus alcocki Ramadan, 1938	ARIST Arist 2

Aristeus alcocki Ramadan, 1938, Sci.Rep.John Murray Exped., 1933-34, 5:40

FAO Names: Arabian red shrimp (En), Gambon d'Arabie (Fr), Gamba roja arábiga (Sp).

Distribution: Indo-West Pacific: Gulf of Aden; Arabian Sea; India; Bay of Bengal.

Habitat: Depth 270 to 1 086 m. Bottom mud. Marine.

Size: Maximum total length 150 mm, average length 110 mm (δ), 140 mm ($\female$).

Interest to Fishery: Potential. The species is listed by Kurian & Sebastian (1976:95) among (potentially) commercially important prawns in S.W. India, where the species was obtained in small numbers during exploratory trawling.

Aristeus antennatus (Risso, 1816)	ARIST Arist 1

Peneus antennatus Risso, 1816, Hist.Nat.Crust.Nice, 3:96

Synonymy: *Sycionia duvernoii* Risso, 1844 (nomen nudum).

FAO Names: Blue and red shrimp (En), Crevette rouge (Fr), Gamba rosada (Sp).

Local Names: Gamba rosada (official Spanish name), Chorizo blanco, Gamba alistada, Carabinero (Spain), Crevette rouge (France), Gambaru de fundu (Monaco), Gambero rosso chiaro (Italy), Gámbao rossu-ciâeo (Genova, Italy), Ammiru cani (Sicily, Italy), Gambli rossi (Malta), Garída (Greece), Aristit (Israel).

Distribution: Eastern Atlantic: Portugal to the Cape Verde Islands; entire Mediterranean.

Habitat: Depth 200 to 1 440 m. Bottom soft mud. Marine.

Size: Maximum total length 220 mm.

Interest to Fishery: The species is highly esteemed as food. It is fished for by deep-sea trawlers off N.W. Africa and along the Mediterranean coasts of Spain, France, Italy and Malta. It is also taken by Israel trawlers, but less commonly so than *Aristaeomorpha foliacea*, while in the Western Mediterranean the opposite is true. The species is sold fresh.

Aristeus semidentatus Bate, 1881	ARIST Arist 3

Aristeus semidentatus Bate, 1881, Ann.Mag.Nat.Hist., (5)8:189

Synonymy: *Hemipenaeus semidentatus* - Bate, 1888.

FAO Names: Smooth red shrimp (En), Gambon lisse (Fr), Gamba roja lisa (Sp).

Distribution: Indo-West Pacific: Madagascar; Arabian Sea; Malay Archipelago; near Kermadec Islands; Hawaii.

Habitat: Depth 180 to 1 100 m. Bottom mud. Marine.

Size: Maximum total length 90 mm (δ), 178 mm ($\female$).

Interest to Fishery: Potential. So far the species is not yet commercially exploited, but several authors (e.g., Jones, 1967:1337 and Kurian & Sebastian, 1976:95) pointed to its commercial potential in view of the fact that it was obtained in fairly great numbers at exploratory cruises off Cochin, S.W. India.

Aristeus varidens Holthuis, 1952	ARIST Arist 4

Aristeus varidens Holthuis, 1952, Résult.Sci.Expéd.Océanogr.Belge Eaux Côt.Afr.Atl.Sud, 1948-49, 3(2):71

FAO Names: Striped red shrimp (En), Gambon rayé (Fr), Gamba listada (Sp).

Local Names: Listado (Spanish, see Crosnier & Tanter, 1968:3).

Literature: Crosnier & Forest, 1973:288, Figs. 96b,c, 97a-c.

Distribution: Eastern Atlantic: continental shelf of West Africa between Rio de Oro (24°N) and S.W. Africa (18°S).

Habitat: Depth 300 to 1 134 m, most common between 400 and 600 m. Bottom mud. Marine.

Size: Maximum total length 190 mm (♀).

Interest to Fishery: According to Crosnier & Forest (1969:550) the species forms "l'objet d'une pêche commerciale assez active de la part de chalutiers espagnols au large de l'Angola". Crosnier & Tanter (1968:4) mentioned that the species is also fished for by Spanish trawlers off Guinea and Senegal. The prawns are sold frozen.

Aristeus virilis (Bate, 1881)   ARIST Arist 5

Hemipenaeus virilis Bate, 1881, Ann.Mag.Nat.Hist., (5)8:187

Synonymy: *Aristaeus tomentosus* Bate, 1881.

FAO Names: Stout red shrimp (En), Gambon gaillard (Fr), Gambón colorado (Sp).

Literature: Kubo, 1949:194, Figures.

Distribution: Indo-West Pacific: East Africa to Japan, the New Hebrides and Indonesia.

Habitat: Depth 344 to 800 m. Bottom mud and sand. Marine.

Size: Total length 85 to 146 mm (♂), 81 to 190 mm (♀); carapace length 25 to 46 mm (♂), 24 to 52 mm (♀).

Interest to Fishery: Potential. Crosnier & Jouannic (1973:12) listed this species among those that they thought "éventuellement commercialisables" on the continental slope of Madagascar; it was found there together with *Aristeus mahabissae* Ramadan, 1938, the latter in smaller quantities. Kurian & Sebastian (1976:95) listed the species among the commercially important prawns of India, but at the same time stated that "only stray catches have been obtained", probably during exploratory cruises.

Plesiopenaeus edwardsianus (Johnson, 1868)   ARIST Plesio 1

Penaeus edwardsianus Johnson, 1868, Proc.Zool.Soc.Lond., 1867:897,901

Synonymy: *Aristeus edwardsianus* - Miers, 1878; *Aristeus coralinus* Bate, 1888; *Aristaeopsis edwardsiana* - Wood-Mason, 1891; *Aristeus splendens* Richard, 1900.

FAO Names: Scarlet shrimp (En), Gambon écarlat (Fr), Gamba carabinero (Sp).

Local Names: Carabinero (official Spanish name), Langostino moruno, Chorizo rojo (Spain), Crevette impériale, Crevette rouge géante (France), Crevette royale (Morocco), Rote Riesengarnele (Germany).

Literature: Crosnier & Forest, 1973:292, Figs. 98,99a,b.

Distribution: Eastern Atlantic: Portugal to South Africa; not in the Mediterranean. Western Atlantic: Grand Bank (43°42'N) to the Gulf of Mexico, Caribbean Sea and north coast of South America. Also reported from the Indo-West Pacific region, but it is not certain whether this is really the same species.

Habitat: Depth 274 to 1 850 m, most frequently found between 400 and 900 m. Bottom mud. Marine.

Size: Maximum total length 193 mm (♂), 334 mm (♀).

Interest to Fishery: Fished commercially by Spanish trawlers (from Vigo, Huelva, and Cádiz) in the area of Senegal, Guinea and especially off Congo and Angola (4° to 10°S). The shrimps are frozen on board and mainly sold on the Spanish markets (e.g., Barcelona), but also in France (Marseilles). Crosnier & Jouannic (1973:12) reported on a form which they assigned to this species as "éventuelle-ment commercialisable" on the continental shelf of Madagascar.

FAMILY PENAEIDAE Rafinesque, 1815

Penedia - Rafinesque, 1815, Analyse de la Nature, 98

This is the largest of the families of Penaeidea and it contains the greatest number of commer-cially important species of Natantia, among which those that are economically of the greatest value.

Like in the other families, the genera and species are listed here alphabetically.

Artemesia longinaris Bate, 1888   PEN Art 1

Artemesia longinaris Bate, 1888, Rep.Voyage Challenger, (Zool.), 24:281

Synonymy: *Artemesia brevinaris* Nobili, 1901.

FAO Names: Argentine stiletto shrimp (En), Crevette stylet d'Argentine (Fr), Camarón estilete argentino (Sp).

Local Names: Camarón (Argentina, Uruguay), Camarão serrinha, Camarão de Argentina, Camarão ferrinho, Camarão barba branca (Brazil).

Literature: Boschi, 1969.

Distribution: Western Atlantic: east coast of South America from Rio de Janeiro, Brazil (23°S) to Puerto de Rawson, Argentina (43°S).

Habitat: Depth littoral to 68 m. Bottom sand and mud. Temperature 8° to 22°C, mostly between 15° and 21°C. Salinity 32.9 to 35.5‰ Cl.

Size: Maximum total length 106 mm ($\male$), 145 mm, exceptionally 152 mm, ($\female$).

Interest to Fishery: Fished for in the entire area, most intensively on the Argentina coast. The species is caught at the same time as *Pleoticus muelleri*, but due to its smaller size it is of less commercial importance than the latter species. In Argentina the annual catch of this species (in metric tons) amounted to 500 (in 1973), 400 (in 1974), 120 (in 1975) and 255 (in 1976). Aqua-culture experiments with this species have been started in Argentina.

Atypopenaeus formosus Dall, 1957   PEN Aty 1

Atyopenaeus formosus Dall, 1957, Aust.J.Mar.Freshwat.Res., 8:199

FAO Names: Orange shrimp (En), Crevette orange (Fr), Camarón naranja (Sp).

Local Names: Orange prawn, Go-home prawn (Australia).

Distribution: Indo-West Pacific: New Guinea; Papua; northern Australia (Darwin to northern New South Wales).

Habitat: Depth 2 to 9 m. Bottom sandy mud or mud. Marine.

Size: Total length 27 to 75 mm (δ), 44 to 91 mm ($\female$); maximum carapace length 17 mm (δ), 21 mm ($\female$).

Interest to Fishery: Minor. Racek (1959:10) reported the presence of this species in commercial catches in New South Wales (very rare), and Queensland (abundant in higher strata). Munro (1968:14) listed the species among "smaller species regarded as having no commercial value".

| *Atypopenaeus stenodactylus* (Stimpson, 1860) | PEN Aty 2 |

Penaeus stenodactylus Stimpson, 1860, Proc.Acad.Nat.Sci.Phila., 1860:43

Synonymy: *Penaeus podophthalmus* Stimpson, 1860; *Penaeus compressipes* Henderson, 1893; *Atypopenaeus compressipes* - Alcock, 1905; *Parapenaeopsis brevirostris* Kubo, 1936; *Miyadiella pedunculata* Kubo, 1949; *Miyadiella podophthalmus* - Holthuis, 1955.

FAO Names: Periscope shrimp (En), Crevette périscope (Fr), Camarón periscopio (Sp).

Local Names: Maimai ebi (Japan).

Distribution: Indo-West Pacific: India to the Malay Archipelago, Hong Kong and Japan.

Habitat: Depth 11 to 27 m. Bottom mud. Marine.

Size: Maximum total length 40 mm (δ), 50 mm ($\female$).

Interest to Fishery: The species is caught in large numbers throughout the year on the west coast of India, in small numbers on the east coast (Kunju, 1967; Kurian & Sebastian, 1976). It is also of minor economic importance in the Inland Sea of Japan (Yasuda, 1956).

| *Macropetasma africana* (Balss, 1913) | PEN Macro 1 |

Penaeus africanus Balss, 1913, Denkschr.Med.-Naturwiss.Ges.Jena, 7:105

FAO Names: Swimming shrimp (En), Crevette nageuse (Fr), Camarón nadador (Sp).

Local Names: Swimming prawn (South Africa).

Distribution: South West Africa and South Africa (Kunene River to St. Lucia).

Habitat: Depth littoral zone to 28 m. Marine and estuarine.

Size: Maximum total length 67 mm ($\female$); mature at about 33 mm.

Interest to Fishery: At present slight, but perhaps greater in the future. Day (1969:102) stated that the species is "netted in the shallows on surf-beaches and occasionally in estuaries" between False Bay and St. Lucia. According to Longhurst (1970:299,300) abundant stocks have been revealed at the coast of S.W. Africa, but "no commercial exploitation appears to have yet occurred". The species is considered of possible future importance commercially.

| *Metapenaeopsis acclivis* (M.J. Rathbun, 1902) | PEN Meta 1 |

Parapenaeus acclivis M.J. Rathbun, 1902, Proc.U.S.Natl.Mus., 26:41

Synonymy: *Metapenaeus acclivis* - Alcock, 1905; *Penaeopsis acclivis* - De Man, 1911; *Erythropenaeus acclivis* - Kishinouye, 1929.

FAO Names: Tora velvet shrimp (En), Crevette chamois tora (Fr), Camarón gamuza tora (Sp).

Local Names: Tora ebi (Japan).

Distribution: Indo-West Pacific: Japan.

Habitat: Depth 9 to 46 m. Marine.

Size: Maximum total length 90 mm.

Interest to Fishery: In several areas of the Inland Sea of Japan *M. acclivis* is an economically important species, belonging to the three most abundant species there (Yasuda, 1956:379; 1957:30).

Metapenaeopsis andamanensis (Wood-Mason, 1891)	PEN Meta 2

Metapenaeus philippinensis andamanensis Wood-Mason, 1891, Ann.Mag.Nat.Hist., (6)8:271

Synonymy: *Penaeus (Metapenaeus) coniger andamanensis* - Alcock, 1901; *Penaeopsis coniger andamanensis* - De Man, 1911.

FAO Names: Rice velvet shrimp (En), Crevette chamois des rizières (Fr), Camarón gamuza de arrozal (Sp).

Distribution: Indo-West Pacific: India; Malaya; South China Sea; Japan.

Habitat: Depth 150 to 350 m. Marine.

Size: Maximum total length 135 mm.

Interest to Fishery: So far not fished commercially, but according to Crosnier & Jouannic (1973:10) "éventuellement commercialisable" on the continental shelf of Madagascar. Also Jones (1969:747) and Kurian & Sebastian (1976:96) were of the opinion that the species may be of future importance for a fishery off the west coast of India, and its economic potentialities are to be studied. Yasuda (1957:30) listed "*Heterocarpus coniger*" among the commercially important shrimps of the Inland Sea of Japan: possibly the present species is meant.

Remarks: See also under *Metapenaeopsis philippii* (Bate, 1881).

Metapenaeopsis barbata (De Haan, 1844)	PEN Meta 3

Penaeus barbatus De Haan, 1844, In Von Siebold, Fauna Japonica, Crustacea, (6/7):Pl. 46, Fig. 3

Synonymy: *Parapenaeus barbatus* - Smith, 1885; *Parapenaeus akayebi* M.J. Rathbun, 1902; *Trachypeneus barbatus* - Alcock, 1905; *Penaeus (Metapenaeus) akayebi* - De Man, 1907; *Penaeopsis barbatus* - De Man, 1911; *Penaeopsis akayebi* - De Man, 1911; *Erythropenaeus akayebi* - Kishinouye, 1929.

FAO Names: Whiskered velvet shrimp (En), Crevette chamois barbulée (Fr), Camarón gamuza barbudo (Sp).

Local Names: Aka ebi (Japan), Chat mai ha, Red rice prawn (Hong Kong).

Distribution: Indo-West Pacific: Japan; Hong Kong; Taiwan; Thailand; Indonesia; Malaya.

Habitat: Depth 20 to 70 m. Bottom mud, sometimes rocky. Marine.

Size: Maximum total length 108 mm.

Interest to Fishery: *Metapenaeopsis barbata* forms a rather important part of the shrimp caught in the Inland Sea of Japan. According to Longhurst (1970:290) it forms, with *Trachypenaeus curvirostris* and *Parapenaeopsis tenella* 45% of the catches, but is of course commercially of less value than the large species. In Thailand, Singapore and Malaya the species also forms part of the commercial shrimp catches (Longhurst, 1970:285,289).

| Metapenaeopsis borradailei (De Man, 1911) | PEN Meta 4 |

Penaeopsis borradailei De Man, 1911, <u>Siboga Exped.Mon.</u>, 39(a):73.

FAO Names: Reef shrimp (En), Crevette des récifs (Fr), Camarón de arrecife (Sp).

Literature: Dall, 1957:174, Fig. 13.

Distribution: Indo-West Pacific: Laccadive Archipelago; Indonesia (Sumatra, Moluccas, Lesser Sunda Islands); Australia (Torres Strait).

Habitat: Depth 1 to 3 m. Coral reefs. Marine.

Size: Total length 23.5 to 39 mm (δ), 24 to 64 ($\female$).

Interest to Fishery: Motoh (1977:6) listed the species as a commercially important penaeid, and referred to Munro (1968). Munro (1968:14), however, ranged the species among the "smaller species regarded as having no commercial value". The fact that *M. borradailei* is a rare species and seems to be restricted to coral reefs, makes it unlikely that it ever will become of commercial interest.

| Metapenaeopsis crassissima Racek & Dall, 1965 | PEN Meta 5 |

Metapenaeopsis crassissima Racek & Dall, 1965, <u>Verh.K.Ned.Akad.Wet.(Natuurkd.)</u>, (2)56(3):26

FAO Names: Stout velvet shrimp (En), Crevette chamois gaill (Fr), Camarón gamuza toro (Sp).

Distribution: Indo-West Pacific: Western Australia; South Australia.

Habitat: Depth 7 to 18 m. Bottom mud. Marine.

Size: Maximum total length 140 mm.

Interest to Fishery: Listed by Racek (1973:155,159) among the prawns of commercial importance, in which he included the species which, because of their size or abundance are considered to be able "to support an organized fishery".

| Metapenaeopsis dalei (M.J. Rathbun, 1902) | PEN Meta 6 |

Parapenaeus dalei M.J. Rathbun, 1902, <u>Proc.U.S.Natl.Mus.</u>, 26:40

Synonymy: *Metapenaeus dalei* - Alcock, 1905; *Penaeopsis dalei* - De Man, 1911; *Ceratopenaeus dalei* - Kishinouye, 1929.

FAO Names: Kishi velvet shrimp (En), Crevette chamois kishi (Fr), Camarón gamuza kishi (Sp).

Local Names: Kishi ebi (Japan).

Distribution: Indo-West Pacific: Japan; Korea; North China.

Habitat: Depth 33 to 132 m. Marine.

Size: Maximum total length 73 mm (δ), 76.3 mm ($\female$); maximum carapace length 18.9 mm (δ), 21.4 mm ($\female$).

Interest to Fishery: The species is of commercial interest in Korea (Yoshida, 1941:15), North China (Liu, 1955:18) and the Inland Sea of Japan (Yasuda, 1956:383; 1957:30), but evidently nowhere of major importance.

Metapenaeopsis goodei (Smith, 1885) — PEN Meta 7

Parapenaeus goodei Smith, 1885, <u>Proc.U.S.Natl.Mus.</u>, 8:176

Synonymy: *? Penaeus pubescens* Stimpson, 1871; *Archipenaeopsis vestitus* Bouvier, 1905; *Parapenaeopsis rathbuni* Bouvier, 1905; *Metapenaeus goodei* - Alcock, 1905; *Penaeopsis goodei* - Bouvier, 1908; *Penaeopsis vestitus* - Schmitt, 1924.

FAO Names: Caribbean velvet shrimp (En), Crevette chamois caraïbe (Fr), Camarón gamuza del Caribe (Sp).

Distribution: Western Atlantic: Bermuda; North Carolina (U.S.A.) to Bahia (Brazil); West Indies.

Habitat: Depth 20 to 300 m. Bottom sand, mud. Marine.

Size: Maximum carapace length 19 mm (δ), 21 mm ($\female$).

Interest to Fishery: The species is fished for food off N. and N.E. Brazil (Pará, Maranhão, Ceará, Rio Grande do Norte, Alagoas and Espíritu Santo). It is of secondary importance commercially and is eaten fresh or used for the preparation of regional dishes. Because of its small size and rather hard shell it is not probable that the species will be utilized, except when caught as an admixture in catches of larger species.

Metapenaeopsis hilarula (De Man, 1911) — PEN Meta 8

Penaeopsis hilarulus De Man, 1911, <u>Siboga Exped.Mon.</u>, 39(a):8,71

FAO Names: Minstrel shrimp (En), Crevette chamois ménestrel (Fr), Camarón gamuza bardo (Sp).

Literature: De Bruin, 1965:81, Figs. 1b,d.

Distribution: Indo-West Pacific: S.E. Africa to Malaya.

Habitat: Depth 30 to 35 m. Marine.

Size: Total length 52 to 57 mm (δ), 50 to 70 mm ($\female$); carapace length 8.5 to 11 mm (δ), 10 to 15 mm ($\female$).

Interest to Fishery: Minor. Muthu (1971:150) reported this species from commercial catches made off the east coast of India (Visakhapatnam and Kakinada).

Remarks: For the taxonomic status of this species and its relation to *M. mogiensis*, see under the latter.

Metapenaeopsis lamellata (De Haan, 1844) — PEN Meta 9

Penaeus lamellatus De Haan, 1844, <u>In</u> Von Siebold, Fauna Japonica, Crustacea, (6/7):Pl. 46, Fig. 4

Synonymy: *Parapenaeus lamellatus* - M.J. Rathbun, 1902; *Metapenaeus lamellatus* - Alcock, 1905; *Penaeopsis lamellatus* - De Man, 1911; *Ceratopenaeus lamellatus* - Kishinouye, 1929.

FAO Names: Humpback shrimp (En), Crevette bossue (Fr), Camarón jorobado (Sp).

Local Names: Hokkoku ebi (Japan), Hunchback prawn, Humpback prawn (Australia).

Distribution: Indo-West Pacific: Japan; Malaysia; tropical Australia.

Habitat: Depth 31 to 200 m. Bottom coral. Marine.

Size: Maximum total length 66.3 mm (♂), 75 mm (♀); carapace length 15 mm (♂), 19 mm (♀).

Interest to Fishery: The species is fished commercially in Japan. Kubo (1949:431) mentioned it from the Tokyo fish market, while Yasuda (1957:30) listed it among the species important in the fishery in the Inland Sea of Japan. The nature of the bottom where the species is found makes that it will probably never be of very great commercial value.

Metapenaeopsis lata Kubo, 1949 PEN Meta 10

Metapenaeopsis latus Kubo, 1949, J.Tokyo Coll.Fish., 36(1):434

FAO Names: Broad velvet shrimp (En), Crevette chamois trappue (Fr), Camarón gamuza espaldudo (Sp).

Distribution: Indo-West Pacific: Japan.

Habitat: Depth 350 m. Marine.

Size: Total length 59 mm (♂); carapace length 15.2 mm (♀).

Interest to Fishery: The species is only included here because it was listed as "important in fishery" in the Inland Sea of Japan by Yasuda (1957:30,36).

Metapenaeopsis mogiensis (M.J. Rathbun, 1902) PEN Meta 11

Parapenaeus mogiensis M.J. Rathbun, 1902, Proc.U.S.Natl.Mus., 26:39

Synonymy: *Metapenaeus mogiensis* - M.J. Rathbun, 1906; *Ceratopenaeus mogiensis* - Kishinouye, 1929.

FAO Names: Mogi velvet shrimp (En), Crevette chamois mogi (Fr), Camarón gamuza mogi (Sp).

Literature: De Bruin, 1965:81-84, Figs. 1,2.

Distribution: Indo-West Pacific: Red Sea and India to Japan and N.E. Australia.

Habitat: Depth 11 to 30 m. Marine.

Size: Maximum total length 69 mm (♂), 90 mm (♀); carapace length 10 to 14.5 mm (♂), 8 to 19 mm (♀).

Interest to Fishery: Minor. The species is listed by Kurian & Sebastian (1976:96) among commercially important prawns of India, but they refer only to stray catches, probably obtained during exploratory trawling. Muthu (1971:148) listed the species from commercial catches taken off the east coast of India (Visakhapatnam and Kakinada).

Remarks: The present knowledge of the taxonomic status of *M. mogiensis* and related species is rather confused. Older authors synonymized *M. mogiensis* and *M. hilarula* (De Man, 1911). De Bruin (1965:82-84, Fig. 1) showed that the two species are distinct. Recently Starobogatov (1972:376,405-406, Pl. 10,Figs. 128,129, Pl. 11, Figs. 158,159) considered the Ceylon material, which De Bruin assigned to *M. mogiensis* and *M. hilarula*, different from either species and made it the types of two new species, *M. bruini* and *M. ceylonensis* respectively.

Metapenaeopsis novaeguineae (Haswell, 1879) PEN Meta 12

Penaeus novae-guineae Haswell, 1879, Proc.Linn.Soc.N.S.W., 4:43

Synonymy: *Penaeopsis novae-guineae* - Gee, 1925.

FAO Names: Northern velvet shrimp (En), Crevette chamois nordique (Fr), Camarón gamuza norteño (Sp).

Local Names: Northern velvet prawn (Australia).

Distribution: Indo-West Pacific: tropical Autralian waters; New Guinea.

Habitat: Marine.

Size: Maximum total length 101 mm.

Interest to Fishery: Cited by Racek (1959:10) under the name *Penaeopsis (Metapenaeopsis) barbata* as abundant in commercial catches in Queensland, rare in New South Wales.

Remarks: In older literature numerous species have been confused under the name *M. novaeguineae*.

Metapenaeopsis palmensis (Haswell, 1879)	PEN Meta 13

Penaeus palmensis Haswell, 1879, Proc.Linn.Soc.N.S.W., 4:43

Synonymy: *Metapenaeus palmensis* - Alcock, 1905; *Penaeopsis palmensis* - De Man, 1911; *Metapenaeopsis barbeensis* Hall, 1962.

FAO Names: Southern velvet shrimp (En), Crevette chamois méridionale (Fr), Camarón gamuza sureño (Sp).

Local Names: Southern velvet prawn (Australia).

Distribution: Indo-West Pacific: Malay Archipelago and northern Australia (from Shark Bay, Western Australia, to Sydney, New South Wales).

Habitat: Depth 18 to 22 m. Bottom mud. Marine.

Size: Maximum total length 105 mm.

Interest to Fishery: Cited by Racek (1959:10), under the name *Penaeopsis (Metapenaeopsis) novae-guineae*, as a species abundant in commercial prawn catches off New South Wales and Queensland. But their small size "renders them commercially unimportant" (Racek, 1957:12).

Metapenaeopsis philippii (Bate, 1881)	PEN Meta 14

Penaeus philippii Bate, 1881, Ann.Mag.Nat.Hist., (5)8:181

Synonymy: *Penaeus philippinensis* Bate, 1888; *Penaeopsis philippii* - De Man, 1911; *Penaeopsis philippinensis* - De Man, 1911; *Leptopenaeus philippinensis* - Kishinouye , 1929; *Penaeopsis (Metapenaeus) philippii* - Ramadan, 1938.

FAO Names: Philip velvet shrimp (En), Crevette chamois philippe (Fr), Camarón gamuza Felipe (Sp).

Literature: Champion, 1973:187-195.

Distribution: Indo-West Pacific: East Africa to the Philippines.

Habitat: Depth 150 to 894 m. Marine.

Size: Maximum total length 130 mm.

Interest to Fishery: Of potential commercial importance off S.W. India; caught in good numbers off the Kerala coast during exploratory trawling (Kurian & Sebastian, 1976:96).

Remarks: Due to the confusion that has existed concerning the identity or distinctness of this species, *M. coniger* (Wood-Mason, 1891), *M. andamanensis* (Wood-Mason, 1891) and other related species, previous records have to be considered with some reserve.

| *Metapenaeopsis rosea* Racek & Dall, 1965 | PEN Meta 15 |

Metapenaeopsis rosea Racek & Dall, 1965, Verh.K.Ned.Akad.Wet.(Natuurkd.), (2)56(3):29

FAO Names: Pink velvet shrimp (En), Crevette chamois rosée (Fr), Camarón gamuza rosado (Sp)

Distribution: Indo-West Pacific: northern and northeastern Australia.

Habitat: Depth 7 to 29 m. Marine.

Size: Maximum total length 120 mm.

Interest to Fishery: Listed by Racek (1973:155,159) among the species of commercial importance.

| *Metapenaeopsis stridulans* (Alcock, 1905) | PEN Meta 16 |

Metapenaeus stridulans Alcock, 1905, Ann.Mag.Nat.Hist., (7)16:518,526

Synonymy: *Penaeopsis stridulans* - De Man, 1911.

FAO Names: Fiddler shrimp (En), Crevette violoneux (Fr), Camarón violinista (Sp).

Distribution: Indo-West Pacific: Arabian Sea to the Malay Archipelago, New Guinea and New Britain.

Habitat: Depth 9 to 90 m. Marine.

Size: Maximum total length 100 mm.

Interest to Fishery: In the northern Arabian Sea the fishery for this species is of minor importance (Tirmizi, in Litt.). Near Bombay it is caught in fairly large numbers (in "dol" nets) especially in October and November (Kurian & Sebastian, 1976:96). It is likewise fished for in Sri Lanka (Longhurst, 1970:283) and Malaya (Tham, 1968:212).

| *Metapenaeopsis toloensis* Hall, 1962 | PEN Meta 17 |

Metapenaeopsis toloensis Hall, 1962, Fish.Publ.Colon.Off.(U.K.), 17:33

FAO Names: Tolo velvet shrimp (En), Crevette chamois tolo (Fr), Camarón gamuza tolo (Sp).

Distribution: Indo-West Pacific: Sri Lanka; Malaya.

Habitat: Depth 69 to 73 m. Marine.

Size: Maximum carapace length 24 mm.

Interest to Fishery: Cited by Longhurst (1970:283) as abundant in shrimp catches along the east coast of Sri Lanka, but of less importance than some *Penaeus* species.

| *Metapenaeus affinis* (H. Milne Edwards, 1837) | PEN Metap 1 |

Penaeus affinis H. Milne Edwards, 1837, <u>Hist.Nat.Crust.</u>, 2:416

Synonymy: *Penaeus mutatus* Lanchester, 1901; *Parapenaeus affinis* - M.J. Rathbun, 1902; *Metapenaeus mutatus* - Nobili, 1903; *Penaeopsis affinis* - De Man, 1911; *Metapenaeus necopinans* Hall, 1956.

FAO Names: Jinga shrimp (En), Crevette jinga (Fr), Camarón jinga (Sp).

Local Names: Jinga (Bombay, N.W. India), Kazhantan chemeen (S.W. India), Chingri (Bengal, N.E. India), Chung Ha, Middle prawn (Hong Kong; also used for other species of the genus).

Literature: George, 1970.

Distribution: Indo-West Pacific: Arabian Sea to the Malay Archipelago and Hong Kong.

Habitat: Depth 5 to 92 m. Bottom mud. Marine.

Size: Maximum total length 222 mm (exceptional), usually not more than 170 mm.

Interest to Fishery: The fishery for this species is of major importance in Pakistan; the species is also regularly fished for in the Persian Gulf. Along the west coast of India and the southern part of the east coast *M. affinis* is commercially the most important species of *Metapenaeus*. It is also important in Sri Lanka, the east and west coast of Malaya and in Hong Kong. In Bangladesh the shrimps are exported both frozen and canned; for local consumption they are peeled and cooked or fried, and used for the preparation of paste and shrimp meal. In Malaya it also forms the subject of a pond fishery.

| *Metapenaeus alcocki* George & Rao, 1968 | PEN Metap 2 |

Metapenaeus alcocki George & Rao, 1968, <u>J.Mar.Biol.Assoc.India</u>, 8:146

FAO Names: Fire shrimp (En), Crevette étincelle (Fr), Camarón foguete (Sp).

Distribution: Indo-West Pacific: Gulf of Kutch, India.

Habitat: Depth 3 to 12 m. Marine.

Size: Total length 97 mm ($\male$), 44 to 87 mm ($\female$); carapace length 23 mm ($\male$), 11 to 19 mm ($\female$).

Interest to Fishery: Minor. Listed by Kurian & Sebastian (1976:96) among the commercially important prawns of India, but with the annotation that only "very small numbers" are caught.

| *Metapenaeus bennettae* Racek & Dall, 1965 | PEN Metap 3 |

Metapenaeus bennettae Racek & Dall, 1965, <u>Verh.K.Ned.Akad.Wet.(Natuurkd.)</u>, (2)56(3):74

Synonymy: In some papers the present species has been erroneously indicated as *M. mastersii* (Haswell), which name actually is a synonym of *M. ensis* (see there). Western Australian specimens identified as *M. bennettae*, usually are *M. dalli*.

FAO Names: Greentail shrimp (En), Crevette queue verte (Fr), Camarón rabo verde (Sp).

Local Names: Greentail prawn, Inshore greasy back prawn, Bay prawn, River prawn (Australia).

Literature: Kirkegaard & Walker, 1970a.

Distribution: Indo-West Pacific: east coast of Australia (Queensland, New South Wales).

Habitat: Depth 0 to 30 m. Estuarine and marine.

Size: Maximum total length 77 mm (♂), 109 mm (♀).

Interest to Fishery: The species is the subject of a "thriving seasonal fishery in Moreton Bay (South Queensland) and, to a lesser extent, the Brisbane River" (Grant, 1965:243). It occurs also abundantly in commercial catches made in New South Wales, being the third most important species of prawn of that state.

Metapenaeus brevicornis (H. Milne Edwards, 1837)	PEN Metap 4

Penaeus brevicornis H. Milne Edwards, 1837, Hist.Nat.Crust., 2:417

Synonymy: *Penaeus avirostris* Dana, 1852; *Metapenaeus avirostris* - Nobili, 1903; *Penaeopsis brevicornis* - De Man, 1911; *Penaeopsis avirostris* - De Man, 1911.

FAO Names: Yellow shrimp (En), Crevette jaune (Fr), Camarón amarillo (Sp).

Local Names: Dhanbone chingri (Calcutta, India), Koraney (or Karaney) chingri, Honye chingri, Kucho chingri, Saga chingri (Bangladesh), Udang kuning, Yellow prawn (Singapore; Indonesia), Udang tjendana, Udang baratan (Indonesia), Kung lee (Thailand).

Literature: George, 1970c.

Distribution: Indo-West Pacific: Arabian Sea off Pakistan to Malaya, Indonesia and Thailand.

Habitat: Depth 4 to 90 m. Marine to almost fresh.

Size: Maximum total length 152 mm (usually not more than 130 mm). Shigueno (1975:146) mentioned that within 3 to 4 months a length of 80 to 110 mm is reached and a weight of 10 to 15 g.

Interest to Fishery: In Pakistan (Tirmizi, in Litt.) and N.W. India (Ramamurthy, 1967:1430) the species if of moderate to great commercial importance. It is used peeled and cooked or fried and is made to paste or shrimp meal. It is exported canned or frozen. Kurian & Sebastian (1976:96) stated that there is a "good fishery in northern regions of south [recte west] and east coasts [of India]. Juveniles also fished from estuaries". The species is reported to be of importance in the Ganges delta of West Bengal and Bangladesh and along the west coast of Thailand. In Thailand, Malaya and Indonesia it forms an important component of the pond culture shrimps.

Metapenaeus conjunctus Racek & Dall, 1965	PEN Metap 5

Metapenaeus conjunctus Racek & Dall, 1965, Verh.K.Ned.Akad.Wet.(Natuurkd.), (2)56(3):64

FAO Names: Wood shrimp (En), Crevette bois (Fr), Camarón leña (Sp).

Distribution: Indo-West Pacific: Malaya; Borneo.

Habitat: Depth 7 to 9 m. Brackish, estuarine.

Size: Maximum total length 88 mm (♂), 100 mm (♀).

Interest to Fishery: Reported as sold on the fish market in Sandakan, N. Borneo (Racek & Dall, 1965).

| *Metapenaeus dalli* Racek, 1957 | PEN Metap 6 |

Metapenaeus dalli Racek, 1957, <u>Fish.Bull.Fish.Dep.(West.Aust.)</u>, 6:4

Synonymy: In some papers misidentified as *M. bennettae*, or *M. mastersii*.

FAO Names: Western school shrimp (En), Crevette dali (Fr), Camarón dalí (Sp).

Local Names: School prawn (W. Australia).

Distribution: Indo-West Pacific: West coast of Australia; Indonesia.

Habitat: Depth 9 to 33 m. Bottom mud and sand. Estuarine.

Size: Maximum total length 65 mm (δ), 85 mm ($\circ\!\!\!\!\!+$).

Interest to Fishery: According to Longhurst (1970:285), who indicated the species as *M. bennettae*, it is the subject of a "small fishery with handnets in the estuaries of Western Australia ...... the landings are considered negligible for the present purpose".

| *Metapenaeus demani* (Roux, 1921) | PEN Metap 7 |

Penaeopsis demani Roux, 1921, <u>Nova Guinea</u>, 13:599

FAO Names: Demon shrimp (En), Crevette diable (Fr), Camarón diablo (Sp).

Local Names: Demons prawn [sic] (Australia: New Guinea; see Rapson & McIntosh, 1971:17).

Literature: Racek & Dall, 1965:75, Pl. 6, Fig. 5, Pl. 11, Fig. 5.

Distribution: Indo-West Pacific: Southern New Guinea; Queensland.

Habitat: Shallow brackish and salt water (also fresh?).

Size: Total length 73 to 96 mm (δ), 78 to 121 mm ($\circ\!\!\!\!\!+$).

Interest to Fishery: Rapson & McIntosh (1971:17) found the species in small numbers in commercial catches in New Guinea.

| *Metapenaeus dobsoni* (Miers, 1878) | PEN Metap 8 |

Penaeus dobsoni Miers, 1878, <u>Proc.Zool.Soc.Lond.</u>, 1878:302,307.

Synonymy: *Mangalura dobsoni* Miers, 1878; *Penaeopsis dobsoni* - De Man, 1911; *Metapenaeus dobsoni choprai* Nataraj, 1942.

FAO Names: Kadal shrimp (En), Crevette kadal (Fr), Camarón kadal (Sp).

Local Names: Thelly chemmeen (smaller specimens), Poovaalan chemmeen, Kadal chemmeen (larger specimens) (S.W. India), Chingri (east coast of India).

Literature: George, 1970a.

Distribution: Indo-West Pacific: west coast of India to Indonesia and the Philippines.

Habitat: Depth 1 to 37 m. Bottom mud. Marine and brackish water.

Size: Maximum total length 118 mm (δ), 130 mm ($\circ\!\!\!\!\!+$).

Interest to Fishery: The species is reported by Enomoto (1971:1,46) as being commercially important in the Persian Gulf near Kuwait. It forms also the subject of important inshore and trawl fisheries along the west and southwest coast of India; in the state of Kerala a major part of the total prawn catch consists of this species. It is the most abundant species in the prawn catches along the east coast of Sri Lanka, but because of its rather small size it is not the most valuable. In India juveniles are much fished for in the estuaries. In Kerala, *M. dobsoni* is the most important species in the rice field shrimp farming. In Indonesia it is one of the main species in the fishery on the south coast of Java.

Metapenaeus eboracensis Dall, 1957	**PEN Metap 9**

Metapenaeus eboracensis Dall, 1957, Aust.J.Mar.Freshwat.Res., 8:183,193

FAO Names: York shrimp (En), Crevette york (Fr), Camarón york (Sp).

Local Names: York prawn (Australia).

Distribution: Indo-West Pacific: Australia (Northern Territory, Queensland); Papua.

Habitat: Depth 2 to 27 m. Bottom mud. Marine.

Size: Maximum total length 111 mm ($\female$).

Interest to Fishery: Racek (1959:12) gave the present species as the last of seven species (listed in order of their importance) which were captured in payable quantities in Queensland, North of Cape Moreton. Harrison, Kesteven & Setter (1965:11) listed *M. eboracensis* among those shrimp species that "may offer some prospect for commercial fishing development" in the Gulf of Carpentaria, N. Australia.

Metapenaeus elegans De Man, 1907	**PEN Metap 10**

Metapeneus elegans De Man, 1907, Notes Leyden Mus., 29:130

Synonymy: *Penaeopsis elegans* - De Man, 1911; *Metapenaeus singaporensis* Hall, 1956.

FAO Names: Fine shrimp (En), Crevette élégante (Fr), Camarón fino (Sp).

Distribution: Indo-West Pacific: Sri Lanka; Malaya; Indonesia.

Habitat: In inland lagoons and ponds, rare in the sea. Depth 1 to 55 m. Usually in water with low salinity.

Size: Maximum total length 81 mm ($\female$); maximum carapace length 20 mm ($\male$), 29 mm ($\female$).

Interest to Fishery: Caught with traps in Ceylon, and irregularly found in prawn ponds in Singapore. Taken as admixture with other shrimps in Indonesia. Commercial value evidently not high.

Metapenaeus endeavouri (Schmitt, 1926)	**PEN Metap 11**

Penaeopsis endeavouri Schmitt, 1926, Biol.Results Fish.Exped.F.I.S. Endeavour, 1909-14, 5:329

FAO Names: Endeavour shrimp (En), Crevette devo (Fr), Camarón devo (Sp).

Local Names: Endeavour prawn (Australia), Brown prawn (Queensland).

Distribution: Indo-West Pacific: west, north and east coasts of Australia, from Shark Bay (W. Australia) to northern New South Wales.

Habitat: Depth 44 to 48 m. Marine.

Size: Maximum total length 140 mm (δ), 175 mm ($\female$).

Interest to Fishery: Racek (1957:12) stated that in the ocean waters of Queensland "the production of *Penaeus merguiensis* occupies the leading place, with that of ....[several species including]
Metapenaeus endeavouri following". In the other areas it seems to be of very minor importance.
Harrison, Kesteven & Setter (1965:11) cited the present species as offering some prospect for a
commercial fishing development in the Gulf of Carpentaria, N. Australia. It is also taken by trawlers
in the Gulf of Papua, and marketed there as frozen tails.

Metapenaeus ensis (De Haan, 1844)	PEN Metap 12

Penaeus ensis De Haan, 1844, <u>In</u> Von Siebold, Fauna Japonica, Crustacea (6/7):Pl. 46, Fig. 2

Synonymy: *Penaeus mastersii* Haswell, 1879; *Penaeus incisipes* Bate, 1888; *Parapenaeus incisipes*
- M.J. Rathbun, 1902; *Metapenaeus incisipes* - Alcock, 1905; *Metapenaeus mastersii* - Alcock, 1905;
Penaeopsis mastersi - De Man, 1911; *Penaeopsis incisipes* - De Man, 1911; *Penaeopsis ensis* - De Man,
1911. This species has often been confused with *Metapenaeus monoceros*. The name *M. mastersii* has at
times been used for specimens of *M. moyebi* from Malaya, of *M. dalli* from W. Australia, and of
M. bennettae from E. Australia.

FAO Names: Greasyback shrimp (En), Crevette glissante (Fr), Camarón resbaloso (Sp).

Local Names: Yosi ebi, Yoshi ebi (Japan), Sand shrimp (Taiwan), Chung ha, Middle prawn (Hong
Kong; name also used for other species of the genus), Kung takard (Thailand), Udang laki, Udang kaju,
Udang dogol, Udang apiapi (Indonesia), Offshore greasyback prawn (Australia).

Distribution: Indo-West Pacific: Sri Lanka and Malaya to S.E. China, Japan, the Malay Archipelago, New Guinea and western, northern and eastern Australia.

Habitat: Depth 18 to 64 m. Bottom mud. Marine and estuarine.

Size: Maximum total length 132 mm (δ), 159 mm ($\female$); maximum carapace length 35 mm (δ), 42 mm ($\female$).

Interest to Fishery: Of major commercial importance in Singapore, Malaya, Indonesia, the
Philippines and Japan. It forms one of the most important species in the prawn catches in Malaya,
Singapore, Indonesia and possibly also in the Philippines. According to Kurian & Sebastian (1976:97)
the species is the subject of a small fishery on the east coast of India "along with *M. monoceros*".
In Malaya it is one of the dominant species in the prawn pond industry (Johnson, 1966:276), and also
in Thailand, the Philippines and Taiwan it is cultured in fish ponds (Shigueno, 1975). In Japan
M. ensis seems to be caught mainly by trawlers. Kubo (1949:332) reported it from the Tokyo fish
market and Harada (1968:82) reported that it is fished for by commercial fishermen in the Lake Naka-
umi area of Shimane prefecture. Yasuda (1957:196) mentioned its use as bait in Japan.

Metapenaeus insolitus Racek & Dall, 1965	PEN Metap 13

Metapenaeus insolitus Racek & Dall, 1965, <u>Verh.K.Ned.Akad.Wet.(Natuurkd.)</u>, (2)56(3):69

FAO Names: Emerald shrimp (En), Crevette émeraude (Fr), Camarón esmeralda (Sp).

Distribution: Indo-West Pacific: Australia (Northern Territory, Queensland).

Habitat: Depth 13 to 33 m. Bottom mud or sand. Marine.

Size: Total length 50 to 71 mm (δ), 45 to 111 mm ($\female$).

Interest to Fishery: Listed by Motoh (1977:6) among commercially important penaeids, with a
reference to Munro (1968:14), who mentioned the species only in a general statement without making
definitely clear that it is of commercial importance.

Metapenaeus intermedius (Kishinouye, 1900)	PEN Metap 14

Penaeus intermedius Kishinouye, 1900, <u>J.Fish.Bur., Tokyo</u>, 8:21

Synonymy: *Penaeopsis intermedius* De Man, 1911; *Penaeopsis intermedia anchista* De Man, 1920.

FAO Names: Middle shrimp (En), Crevette ceinture (Fr), Camarón cintura (Sp).

Local Names: Hige naga ebi (Japan), Chung ha, Middle prawn (Hong Kong; name used also for other species in the genus).

Distribution: Indo-West Pacific: Japan; Hong Kong; Malaysia; Singapore; Andaman Islands; Indonesia.

Habitat: Depth 12 to 13 m. Bottom mud. Marine.

Size: Maximum total length 79 mm (δ), 142 mm ($\female$).

Interest to Fishery: Longhurst (1970:288,290) indicated that the species is trawled off Singapore and also is taken at Hong Kong. Yokoya (1933:9) reported it from the market at Uwazima, Ehime-ken, Japan and Balss (1914:8) mentioned material from the Singapore market.

Metapenaeus joyneri (Miers, 1880)	PEN Metap 15

Penaeus joyneri Miers, 1880, <u>Ann.Mag.Nat.Hist.</u>, (5)5:458

Synonymy: *Penaeus pallidus* Kishinouye, 1897; *Parapenaeus joyneri* - M.J. Rathbun, 1902; *Penaeopsis joyneri* - De Man, 1911.

FAO Names: Shiba shrimp (En), Crevette siba (Fr), Camarón siba (Sp).

Local Names: Shiba ebi, Siba ebi (Japan), Small white prawn (Hong Kong).

Distribution: Indo-West Pacific: Japan; Korea; China; Hong Kong.

Habitat: Depth 20 m or less. Bottom sand. Marine.

Size: Maximum total length 110 mm (δ), 125 mm ($\female$); maximum carapace length 27 mm (δ), 34 mm ($\female$).

Interest to Fishery: In Japan the species is fished for in the Inland Sea (Longhurst, 1970:290), where it forms about 20% of the catches. It belongs also to the commercially important shrimps of other areas in Japan (e.g., Tokyo Bay), of Korea (Yoshida, 1941:14) and N. China (Liu, 1955:12). The annual catch of the species (in metric tons) in the Republic of Korea was 1 200 (in 1973), 2 144 (in 1974), 1 533 (in 1975), and 2 009 (in 1976).

Metapenaeus kutchensis George, George & Rao, 1963	PEN Metap 16

Metapenaeus kutchensis George, George, & Rao, 1963, <u>J.Mar.Biol.Assoc.India</u>, 5:284

FAO Names: Ginger shrimp (En), Crevette gingembre (Fr), Camarón jengibre (Sp).

Distribution: Indo-West Pacific: Gulf of Kutch, N.W. India.

Habitat: Depth 3 to 12 m. Marine.

Size: Maximum total length 148 mm (δ), 164 mm ($\female$).

Interest to Fishery: "Contributes to a good percentage of the fishery in the Gulf of Kutch area" (Jones, 1967:1335; Ramamurthy, 1967:1424).

Metapenaeus lysianassa (De Man, 1888)	PEN Metap 17

Penaeus lysianassa De Man, 1888, J.Linn.Soc.Lond.(Zool.), 22:290

Synonymy: *Penaeopsis lysianassa* - De Man, 1911; *Metapenaeus lysianassa malaccaensis* Hall, 1962.

FAO Names: Bird shrimp (En), Crevette oiseau (Fr), Camarón parancero (Sp).

Distribution: Indo-West Pacific: West and East coasts of India; Bay of Bengal; Malaya; Thailand; Indonesia.

Habitat: Depth 5 to 9 m. Marine.

Size: Maximum total length 55 mm (♂), 88 mm (♀).

Interest to Fishery: According to Rai (1933:885) the species is of economic value in Bombay, but Jones (1967:1335) stated that "*Metapenaeus lysianassa* has been reported by some to be an important prawn in some parts of the west coast [of India], but this remains to be confirmed". Pannikkar (1937: 345) mentioned *M. lysianassa* among the economically important species of Travancore. Kurian & Sebastian (1976:97), although including the species in their list of commercially important prawns of India, mentioned that it was taken in "stray catches only". Ahmad (1957) mentioned the species from Bangladesh, but it is not clear from his account whether the species is there of commercial importance. Longhurst (1970:288) cited the fishery in Singapore, while Racek & Dall (1965:79) reported upon specimens obtained at the fish market of Sandakan, North Borneo.

Metapenaeus macleayi (Haswell, 1879)	PEN Metap 18

Penaeus macleayi Haswell, 1879, Proc.Linn.Soc.N.S.W., 4:40

Synonyms: *Penaeopsis macleayi* - De Man, 1911; *Penaeus haswelli* Phillips, 1925.

FAO Names: Eastern school shrimp (En), Crevette de maclay (Fr), Camarón maclayo (Sp).

Local Names: School prawn, White River prawn (Australia).

Literature: Kirkegaard & Walker, 1970c.

Distribution: Indo-West Pacific: East coast of Australia from S. Queensland to N. Victoria, most common in New South Wales.

Habitat: Depth 22 to 37 m, juveniles in shallower water. Marine and estuarine.

Size: Maximum total length 162 mm.

Interest to Fishery: "This is the most important commercial species of the New South Wales prawn industry" (Racek, 1955:229). It is not very common in Queensland or Victoria.

Metapenaeus monoceros (Fabricius, 1798)	PEN Metap 19

Penaeus monoceros Fabricius, 1798, Suppl.Ent.Syst., 409

Synonymy: *Penaeopsis monoceros* - De Man, 1911. The records of *M. monoceros* from the area E. and N. of that indicated here, usually pertain to *M. ensis*.

FAO Names: Speckled shrimp (En), Crevette mouchetée (Fr), Camarón moteado (Sp).

Local Names: Speckled prawn, Ginger prawn (S.E. Africa), Kamba, Kamba ndogo (Swahili language, E. Africa), patsanorana (Madagascar; a name also used for other species of prawn), Koraney chingri, Honye chingri (Calcutta, India), Honye chingri, Karkaria chingri, Karaney chingri, Kucho chingri and Lallia chingri (Bangladesh), Klipa kasha (Israel).

Literature: George, 1970b.

Distribution: Indo-West Pacific: E. and S.E. Africa (from Durban north), Red Sea to the Bay of Bengal. Eastern Atlantic: entered into the eastern Mediterranean (Turkey, Syria, Lebanon, Israel, Egypt) through the Suez Canal.

Habitat: Depth 1 to 60 m (mostly between 10 and 30 m), some reports from greater depths (up to 170 m). Bottom sandy mud. Salinity 5 to 35°/oo. Brackish to marine.

Size: Maximum total length 150 mm ($\male$), 195 mm ($\female$); maximum carapace length 50 mm ($\female$).

Interest to Fishery: Of commercial value almost throughout its range. In Eastern South Africa it is of medium importance, the specimens trawled offshore are used for food, sold whole or peeled and used as delicacy in restaurants, etc.; those fished inshore are usually used as bait. In Mozambique the species is an important fishery object. In Tanzania and Kenya the fishery is of minor to moderate importance, the specimens are used here as food as such, being consumed mostly whole and fried, juveniles are also used (whole and peeled) in local dishes. *Metapenaeus monoceros* is one of the dominant species in the inshore fishery along the east coast of Madagascar. In Somalia, the Gulf of Aden and in Yemen it is of some commercial importance. In the southern Red Sea it is caught by trawlers, but there seem to be no extensive shrimp resources there (Ben-Tuvia, 1968). In Pakistan the species is of moderate importance in the offshore fishery, and is exported frozen and canned, and used locally peeled and cooked or fried in paste. Along the Indian coast the species is fished both offshore and inshore, its importance varies from place to place. Kurian & Sebastian (1976:97) remarked that in India it forms a "very important fishery of commercial importance". Both along the Kerala coast (S.W. India) and in the Ganges delta, the species plays a minor role in rice field shrimp farming. In Bangladesh there is an inshore fishery for this species. In the Mediterranean *Metapenaeus monoceros* is taken by trawlers off the south coast of Turkey, on the continental shelf off Israel, and off Alexandria, Egypt.

Metapenaeus moyebi (Kishinouye, 1896)	PEN Metap 20

Penaeus moyebi Kishinouye, 1896, Zool.Mag.Tokyo, 8:373

Synonymy: *Metapenaeus burkenroadi* Kubo, 1954.

FAO Names: Moyebi shrimp (En), Crevette moyebi (Fr), Camarón moyebi (Sp).

Local Names: Mo ebi (Japan), Chung ha, Middle prawn (Hong Kong; names also used for other species of the genus).

Distribution: Indo-West Pacific: Southern India and Sri Lanka to Japan, the Malay Archipelago and N. Queensland (Australia).

Habitat: Depth 5.5 to 45 m. Bottom mud. Marine and brackish water.

Size: Maximum total length 97 mm; maximum carapace length 17.5 mm ($\female$).

Interest to Fishery: The present species (usually cited in the literature concerning the area as *Metapenaeus mastersii* but incorrectly so) is of importance in the prawn pond culture of Malay and Singapore. It is also of economic importance in the Philippines (Longhurst, 1970:290) and Japan (where, until 1954, it was usually, incorrectly, indicated as *M. affinis*). Yasuda (1957:30; 1957a: 196) mentioned that the present species is of economic importance in the Inland Sea of Japan, where it forms part of the trawl catches; it is used as bait. Kurian & Sebastian (1976:96) listed the present species (as *M. burkenroadi*) among the commercially important species of India with the remark "a few recorded recently".

Remarks: In an unillustrated preliminary paper written in Japanese and entitled "Japanese Penaeid shrimps and their classification" Kishinouye (1896:372-374) gave a key to the Japanese Penaeidae known to him, all of which were placed by him in the genus *Penaeus*. All but one of the species dealt with by Kishinouye were referred to forms described previously by other authors; the one exception is *Penaeus moyebi* which was new. With *Penaeus monoceros* Fabricius, 1798, and *P. affinis* H. Milne Edwards, it formed a (triple) couplet in Kishinouye's key, and the three species were there given the numbers, 7, 8 and 9 respectively. In Kishinouye's (1900) final monograph "Japanese species of the genus *Penaeus*", which has both an English and Japanese text and was profusely illustrated, the names given to the three just mentioned species are quite different from those used in 1896. The species 7, 8 and 9 of 1896, in 1900 were given the names *P. affinis* H. Milne Edwards, 1837 *P. joyneri* Miers, 1880 and *P. incisipes* Bate, 1888, respectively. After 1900 the name *Penaeus* (or *Metapenaeus*, or *Penaeopsis*) *affinis* was commonly used for species 7 and, being a junior synonym, the name *P. moyebi* was completely forgotten. In 1954, however, Kubo (1954:92) showed that the Japanese species then currently identified as *Metapenaeus affinis* is different from the true *Metapenaeus affinis* (H. Milne Edwards, 1837) from India and Pakistan. Kubo therefore proposed the new name *Metapenaeus burkenroadi* for the Japanese species. As the available name *Penaeus moyebi* Kishinouye, 1896, for the same species is older, it has priority and should be used, *M. burkenroadi* Kubo, 1954, falling as a junior synonym. For this reason the less familiar name *Metapenaeus moyebi* (Kishinouye, 1896) is adopted here for the present species.

Metapenaeus papuensis Racek & Dall, 1965	PEN Metap 21

Metapenaeus papuensis Racek & Dall, 1965, <u>Verh.K.Ned.Akad.Wet.(Natuurkd.)</u>, (2)56(3):66

FAO Names: Papua shrimp (En), Crevette papou (Fr), Camarón papuense (Sp).

Distribution: Indo-West Pacific: Papua and New Guinea.

Habitat: Marine.

Size: Maximum total length 110 mm.

Interest to Fishery: Listed by Racek (1973:155,160) among the Indo-West Pacific penaeid prawns of commercial importance.

Metapenaeus stebbingi Nobili, 1904	PEN Metap 22

Metapenaeus stebbingi Nobili, 1904, <u>Bull.Mus.Hist.Nat., Paris</u>, 10:229

Synonymy: *Penaeopsis stebbingi* - De Man, 1911; *Mangalura stebbingi* - Burkenroad, 1959; *Metapenaeopsis stebbingi* - Kensley, 1969.

FAO Names: Peregrine shrimp (En), Crevette faucon (Fr), Camarón peregrino (Sp).

Distribution: Indo-West Pacific: E. Africa and Red Sea to Pakistan and N.W. India (Kutch). Eastern Atlantic: the species has entered the eastern Mediterranean through the Suez Canal and has been found as far north as the Israel coast.

Habitat: Depth down to 90 m. Bottom mud, or sandy mud. Marine.

Size: Maximum total length 139 mm, usually much smaller.

Interest to Fishery: Gorgy (1966:62) mentioned that *M. stebbingi* is caught in the Mediterranean coast near Alexandria, Egypt, where it, *Penaeus japonicus*, *P. semisulcatus* and *Metapenaeus monoceros* "constituent une partie importante des apports des chalutiers". Also in the Red Sea and the Gulf of Aden the species is caught for commercial purposes: Gurney (1927:228) reported that the species was sold for bait in Suez, and Burkenroad (1959:87) reported upon material obtained at the Suez market. Gorgy (1966a:103) mentioned *M. stebbingi* from the Suez Canal (Timsah and Bitter Lakes) and the Gulf of Suez where it is trawled. Ben-Tuvia (1968:51) listed the species among those trawled in the southern Red Sea by Israel trawlers, but it evidently is only of minor importance there. Tirmizi (in Litt.) indicated *Metapenaeus stebbingi* as of major commercial importance on the Pakistan coast, where it is trawled, and exported frozen or canned, while it also is peeled, and cooked or fried, and used as shrimp meal and in paste. Kurian & Sebastian (1976:97) mention "stray catches only" of this species from N.W. India. In Madagascar *M. stebbingi* is reported to form a minor part of commercial catches made along the west and north-west coasts.

Metapenaeus tenuipes Kubo, 1949	PEN Metap 23

Metapenaeus tenuipes Kubo, 1949, J.Tokyo Coll.Fish., 36(1):348

Synonymy: *Metapenaeus spinulatus* Kubo, 1949.

FAO Names: Stork shrimp (En), Crevette cigogne (Fr), Camarón cigueña (Sp).

Distribution: Indo-West Pacific: Thailand; W. Indonesia; Malaya; Singapore.

Habitat: Depth 4 to 27 m. Marine.

Size: Maximum total length 97 mm.

Interest to Fishery: The species is taken in commercial catches in Malaya (Hall, 1961:86).

Parapenaeopsis acclivirostris Alcock, 1905	PEN Para 1

Parapenaeopsis acclivirostris Alcock, 1905, Ann.Mag.Nat.Hist., (7)16:522

FAO Names: Hawknose shrimp (En), Crevette aquiline (Fr), Camarón aguileño (Sp).

Literature: Alcock, 1906:42, Pl. 8, Fig.27; Tirmizi & Bashir, 1973:58, Figs. 40L-P, 42.

Distribution: Indo-West Pacific: South and East Africa to India.

Habitat: Depth 24 to 48 m. Marine.

Size: Maximum total length 47 mm (δ), 73 mm ($\female$); carapace length 7 to 18.5 mm.

Interest to Fishery: Minor. Kunju (1967:1384) listed this species as "occurring in the fishery" off the Maharashtra coast of India. Kurian & Sebastian (1976:97) mentioned that the species is found in India "in small numbers with other commercial species".

Parapenaeopsis arafurica Racek & Dall, 1965	PEN Para 2

Parapenaeopsis arafurica Racek & Dall, 1965, Verh.K.Ned.Akad.Wet.(Natuurkd.), (2)56(3):102

FAO Names: Arafura shrimp (En), Crevette arafura (Fr), Camarón arafura (Sp).

Distribution: Indo-West Pacific: Australia (Northern Territory) and New Guinea (Gulf of Papua).

Habitat: Depth 16 m. Bottom mud. Marine.

Size: Total length 41 to 58 mm (δ), 51 to 78 mm ($\female$).

Interest to Fishery: Listed by Motoh (1977:6), who referred to Munro (1968), as a commercially important penaeid. Munro (1968:14), however, ranged the species among "smaller species regarded as having no commercial value".

Parapenaeopsis atlantica Balss, 1914

Parapenaeopsis atlantica Balss, 1914, Zool.Anz., 44:593

Synonymy: *Trachypenaeus constrictus africana* Balss, 1916.

FAO Names: Guinea shrimp (En), Crevette guinéenne (Fr), Camarón guineo (Sp).

Local Names: Tshengtsheng, Song (Ga language, Ghana), Sesew, Asisi (Winnebah language, Ghana), Bolu (Ewe language, Ghana), Musombé (Subu language, Cameroon), Mikossa (Vili language, Congo), Petite crevette (Congo).

Distribution: Eastern Atlantic: West African coast from Senegal to Angola.

Habitat: Depth 1 to 60 m (most abundant between 10 and 40 m). Bottom mud or sandy mud. Temperature not less than 16°C. Marine and estuarine.

Size: Maximum total length 173 mm (usually less: 60 to 90 mm (δ), 90 to 140 mm ($\female$).

Interest to Fishery: The species is fished for practically throughout its range, but is not of such abundance that it is anywhere the main subject of the fishery. In the Ivory Coast, Cameroon and Congo (Brazzaville) it is fished by trawlers (Crosnier & Bondy, 1957:5,6), while also in Nigeria trawl fishing for the species has started (Thomas, 1969:415). Since the species occurs abundantly in shallow waters it forms the object of native inshore fisheries. Irvine (1947:308) mentioned that in Ghana these prawns are highly esteemed as food. Monod (1927:594) and Balss (1914a:593) mentioned their capture in fish traps in Cameroon.

Parapenaeopsis cornuta (Kishinouye, 1900)

Penaeus cornutus Kishinouye, 1900, J.Fish.Bur., Tokyo, 8:23

FAO Names: Coral shrimp (En), Crevette corail (Fr), Camarón coral (Sp).

Local Names: Coral prawn (Australia).

Literature: Kubo, 1949:374, Figures; Dall, 1957:215, Fig. 26.

Distribution: Indo-West Pacific: India to Japan and N. Australia.

Habitat: Depth 1 to 37 m. Marine.

Size: Total length 48.5 to 83 mm (δ), 49 to 82 mm ($\female$); maximum carapace length 24 mm.

Interest to Fishery: Minor. Muthu (1971:147) reported the species from commercial catches landed at the east coast of India (Visakhapatnam and Kakinada). Kunju (1967:1384) listed it as occurring in the fishery of the Maharashtra coast of India.

Parapenaeopsis coromandelica Alcock, 1906

Parapenaeopsis stylifera coromandelica Alcock, 1906, Cat. Indian Decap.Crust., 3(1):37

FAO Names: Coromandel shrimp (En), Crevette coromandel (Fr), Camarón coromandel (Sp).

Distribution: Indo-West Pacific: East coast of India, and Sri Lanka to Indonesia.

Habitat: Depth 7 to 11 m. Marine.

Size: Maximum total length 120 mm (δ and $\female$).

Interest to Fishery: Menon (1956:346) listed the present species under the "prawns of commercial value in India". Tham (1968:212), indicated it as commonly found in shrimp catches in Malaysia. De Bruin (1965:99) noted it to be very abundant off the west coast of Sri Lanka. Longhurst (1970:282, 284), who confirmed the commercial possibilities of the species in Sri Lanka, also thought it to be of potential value off the west coast of Thailand. The same author (Longhurst, 1970:285) indicated that the inshore fisheries along the north west coast of Malaya are dominated by two *Parapenaeopsis* species, the less important of these being *P. coromandelica*.

Remarks: Many authors treated this form as a subspecies of *P. stylifera*. As the two are clearly distinct, and as the subspecific status of most marine crustacea is not well enough known, we follow here Hall (1962) in treating the present form as a full species.

| *Parapenaeopsis hardwickii* (Miers, 1878) | PEN Para 6 |

Penaeus hardwickii Miers, 1878, Proc.Zool.Soc.Lond., 1878:300,306

Synonymy: *Parapenaeopsis sculptilis hardwickii* - Alcock, 1906.

FAO Names: Spear shrimp (En), Crevette javelot (Fr), Camarón lanzón (Sp).

Local Names: Hard spear prawn (Hong Kong).

Distribution: Indo-West Pacific: Pakistan to China and Indonesia.

Habitat: Depth 5 to 90 m. Marine.

Size: Maximum total length 135 mm ($\female$).

Interest to Fishery: Of minor commercial importance in Pakistan (Tirmizi, in Litt.) and N.W. India (Jones, 1967:1336; Longhurst, 1970:281), where it is commonly found in trawler catches. Kurian & Sebastian (1976:98) reported "good fishery for the species near Bombay, and less so on the east coast of India in the Godavery estuary". Along the west coast of Malaya and probably also that of Thailand, the species dominates in the inshore fishery (Longhurst, 1970:284,285). Near Singapore it is found in the offshore catches made by trawlers (Longhurst, 1970:288).

| *Parapenaeopsis hungerfordi* Alcock, 1905 | PEN Para 7 |

Parapenaeopsis hungerfordi Alcock, 1905,   Ann.Mag.Nat.Hist., (7)16:522,530

FAO Names: Dog shrimp (En), Crevette chien (Fr), Camarón perro (Sp).

Local Names: Dog prawn (Hong Kong).

Distribution: Indo-West Pacific: Malaya and Indonesia to S. China.

Habitat: Depth 5 to 13 m. Marine.

Size: Maximum total length 104 mm.

Interest to Fishery: According to Tham (1968:212) the species is commonly found in shrimp catches in Malaya, while Longhurst (1970:284) indicated that it is one of the dominant species in catches made off N.W. Malaysia and probably also off the west coast of Thailand.

| *Parapenaeopsis maxillipedo* Alcock, 1905 | PEN Para 8 |

Parapeneopsis maxillipedo Alcock, 1905, Ann.Mag.Nat.Hist., (7)16:522,527

Synonymy: *Parapenaeopsis cornuta maxillipedo* - Racek & Dall, 1965.

FAO Names: Torpedo shrimp (En), Crevette torpille (Fr), Camarón torpedo (Sp).

Distribution: Indo-West Pacific: from the west coast of India and Sri Lanka to Malaya, the Philippines, Indonesia, New Guinea and northern Australia.

Habitat: Depth 9 to 11 m. Bottom mud. Marine.

Size: Maximum total length up to 121 mm.

Interest to Fishery: The species is reported to be of commercial value in Bombay waters (Kunju, 1967:1385). According to Tham (1968:212) it is commonly found in commercial catches made in Malayan waters.

Parapenaeopsis nana Alcock, 1905	PEN Para 9

Parapenaeopsis nana Alcock, 1905, Ann.Mag.Nat.Hist., (7)16:522,529

FAO Names: Dwarf shrimp (En), Crevette naine (Fr), Camarón enano (Sp).

Literature: Alcock, 1906:41, Pl. 8, Fig. 26.

Distribution: Indo-West Pacific: India; Sri Lanka.

Habitat: Depth 7 to 124 m. Marine.

Size: Maximum total length 55 mm; carapace length 10.5 to 12 mm (δ), 11 to 12 mm ($\stackrel{\circ}{+}$).

Interest to Fishery: Little or none. Kurian & Sebastian (1976:98) listed the species among the commercially important prawns of India, but remarked that the specimens have been taken only in stray catches on the east coast.

Parapenaeopsis probata Hall, 1961	PEN Para 10

Parapenaeopsis probata Hall, 1961, Bull.Raffles Mus., 26:96

Synonymy: According to De Bruin (1965:96) *Parapenaeopsis probata* is a synonym of *P. uncta* Alcock, 1905.

FAO Names: Parole shrimp (En), Crevette parole (Fr), Camarón parolo (Sp).

Distribution: Indo-West Pacific: Kuwait; Malaya; Singapore.

Habitat: Depth 44 to 82 m. Bottom clean. Marine.

Size: Maximum carapace length 22 mm (δ), 31 mm ($\stackrel{\circ}{+}$).

Interest to Fishery: The species is mentioned by Longhurst (1970:288) as a species taken from trawl catches off Singapore.

Parapenaeopsis sculptilis (Heller, 1862)	PEN Para 11

Penaeus sculptilis Heller, 1862, Verh.Zool.-Bot.Ges.Wien, 12:528

Synonymy: *? Parapenaeopsis sculptilis cultrirostris* Alcock, 1906; *? Parapenaeopsis cultrirostris* - Kubo, 1949.

FAO Names: Rainbow shrimp (En), Crevette arc-en-ciel (Fr), Camarón arco iris (Sp).

Local Names: Kiddi (Pakistan; a name also used for other species of approximately the same size), Baga tara ichha, Bagtara chingri (Bangladesh), Rainbown prawn, Coral prawn (Australia).

Literature: Kirkegaard & Walker, 1970b.

Distribution: Indo-West Pacific: from Pakistan to Malaya, Hong Kong, the Philippines, Indonesia, New Guinea and N. Australia.

Habitat: Depth 35 to 90 m. Marine.

Size: Maximum total length 170 mm.

Interest to Fishery: In Pakistan the species is of moderate importance; it is peeled and is exported frozen and canned, it is also cooked and fried and used as shrimp meal and in shrimp paste (Tirmizi, in Litt.). In India it occurs in commercial catches off Bombay and off the Ganges delta (Jones, 1967:1336). Kurian & Sebastian (1976:98) mentioned that there is "a small fishery in the northern east and west coasts" of India. In Bangladesh it "is found in abundance in the estuaries"... "and provides a lucrative fishery" (Ahmad, 1957:13). Also in Malaya and Singapore it is of commercial importance (Tham, 1968:212, for Malaya; Kubo, 1949:390 mentioned a specimen from the Singapore fish market). In Australia the species is of commercial value North of Cape Moreton, Queensland (Racek, 1959:12). Grant (1965:242) remarked that "it is a popular bait species on the Central Queensland coast".

| *Parapenaeopsis stylifera* (H. Milne Edwards, 1837) | PEN Para 12 |

Penaeus styliferus H. Milne Edwards, 1837, Hist.Nat.Crust., 2:418

Synonymy: *Penaeopsis stylifera* - Bate, 1881.

FAO Names: Kiddi shrimp (En), Crevette kidi (Fr), Camarón kidi (Sp).

Local Names: Kiddi (Pakistan, also used for other species of about the same size).

Literature: Rao, 1970.

Distribution: Indo-West Pacific: Kuwait; Pakistan; India (mainly on the west coast and southern part of the east coast); Sri Lanka; Bangladesh.

Habitat: Depth 20 to 90 m. Marine.

Size: Maximum total length 145 mm.

Interest to Fishery: The species is of major commercial importance in Pakistan (Tirmizi, in Litt.), and all along the west coast of India: Kutch (Ramamurthy, 1967:1426), Bombay (Jones, 1967:1336), Karwar (Radakrishnan, 1967:1422) and Travancore in present Kerala State, where according to Chopra (1943:3) the species "is fished on a very large scale in the littoral regions". Ahmad (1957:12) listed it among the economic prawns of Bangladesh.

| *Parapenaeopsis tenella* (Bate, 1888) | PEN Para 13 |

Penaeus tenellus Bate, 1888, Rep.Voyage Challenger, (Zool.), 24:270

Synonymy: *Penaeus crucifer* Ortmann, 1890; *Metapenaeus tenellus* - Alcock, 1905; *Metapenaeus crucifer* - Alcock, 1905.

FAO Names: Smoothshell shrimp (En), Crevette glabre (Fr), Camarón liso (Sp).

Local Names: Subesube ebi (Japan), Smooth shelled prawn (Hong Kong).

Distribution: Indo-West Pacific: from Japan and Korea south to northern Australia, New Guinea, Indonesia, Malaya, Bangladesh, India, Sri Lanka, and Pakistan.

Habitat: Depth 5.5 to 16 m. Marine.

Size: Maximum total length 42 mm (δ), 67 mm ($\female$); maximum carapace length 16.5 mm (δ), 19 mm ($\female$).

Interest to Fishery: The species is listed under the economically important shrimps of Korea (Yoshida, 1941:15), and of N. China (Liu, 1955:16). Yasuda (1957:30) mentioned it as one of the species that are important in the shrimp fishery in the Inland Sea of Japan. Tham (1968:212) listed it as commonly found in the shrimp catches of Malaya. According to Kurian & Sebastian (1976:98) in India it is caught in small numbers only (Palk Bay and Gulf of Mannar). Muthu (1971:147) mentioned specimens from commercial catches landed at Visakhapatnam and Kakinada (east coast of India). According to Tirmizi (in Litt.) it is of minor commercial value in Pakistan.

Parapenaeopsis uncta Alcock, 1905	PEN Para 14

Parapenaeopsis uncta Alcock, 1905, Ann.Mag.Nat.Hist., (7)16:522

Synonymy: According to De Bruin (1965:96) *Parapenaeopsis probata* Hall, is a synonym.

FAO Names: Uncta shrimp (En), Crevette uncta (Fr), Camarón unta (Sp).

Local Names: Kiddi (Pakistan, a name also used for other species of about the same size).

Distribution: Indo-West Pacific: the species has been reported from Pakistan, India, Bangladesh and Sri Lanka.

Habitat: Depth 5 to 82 m. Marine.

Size: Maximum total length 120 mm.

Interest to Fishery: Qureshi (1956:362) and Qureshi & Hashmi (1965:73) mentioned the species as occurring in commercial catches in Pakistan. Rai (1933:886) reported it among the species caught near Bombay. Kurian & Sebastian (1976:98) recorded "stray catches only" from India. Ahmad (1957:14) listed it among the prawns fished for in Bangladesh. The importance of the fishery cannot be very great as Tirmizi (in Litt.) does not list it for Pakistan and neither Jones (1967) nor Tham (1968) give it among the commercial prawns of India.

Parapenaeopsis venusta De Man, 1907	PEN Para 15

Parapenaeopsis venusta De Man, 1907, Notes Leyden Mus., 29:134

FAO Names: Adonis shrimp (En), Crevette adonis (Fr), Camarón adonis (Sp).

Literature: De Man, 1911:93; De Man, 1913, Pl. 9, Fig. 30; Dall, 1957:220, Fig. 28.

Distribution: Indo-West Pacific: Malaya; Indonesia; Australia (Queensland).

Habitat: Depth 11 to 44 m. Bottom sand, shells, stones and mud. Marine.

Size: Total length 37 to 45 mm ($\female$); carapace length 0.9 mm (δ), 1.3 mm ($\female$).

Interest to Fishery: Listed among the commercially important penaeids by Motoh (1977:6), who based himself on Munro (1968:14). The latter, however, ranged the species among "smaller species regarded as having no commercial value". Also the rarity of the species (only a few specimens have been reported upon) makes it unlikely that it ever will become of commercial value.

Parapenaeus australiensis Dall, 1957	PEN Parap 2

Parapenaeus australiensis Dall, 1957, Aust.J.Mar.Freshwat.Res., 8:179

FAO Names: Australian rose shrimp (En), Crevette rose australienne (Fr), Camarón rosado australiano (Sp).

Distribution: Indo-West Pacific: Eastern Australia.

Habitat: Depth 124 to 180 m. Marine.

Size: Maximum total length 160 mm.

Interest to Fishery: Listed as commercially important by Racek (1973:155,161).

Parapenaeus fissurus (Bate, 1881)	PEN Parap 3

Penaeus fissurus Bate, 1881, <u>Ann.Mag.Nat.Hist.</u>, (5)8:180

FAO Names: Neptune rose shrimp (En), Crevette neptune (Fr), Camarón rosado neptuno (Sp).

Distribution: Indo-West Pacific: from East Africa and the Red Sea through India and Malaya to Japan, the Philippines and Indonesia.

Habitat: Depth 50 to 274 m. Bottom mud and sand. Marine.

Size: Maximum total length 78 mm (δ), 107 mm ($\female$); maximum carapace length 20 mm (δ), 31.5 mm ($\female$). Kurian & Sebastian (1976:99) gave the total length as 120 mm, while Crosnier & Jouannic (1973:10) indicated it as 140 mm.

Interest to Fishery: Crosnier & Jouannic (1973:10) listed *P. fissurus* as one of the species "éventuellement commercialisables" on the continental shelf of Madagascar. Kurian & Sebastian (1976: 99) included the species among the commercially important prawns of India, but stated that it is taken in "stray catches only". According to Yasuda (1957:30) *P. fissurus* belongs to those shrimps that are important in the fishery in the Inland Sea of Japan. Judging by Yoshida's (1941:17, Fig. 10) figure of petasma of his material of *"P. fissurus"* from the fishmarket at Fusan, Korea, this does not belong to the present species but to *P. lanceolatus*.

Parapenaeus investigatoris Alcock & Anderson, 1899	PEN Parap 4

Parapenaeus investigatoris Alcock & Anderson, 1899, <u>Ann.Mag.Nat.Hist.</u>, (7)3:279

FAO Names: Explorer rose shrimp (En), Crevette rose chercheuse (Fr), Camarón explorador (Sp).

Literature: Kubo, 1949:406, Figures.

Distribution: Indo-West Pacific: S.E. Africa and Gulf of Aden to the Malay Archipelago and Japan.

Habitat: Depth 220 to 1 240 m. Marine.

Size: Total length 62 to 76 mm (δ), 73 to 82 mm ($\female$); carapace length 14 to 15 mm (δ), 18 mm ($\female$).

Interest to Fishery: Minor. Included by Kurian & Sebastian (1976:99) among the Indian prawns of commercial importance with the annotation that it is "recorded in small numbers " and taken "mostly in the Gulf of Mannar, off Pulicat Lake and Andamans. Also off Cochin in deep-sea trawling".

Parapenaeus lanceolatus Kubo, 1949	PEN Parap 5

Parapenaeus lanceolatus Kubo, 1949, <u>J.Tokyo Coll.Fish.</u>, 36(1):405

FAO Names: Lancer rose shrimp (En), Crevette rose lancier (Fr), Camarón rosado lanzón (Sp).

Distribution: Indo-West Pacific: Japan; Korea.

Habitat: Depth 300 to 350 m. Marine.

Size: Maximum total length 75 mm (♂); maximum carapace length 20 mm (♂).

Interest to Fishery: Yasuda (1957:30) listed this species, together with *P. fissurus* as being important in the prawn fishery in the Inland Sea of Japan. Yoshida (1941:17) mentioned this species, under the name *P. fissurus*, in his list of economic important marine shrimps of Korea, his material was obtained at the Fusan fishmarket; Yoshida's Figure 10, showing the petasma of his specimens, indicate that what he had was not *P. fissurus* but *P. lanceolatus*.

Parapenaeus longipes Alcock, 1905	PEN Parap 6

Parapenaeus longipes Alcock, 1905, Ann.Mag.Nat.Hist., (7)6:520,525

FAO Names: Flamingo shrimp (En), Crevette flamand (Fr), Camarón flamenco (Sp).

Literature: Racek & Dall, 1965:52, Pl. 5, Fig. 5, Pl. 10, Fig. 6; Tirmizi & Bashir, 1973:63, Figs. 43,44.

Distribution: Indo-West Pacific: East Africa to the Malay Archipelago and Japan.

Habitat: Depth 13 to 88 m. Marine

Size: Total length 50 to 76 mm (♂), 61 to 79 mm (♀).

Interest to Fishery: Minor or nil. Listed by Kurian & Sebastian (1976:99) among the Indian prawns of commercial importance and said to be "recorded in small numbers" in "Mangalore and Cochin, off Ganjam, Vizagapatnam and river Hoogly".

Parapenaeus longirostris (Lucas, 1846)	PEN Parap 1

Penaeus longirostris Lucas, 1846, Explor.Sci.Algér.(Zool.), 1(1):46

Synonymy: *Peneus cocco* Prestandrea, 1833; *Penaeus bocagei* Johnson, 1863; *Penaeus politus* Smith, 1881; *Parapenaeus politus* - Smith, 1886; *Neopenaeopsis paradoxus* Bouvier, 1905; *Parapenaeus paradoxus* - Bouvier, 1908; *Penaeopsis paradoxus* - Schmitt, 1926. The species has often been, incorrectly, indicated with the name *Parapenaeus membranaceus*; the true *Penaeus membranaceus* Risso, however, is a *Solenocera*.

FAO Names: Deep-water rose shrimp (En), Crevette rose du large (Fr), Camarón de altura (Sp).

Local Names: Camarão da costa (Portugal), Gamba (official Spanish name), Gamba blanca (Spain), Crevette rose du large (France, Tunisia, Algeria, Morocco), Gambero bianco, Gambero rosa (Italy) Ammiru biancu (Sicily, Italy), Garidáki (Greece), Karides (Turkey), Bar-penon (Israel), Gembri sghir (Tunisia), Crevette de chalut (Morocco), Rosa Garnele (Germany), Petite crevette, Crevette des grands fonds (Senegal).

Distribution: East Atlantic: from Portugal to Angola, also in the entire Mediterranean. West Atlantic: from Massachusetts, U.S.A. to French Guiana.

Habitat: Depth 20 to 700 m, but usually between 150 and 400 m. Bottom mud or muddy sand. Marine.

Size: Maximum total length 160 mm (♂), 186 mm (♀), usually shorter 140 mm (♂), 160 mm (♀).

Interest to Fishery: Along the Mediterranean coast of Spain the species is much fished for and sold cooked or salted (Zariquiey Alvarez, 1968:55). Longhurst (1970:267) indicated that this is the

most important commercial species of the Mediterranean coasts of Spain, France and Italy. Also in
Algeria, Tunisia, Greece and Turkey the species is of commercial value, although on a lesser scale.
Outside the Mediterranean the species is fished by trawlers in the area between S. Portugal and Rio de
Oro and off Senegal; however, it is not of great importance there. In the southern part of the Gulf
of Guinea the fishery for the species at depths between 200 and 325 m is very productive, with a
daily yield per trawler of more than 1 t (average) to 3 t (maximum) (Crosnier & Forest, 1973:304).

| *Parapenaeus sextuberculatus* Kubo, 1949 | PEN Parap 7 |

Parapenaeus sextuberculatus Kubo, 1949, J.Tokyo Coll.Fish., 36(1):403

FAO Names: Domino shrimp (En), Crevette domino (Fr), Camarón dominó (Sp).

Distribution: Indo-West Pacific: Madagascar to Japan.

Habitat: Depth 250 to 350 m. Marine.

Size: Maximum total length 140 mm.

Interest to Fishery: Potential. Crosnier & Jouannic (1973:11) listed the species as "éventuellement commercialisable" on the continental slope of Madagascar.

| *Penaeopsis rectacuta* (Bate, 1888) | PEN Pe 1 |

Penaeus rectacutus Bate, 1888, Ann.Mag.Nat.Hist., (5)8:180

Synonymy: *Metapenaeus rectacutus* - Wood-Mason, 1891; *Parapenaeus rectacutus* - Alcock, 1901.

FAO Names: Needle shrimp (En), Crevette aiguille (Fr), Camarón aguja (Sp).

Distribution: Indo-West Pacific: S.E. Africa and India to Japan, the Philippines, Indonesia and
Fiji.

Habitat: Depth 180 to 750 m. Bottom mud. Marine.

Size: Maximum total length 104 mm (♂), 131 mm (♀); maximum carapace length 24 mm (♂), 34 mm (♀).

Interest to Fishery: Crosnier & Jouannic (1973:12) considered this species "éventuellement
commercialisable" on the continental shelf of Madagascar. In India *P. rectacuta* at present is not yet
commercially fished for, but exploratory work indicated that a commercial fishery might be feasible
off the Indian west coast (Jones, 1967:1337; Longhurst, 1970:282; Kurian & Sebastian, 1976:99).
Domantay (1956:363) listed the species among the economically important prawns in the Philippines.

| *Penaeopsis serrata* Bate, 1881 | PEN Pe 2 |

Penaeopsis serratus Bate, 1881, Ann.Mag.Nat.Hist., (5)8:183

Synonymy: *Parapenaeus megalops* Smith, 1885; *Artemesia talismani* Bouvier, 1905; *Penaeopsis
serratus antillensis* A. Milne Edwards & Bouvier, 1909; *Penaeopsis megalops* - De Man, 1911. This is a
different species from the Indo-West Pacific *Penaeus serratus* Bate, 1881 (Ann.Mag.Nat.Hist., (5)8:182),
which also belongs to the present genus and which should correctly be known as *Penaeopsis challengeri*
De Man, 1911.

FAO Names: Megalops shrimp (En), Crevette megalops (Fr), Camarón megalops (Sp).

Distribution: Eastern Atlantic: off N.W. Africa (Morocco, Rio de Oro). Western Atlantic:
North Carolina (U.S.A.) to Surinam; Bahamas Islands; Gulf of Mexico; Caribbean Sea.

Habitat: Depth 120 to 640 m. Marine.

Size: Maximum total length 105 mm (δ), 140 mm ($\female$); maximum carapace length 37 mm (δ), 54 mm ($\female$).

Interest to Fishery: According to Longhurst (1970:275,300) the species is of potential commercial importance both in the Western Atlantic and in the Eastern Atlantic.

Penaeus (Farfantepenaeus) aztecus Ives, 1891	PEN Pen 2

Penaeus brasiliensis aztecus Ives, 1891, Proc.Acad.Nat.Sci.Phila., 43:190,191,199

Synonymy: *Penaeus (Melicertus) aztecus aztecus* - Perez-Farfante, 1969.

FAO Names: Northern brown shrimp (En), Crevette royale grise (Fr), Camarón café norteño (Sp).

Local Names: Brown shrimp, Brownie, Green lake shrimp, Red shrimp, Redtail shrimp, Golden shrimp, Native shrimp (U.S.A.), Camarón café, Camarón moreno, Camarón pardo (Mexico). Before 1939 this species was not distinguished from the other East American species of the subgenus *Farfantepenaeus,* all of which were then indicated as *Penaeus brasiliensis.* In 1967 two subspecies of *P. aztecus* were recognized, which at present are considered good species: *P. aztecus* and *P. subtilis.*

Literature: Pérez-Farfante, 1969; Cook & Lindner, 1970.

Distribution: Western Atlantic: Atlantic coast of U.S.A. from Massachusetts to Texas; east coast of Mexico from Tamaulipas to Campeche.

Habitat: Depth 4 to 160 m, highest densities between 27 and 54 m. Bottom mud or peat, often with sand, clay or broken shells. Salinity: the adults are marine, the juveniles estuarine and marine.

Size: Maximum total length 195 mm (δ), 236 mm ($\female$).

Interest to Fishery: Off North Carolina this is the most important *Penaeus* species. Also along the north and east coast of the Gulf of Mexico it is of great commercial value, although sometimes surpassed by *P. setiferus*; the grounds off Texas are by far the most important. In 1976, 61 873 metric tons of the species were landed in the U.S.A. Aquaculture experiments with *P. aztecus* have been undertaken in the U.S.A.

Penaeus (Farfantepenaeus) brasiliensis Latreille, 1817	PEN Pen 3

Penaeus brasiliensis Latreille, 1817, Nouv.Dict.Hist.Nat., 25:156

Synonymy: *Penaeus (Melicertus) brasiliensis* - Perez-Farfante, 1969.

FAO Names: Redspotted shrimp (En), Crevette royale rose (Fr), Camarón rosado con manchas (Sp).

Local Names: Pink spotted shrimp, Spotted pink shrimp, Brown shrimp, Caribbean brown shrimp (U.S.A.), Camarón rojo (Cuba, Nicaragua), Langostino rosado con manchas, Camarón rosado con manchas, Langostino amarillo (Venezuela), Camarão rosa, Camarão lixo (Brazil).

Literature: Pérez-Farfante, 1969.

Distribution: Western Atlantic: Atlantic coast of America from North Carolina (U.S.A) to Rio Grande do Sul (Brazil); Bermuda; West Indies.

Habitat: Depth 3 to 365 m, most abundant at 45 to 65 m. Bottom mud, mud and sand. Juveniles are estuarine, adults marine.

Size: Maximum total length 191 mm (♂), 150 mm (♀).

Interest to Fishery: In the northern part of its range (West Indies, coast of U.S.A.) it usually forms a small percentage of the total shrimp catch. It is quite important in some localities on the Caribbean coast of Central and South America (Quintana Roo (Mexico), Nicaragua, E. Venezuela), and is especially important off the Atlantic coast of South America from Guyana to northern Brazil (Baia de Marajó), where it produces "gigantic catches" (Pérez-Farfante, 1969:576). In northeastern Brazil the commercial value of the species is limited, but more to the south, in Rio de Janeiro state it is quite important again.

| *Penaeus (Farfantepenaeus) brevirostris* Kingsley, 1878 | PEN Pen 9 |

Penaeus brevirostris Kingsley, 1878, Proc.Acad.Nat.Sci.Phila., 1878:98

FAO Names: Crystal shrimp (En), Crevette cristal (Fr), Camarón cristal (Sp).

Local Names: Camarón rojo (Mexico, Nicaragua, Panama, Ecuador), Camarón cristalino, Camarón cristal (Mazatlán, Mexico), Pink shrimp (Panama).

Distribution: Eastern Pacific: Sinaloa (Mexico) to northern Peru and the Galápagos Islands.

Habitat: Depth 36 to 120 m. Bottom mud, sandy mud. Marine.

Size: Maximum total length, 150 mm (♂), 170 mm (♀); maximum carapace length 56 mm.

Interest to Fishery: In Mexico the species is of considerable importance, although less so than the other species of *Penaeus* taken on the west coast. It is sold fresh or frozen. Also in Panama and Ecuador the present species is fished, but seems to be of minor or moderate importance.

| *Penaeus (Farfantepenaeus) californiensis* Holmes, 1900 | PEN Pen 10 |

Penaeus californiensis Holmes, 1900, Occas.Pap.Calif.Acad.Sci., 7:218

FAO Names: Yellowleg shrimp (En), Crevette pattes jaunes (Fr), Camarón patiamarillo (Sp).

Local Names: Camarón café, Café brown shrimp (Mexico, Nicaragua, Ecuador), Camarón kaki, Camarón pata amarilla (Mexico).

Distribution: Eastern Pacific: California (U.S.A.) to Paita (Peru).

Habitat: Depth 15 to 100 m, most abundant between 25 to 50 m. Bottom mud or sandy mud. Marine; juveniles rarely estuarine.

Size: Maximum total length 160 mm (♂), 209 mm (♀); maximum carapace length 55 mm (♀).

Interest to Fishery: The species is of considerable importance in the offshore fishery off Mexico, forming about 75% of the catch of Mexican Pacific shrimp trawlers. Also in Guatemala, Costa Rica, Panama and Ecuador the species is fished. In Ecuador it was so far of little importance but since 1963 the landings increased there notably.

| *Penaeus (Farfantepenaeus) duorarum* Burkenroad, 1939 | PEN Pen 4 |

Penaeus duorarum Burkenroad, 1939, Bull.Bingham Oceanogr.Collect., Yale Univ., 6(6):31

Synonymy: *Penaeus (Melicertus) duorarum duorarum* - Perez-Farfante, 1969. Until 1939 this species was not distinguished from *Penaeus brasiliensis* and the latter name was then used to indicate all Western Atlantic species of the subgenus *Farfantepenaeus*. In 1967 Pérez-Farfante recognized two sub-species of *P. duorarum: P. d. duorarum* and *P. d. notialis*. The latter is now treated as a distinct species.

FAO Names: Northern pink shrimp (En), Crevette rodché du nord (Fr), Camarón rosado norteño (Sp).

Local Names: Pink shrimp, Spotted shrimp, Pink-spotted shrimp, Brown-spotted shrimp, Grooved shrimp, Green shrimp, Pink night shrimp, Red shrimp, Hopper, Skipper, Pushed shrimp, Bait shrimp (U.S.A.), Camarón rosado (Mexico).

Literature: Pérez-Farfante, 1969; Costello & Allen, 1970.

Distribution: Western Atlantic: Bermuda; Atlantic coast of the U.S.A. from Maryland to Texas; east coast of Mexico from Tamaulipas to Quintana Roo.

Habitat: Depth 2 to 70 m, rarely to 230 m, most abundant between 11 and 36 m. Bottom firm mud and silt with sand and shells. Juveniles can and do live in water with low salinities, adults are marine.

Size: Maximum total length 269 mm (δ), 280 mm ($\female$).

Interest to Fishery: Of great commercial value in the Gulf of Mexico; most intensively fished in the Tortugas area and in the Gulf of Campeche, but also off N.W. Florida and W. Texas. In 1976, 11 291 metric tons were landed in U.S.A. Used for consumption and bait.

Penaeus (Farfantepenaeus) notialis Pérez-Farfante, 1967	PEN PEN 5

Penaeus duorarum notialis Pérez-Farfante, 1967, Proc.Biol.Soc.Wash., 80:94

Synonymy: *Penaeus duorarum* var. *cameronensis* Rossignol & Repelin, 1962 (unavailable name). *Penaeus (Melicertus) duorarum notialis* - Perez-Farfante, 1969. Until 1967 this species was not distin-guished from *P. duorarum*; in 1967 it was first considered a subspecies *of Penaeus duorarum*, later the two were found to be distinct species.

FAO Names: Southern pink shrimp (En), Crevette rodché du Sud (Fr), Camarón rosado sureño (Sp).

Local Names: Candied shrimp (U.S.A.), Camarón acaramelado, Camarón cocinero, Camarón carbonero (Cuba), Pink shrimp (British Honduras), Camarón rojo (Nicaragua), Langostino amarillo, Langostino rosado, Camarón rosado sin mancha (Venezuela), Camarão rosa (Brazil), Crevette grosse, Crevette blanche (Senegal), Bangbo (Ivory Coast), Degon (Dahomey), Mudionga (Cameroon), Rozovoi krevetki (U.S.S.R.).

Distribution: Eastern Atlantic: West African coast from Mauritania to Angola. Western Atlantic: Greater Antilles from Cuba to the Virgin Islands; Atlantic coast of Middle and South America from S. Mexico (Quintana Roo) to Brazil (S. to Rio de Janeiro).

Habitat: Depth 3 to 100 m, rarely as deep as 700 m, usually between 3 and 50 m. Bottom mud or sandy mud, and sandy patches among rocks. Marine; juveniles estuarine.

Size: Maximum total length 175 mm (δ), 192 mm ($\female$); maximum carapace length 41 mm (δ), 48 mm ($\female$).

Interest to Fishery: With *Penaeus (Litopenaeus) schmitti* the most important commercial shrimp of the Greater Antilles and the Atlantic coast of Central America, Venezuela and various areas of Brazil, both on a local and commercial scale. The species is also the subject of important fisheries in West Africa, both locally and by foreign trawlers. Aquaculture experiments with this species have been undertaken in Cuba.

| *Penaeus (Farfantepenaeus) paulensis* Pérez-Farfante, 1967 | PEN Pen 11 |

Penaeus (Melicertus) paulensis Pérez-Farfante, 1967, Proc.Biol.Soc.Wash., 80:84,86,87,93

Synonymy: Until 1967 this species was confused either with *Penaeus brasiliensis* or *P. aztecus*.

FAO Names: São Paulo shrimp (En), Crevette de São Paulo (Fr), Camarón de São Paulo (Sp).

Local Names: Camarão rosa (Brazil), Langostino (Uruguay), Camarón (Uruguay, for small specimens).

Literature: Pérez-Farfante, 1969.

Distribution: Western Atlantic: Brazil (from Cabo Frio, Estado de Rio de Janeiro) south to Argentina (38°30'S).

Habitat: Depth 1 to 130 m, mostly between 36 and 54 m. Bottom mud. Marine.

Size: Maximum total length 171 mm (δ), 215 mm ($\female$); maximum carapace length 40 mm (δ), 54 mm ($\female$).

Interest to Fishery: There are inshore fisheries for this species both in Brazil and Uruguay, while in the northern part of its range in Brazil there is also an offshore fishery. The possibility of its culture in Uruguay is under study (Villegas, 1974).

| *Penaeus (Farfantepenaeus) subtilis* Pérez-Farfante, 1967 | PEN Pen 8 |

Penaeus aztecus subtilis Pérez-Farfante, 1967, Proc.Biol.Soc.Wash., 80:87

Synonymy: *Penaeus (Melicertus) aztecus subtilis* - Pérez-Farfante, 1969. Until 1967 this species was not distinguished from *Penaeus aztecus* then at first it was considered a subspecies of *P. aztecus*, but at present the two are treated as distinct species.

FAO Names: Southern brown shrimp (En), Crevette café (Fr), Camarón café sureño (Sp).

Local Names: Brown shrimp, Dark shrimp (U.S.A.), Camarón café (Cuba, Nicaragua), Camarón marrón, Langostino amarillo (Venezuela), Short feelered prawn (Guyana), Camarão lixo, Camarão vermelho, Camarão branco, Cabeçudo (Brazil).

Literature: Pérez-Farfante, 1969.

Distribution: Western Atlantic: West Indies from the Greater Antilles south; Atlantic coast of Central and South America from Honduras to Brazil (Rio de Janeiro State).

Habitat: Depth 1 to 190 m. Bottom mud, and mud with sand or shells. Adults are marine, juveniles usually estuarine and marine, sometimes hypersaline.

Size: Maximum total length 152 mm (δ), 205 mm ($\female$); maximum carapace length 36 mm (δ), 55 mm ($\female$).

Interest to Fishery: The species is fished throughout its range, often forming part of catches of other shrimps. The young are often caught in estuarine waters of northern South America, adults are fished for in Venezuela and Brazil.

| *Penaeus (Fenneropenaeus) chinensis* (Osbeck, 1765) | PEN Pen 12 |

Cancer chinensis Osbeck, 1765, Reise nach Ostindien und China, 151

Synonymy: *Cancer (Gammarellus) chinensis* - Herbst, 1793; *Penaeus orientalis* Kishinouye, 1918.

FAO Names: Fleshy prawn (En), Crevette charnue (Fr), Camarón carnoso (Sp).

Local Names: Korai ebi (Japan), Fleshy prawn (Hong Kong).

Distribution: Indo-West Pacific: Korea; China; Hong Kong. Records from outside this area are doubtful and may pertain to one of the other *Fenneropenaeus* species.

Habitat: Depth 90 to 180 m. Marine.

Size: Maximum total length 154 mm (δ), 183 mm ($\stackrel{\circ}{+}$); maximum carapace length 42 mm (δ), 55 mm ($\stackrel{\circ}{+}$).

Interest to Fishery: The species is of considerable commercial importance in the Yellow Sea, East China Sea and Korean Bight, where it is trawled. It is sold in Korea, China, Japan and Hong Kong. Frozen (both whole and headed) it is exported to Western Europe. Pond culture for this species has started in South Korea and Japan.

Remarks: The problem of the distinctness of this species from *Penaeus indicus* is still not definitely solved. The name *Penaeus chinensis* has hardly ever been used for the species, which is better known as *P. orientalis*. However, Osbeck's (1765) description is sufficiently clear to make certain that his specimens belonged to the present species; the specific name *chinensis*, being one of the oldest for any penaeid species, has therefore to be used.

Penaeus (Fenneropenaeus) indicus H. Milne Edwards, 1837	PEN Pen 13

Penaeus indicus H. Milne Edwards, 1837, Hist.Nat.Crust., 2:415

Synonymy: *? Palaemon longicornis* Olivier, 1825; *Penaeus indicus longirostris* De Man, 1892.

FAO Names: Indian white prawn (En), Crevette royale blanche (des Indes) (Fr), Camarón blanco de la India (Sp).

Local Names: White prawn (S. Africa, Kenya), Tugela prawn (S. Africa), Kamba weupe, Kamba ndogo (Swahili language, Kenya), Makamba (Sakalave language, Madagascar), Patsa (Hova language, Madagascar), Jaira, Jiaro (Pakistan; used also for other species of *Fenneropenaeus*), Jinga (Bombay, India), Naran, Vella chemmeen (Kerala, India), Yera (Madras, India), Chapda chingri (Calcutta, India; Bangladesh), Chapra chingri, Chamma chingri, Changa chingri (Bangladesh), Udang putih (Indonesia), Hipon putih (Philippines), Indian prawn (Australia).

Literature: Mohamed, 1970 a.

Distribution: Indo-West Pacific: E. and S.E. Africa to S. China, New Guinea and N. Australia.

Habitat: Depth 2 to 90 m. Bottom mud or sand. Adults marine, juveniles estuarine.

Size: Maximum total length 184 mm (δ), 228 mm ($\stackrel{\circ}{+}$), usually much smaller (170 mm); maximum carapace length 56 mm.

Interest to Fishery: In Madagascar, Mozambique, Tanzania, Kenya and Somalia the fishery for this species is of major importance, the species being dominant in the shrimp catches. In Kenya it forms 75 to 90% of the catch (Brusher, 1976). Although the species is of minor importance in Yemen, the Persian Gulf and Pakistan (Tirmizi, in Litt.), in India it is "the most important species" (Jones, 1967:1333), especially in the inshore fishery (see also Kurian & Sebastian, 1976:99). Next to *Metapenaeus dobsoni*, *P. indicus* is the second most important species in the ricefield shrimp farming of the Kerala coast of S.W. India. Also in Bangladesh, Malaya, Thailand, Indonesia and the Philippines the species is of importance, both for offshore fishing and in the pond culture.

Remarks: This species, *P. merguiensis* and *P. penicillatus* have sometimes been confused, and it may be possible that some of the data on the fishery of *P. indicus* provided in the previous paragraph actually refer to either of the other two species.

Penaeus (Fenneropenaeus) merguiensis De Man, 1888		PEN Pen 14

Penaeus merguiensis De Man, 1888, <u>J.Linn.Soc.Lond.(Zool.)</u>, 22:287

Synonymy: *Penaeus indicus merguiensis* - De Man, 1882.

FAO Names: Banana prawn (En), Crevette banana (Fr), Camarón banana (Sp).

Local Names: Jaira, Jiaro (Pakistan, also used for other species of *Fenneropenaeus*), Udang kaki merah (Malaysia), Udang putih (Indonesia), Kung chaebauy (Thailand), Pak ha, White prawn (Hong Kong), Banana prawn, White prawn (Australia).

Literature: Kirkegaard, Tuma & Walker, 1970.

Distribution: Indo-West Pacific: from the Persian Gulf to Thailand, Hong Kong, the Philippines. Indonesia, New Guinea, New Caledonia and N. Australia (north of 29°S).

Habitat: Depth 10 to 45 m. Bottom mud. Estuarine and marine.

Size: Maximum total length 240 mm (♀).

Interest to Fishery: The species is commercially of major importance in the Persian Gulf and in Pakistan (Longhurst, 1970:280,281; Tirmizi, in Litt.). In India this species has often been confused with *P. indicus* so that its present economic status is not quite accurately known, but Jones (1967: 1333) pointed out that it definitely contributes to the commercial fishery along the Karwar coast of W. India. Kurian & Sebastian (1976:100) reported that there is a small fishery for this species "in the middle region of east and west coasts" of India, while "juveniles are fished from estuaries". It is not mentioned for Bangladesh by Ahmad (1957), so that it is possible that a confusion with *P. indicus* has occurred here also. *P. merguiensis* is also important off the northwestern coast of Malaya, and possibly the west coast of Thailand, and the Philippines (Longhurst, 1970:284-290). In Indonesia it is taken by trawlers off E. Sumatra, the south coast of Java, off Borneo and in the Arafura Sea, being the dominant species there. In Australia it is the most important commercial species of Queensland, and also in Western Australia it may become very important (Racek, 1955:222; 1957:12). In the Gulf of Papua it is trawled for; the catch is frozen. It plays a role in pond culture in Thailand (Shigueno, 1975:120) and in Indonesia.

Penaeus (Fenneropenaeus) penicillatus Alcock, 1905		PEN Pen 15

Penaeus indicus penicillatus Alcock, 1905, <u>Ann.Mag.Nat.Hist.</u>, (7)16:525

FAO Names: Redtail prawn (En), Crevette queue rouge (Fr), Camarón rabo colorado (Sp).

Local Names: Jaira, Jiaro (Pakistan, used also for other species of *Fenneropenaeus*), Pak ha, White prawn (Hong Kong), Red-tailed prawn (Taiwan).

Distribution: Indo-West Pacific: from Pakistan to Taiwan and Indonesia.

Habitat: Depth 2 to 90 m. Marine.

Size: Maximum total length 163 mm (♂), 212 mm (♀); carapace length 31 mm (♂), 33 mm (♀).

Interest to Fishery: In Pakistan this species is of major commercial importance (Qureshi, 1956: 362; Tirmizi, in Litt.). There are few records of the commercial importance of the species in India. Kagwade (1967:1379) listed it among the less common forms in the catches off Bombay, and Kunyu (1967: 1385) remarked that it is the main species obtained off the Maharashtra coast (Western India). Kurian & Sebastian (1976:100) reported "small records from Bombay and Orissa". It is possible that many of the records of *Penaeus indicus* from off the Indian coasts pertain to the present species. Ahmad (1957:8) gave it in his list of economic important prawns of Bangladesh, but Qureshi (1956:362) did not. Tham (1968:211) ranged *P. penicillatus* among the species commonly found in shrimp catches in Malaysia.

| Penaeus (Litopenaeus) occidentalis Streets, 1871 | PEN Pen 16 |

Penaeus occidentalis Streets, 1871, Proc.Acad.Nat.Sci.Phila., 1871:243

FAO Names: Western white shrimp (En), Crevette royale blanche (du Pacifique) (Fr), Camarón blanco del Pacifico (Sp).

Local Names: Camarón blanco (Nicaragua, Colombia, Ecuador, Peru), Langostino (Panama, Colombia, Peru).

Distribution: Eastern Pacific: Off Chiapas (Mexico) to Peru.

Habitat: Depth 2 to 20 m. Bottom soft mud. Estuarine (juveniles) and marine (adults).

Size: Maximum total length 215 mm.

Interest to Fishery: The species is of commercial importance almost throughout its range. It is taken by trawlers in El Salvador where it is the third in importance after *P. vannamei* and *P. stylirostris*. In Honduras there is an inland fishery for the juveniles (Lindner, 1957:69). In Panama, Colombia and Ecuador the fishery for this species is of major importance, it is the dominant species there.

| Penaeus (Litopenaeus) schmitti Burkenroad, 1936 | PEN Pen 6 |

Penaeus schmitti Burkenroad, 1936, An.Acad.Bras.Cienc., 8:315

Synonymy: Before 1936 this species was not distinguished from *P. setiferus* and therefore most records of *P. setiferus* from the area of *P. schmitti* pertain actually to the latter species.

FAO Names: Southern white shrimp (En), Crevette ligubam du sud (Fr), Camarón blanco sureño (Sp).

Local Names: White shrimp (U.S.A., British Honduras), Blue shrimp, Green shrimp (U.S.A.), Camarón blanco (Cuba, Honduras, Nicaragua, Venezuela), Camarón casquiazul (Cuba), Chacalín (Nicaragua; for the juveniles only), Langostino blanco (Venezuela), Camarão legítimo, Camarão verdadeiro, Camarão branco, Camarão lixo, Camarão vila franca, Camarão caboclo (Brazil).

Literature: Pérez-Farfante, 1969, 1970.

Distribution: Western Atlantic: Greater Antilles from Cuba to Virgin Islands; Atlantic coast of Central and South America from British Honduras to S. Brazil (28°24'S).

Habitat: Depth 2 to 47 m, most abundant between 15 and 30 m. Bottom soft mud or silt, sometimes with sand. Juveniles found in estuarine areas, the adults are marine.

Size: Maximum total length 175 mm (δ), 235 mm ($\female$).

Interest to Fishery: The species is of considerable commercial importance in Cuba, Belize, Honduras, Nicaragua, Colombia, Venezuela, Guyana, French Guiana, Surinam, and all along the coast of Brazil. It is caught in large quantities and a great percentage is exported. In Cuba aquaculture experiments with this species have started.

| Penaeus (Litopenaeus) setiferus (Linnaeus, 1767) | PEN Pen 7 |

Cancer setiferus Linnaeus, 1767, Syst.Nat., (ed.12)1:1054,1055

Synonymy: *Cancer (Gammarellus) setiferus* - Herbst, 1793; *Astacus setiferus* - Olivier, 1791; *Palaemon setiferus* - Olivier, 1811; *Penaeus orbignyanus* Latreille, 1817; *Penaeus fluviatilis* Say, 1818; *Penaeus setifer* - Agassiz, 1849; *Penaeus gracilirostris* Thallwitz, 1892; *Penaeus setifera* - Cowles, 1930. Before 1936 this species and *P. schmitti* were not distinguished as separate species; therefore several older records of *P. setiferus*, viz. those of specimens outside the area of the present species, pertain to *P. schmitti*.

A recent dispute about whether the name *P. setiferus* or *P. fluviatilis* is the correct name for the present species, has been settled by the International Commission on Zoological Nomenclature in favour of the former of these two names.

FAO Names: Northern white shrimp (En), Crevette ligubam uu nord (Fr), Camarón blanco norteño (Sp).

Local Names: White shrimp, Grey shrimp, Lake shrimp, Green shrimp, Green-tailed shrimp, Blue-tailed shrimp, Rainbow shrimp, Daytona shrimp, Southern shrimp (U.S.A.), Camarón blanco (Mexico).

Literature: Pérez-Farfante, 1969; Lindner & Cook, 1970.

Distribution: Western Atlantic: East coast of U.S.A. from New Jersey to Texas; east coast of Mexico from Tamaulipas to Campeche; especially abundant in the Gulf of Mexico.

Habitat: Depth 2 to 90 m. Bottom mud or peat, sometimes with sand or clay. Marine (adults), and estuarine (juveniles).

Size: Maximum total length 175 mm (δ), 200 mm ($\female$); maximum carapace length 41 mm (δ), 60 mm ($\female$).

Interest to Fishery: The species is fished along the Atlantic coast of U.S.A. from North Carolina to Florida and in the Gulf of Mexico. It is of great economic importance in the United States and Mexico. In 1975 almost 27 000 metric tons were landed in the U.S.A. alone. In Mexico the most important fishery is in the Gulf of Campeche. The species is mostly frozen and canned and exported all over the world. Culture experiments with this species seem to meet with some success (Bardach et al., 1972:613).

Penaeus (Litopenaeus) stylirostris Stimpson, 1874	PEN Pen 17

Penaeus stylirostris Stimpson, 1874, Ann.Lyc.Nat.Hist., New York, 10:134

FAO Names: Blue shrimp (En), Crevette bleue (Fr), Camarón azul (Sp).

Local Names: Camarón azul, Blue shrimp (Mexico), Camarón blanco (Nicaragua, Costa Rica, Panama, Colombia, Ecuador, Peru; also used for the other species of *Litopenaeus*), White shrimp (Panama), Langostino (Panama, Peru; used for all species of *Litopenaeus*), Camarón (El Salvador; for all larger shrimps).

Distribution: Eastern Pacific: from Baja California (Mexico) to Peru.

Habitat: Depth 0 to 27 m, seldom to 45. Bottom mud and clayey or sandy mud. Marine (adults) and estuarine (juveniles).

Size: Maximum total length 230 mm; maximum carapace length 59 mm.

Interest to Fishery: Of major importance on most of the west coast of Mexico, although locally of secondary importance; fished both inshore and offshore. Sold fresh, cooked, dry and frozen. In Guatemala it is fished for inshore and offshore. In El Salvador *Penaeus stylirostris* is the second most important species, it is caught offshore and inshore. In Honduras the inshore fishery is mostly on juveniles of this species and of *P. occidentalis*. These two species are also the most important in Costa Rica and Panama. Farther south the importance of the present species diminishes, being evidently replaced by *P. occidentalis*.

| *Penaeus (Litopenaeus) vannamei* Boone, 1931 | PEN Pen 18 |

Penaeus vannamei Boone, 1931, <u>Bull.Am.Mus.Nat.Hist.</u>, 63:173

FAO Names: Whiteleg shrimp (En), Crevette pattes blanches (Fr), Camarón patiblanco (Sp).

Local Names: Camarón blanco, White shrimp (Mexico; this name is used in several countries, like Nicaragua, Costa Rica, Pańama, Colombia, Ecuador, and Peru for all species of *Litopenaeus*), Camarón patiblanco (Panama), Camarón café (Colombia), Langostino (Peru; a name used for all species of *Litopenaeus*).

Distribution: Eastern Pacific: from Sonora, Mexico, south to northern Peru.

Habitat: Depth 0 to 72 m. Bottom mud. Marine (adults), and estuarine (juveniles).

Size: Maximum total length 230 mm; maximum carapace length 90 mm.

Interest to Fishery: The inshore fishery for this species is of major importance in Mexico, especially in the southern part. It is also taken in considerable quantities by the Mexican offshore trawlers. In Guatemala and El Salvador *P. vannamei* is the dominant species, but its importance seems to diminish farther to the southwest.

| *Penaeus (Marsupenaeus) japonicus* Bate, 1888 | PEN Pen 19 |

Penaeus canaliculatus japonicus Bate, 1888, <u>Rep.Voyage Challenger (Zool.)</u>, 24:245

Synonymy: *Penaeus pulchricaudatus* Stebbing, 1914.

FAO Names: Kuruma prawn (En), Crevette kuruma (Fr), Camarón kuruma (Sp).

Local Names: Ginger prawn (S. Africa), Tiger prawn (Kenya), Kamba, Kamba ndogo (Swahili language, Kenya; used for large, respectively small specimens of all species of commercial penaeids), Kalri (Pakistan, also used for other species of similar size), Flowery prawn (Hong Kong), Banded shrimp (Taiwan), Kuruma ebi (Japan), Saimaki ebi (Japan, juveniles only), Oriental brown shrimp (Korea), Japanese king prawn, Tiger prawn (Australia, New Guinea), Kuruma shrimp (U.S.A.), Kristal (Israel).

Distribution: Indo-West Pacific: from the Red Sea, E. and S.E. Africa to Korea, Japan and the Malay Archipelago, also reported from Fiji. Eastern Atlantic: the species entered the eastern Meidterranean through the Suez Canal and has reached the south coast of Turkey.

Habitat: Depth 0 to 90 m. Bottom sandy mud and sand. Marine.

Size: Maximum total length 190 mm ($\male$), 225 mm ($\female$); maximum carapace length 53 mm ($\male$), 66 mm ($\female$).

Interest to Fishery: On the east and southeast coast of Africa, in Madagascar waters, in the Gulf of Aden, and in the Red Sea the Species is fished, but is of minor commercial importance. In India small fisheries for this species are mentioned for the Bombay and Madras areas (Kurian & Sebastian, 1976:100). Domantay (1956:363) reported it among the commercially important prawns of the Philippines. In Japan the fishery is of major importance, the present species being the most valuable of the commercial shrimps, it is not only trawled but also plays a role in the pond fishery. In New Guinea *P. japonicus* forms a small percentage of commercial catches (Rapson & McIntosh, 1971:17). In the eastern Mediterranean the species is caught by Turkish, Israelian and Egyptian trawlers. It is possible that the records of the fishery for *Penaeus canaliculatus* (see there) in India, Indonesia and the Philippines actually pertain to the present species. Serious and most successful efforts at culturing the species, both in ponds and tanks, are undertaken in Japan (Shigueno, 1975). In some areas outside Japan (e.g., Korea, Taiwan, France) the species is also used in aquaculture experiments.

| *Penaeus (Melicertus) canaliculatus* (Olivier, 1811) | PEN Pen 20 |

Palaemon canaliculatus Olivier, 1811, Encycl.Méthod.Hist.Nat.(Ins.), 8:660

FAO Names: Witch prawn (En), Crevette sorcière (Fr), Camarón brujo (Sp).

Literature: Pérez-Farfante, 1976:23-37, Figs. 1-4.

Distribution: Indo-West Pacific: *Penaeus canaliculatus* has been reported from an extensive area reaching from S.E. Africa to Taiwan, the Malay Archipelago and Polynesia.

Habitat: Depth 33 to 46 m. Marine.

Size: Total length 97 to 120 mm (♂), 131 to 145 mm (♀); carapace length 24.5 to 34 mm (♂), 35 to 40 mm (♀).

Interest to Fishery: Qureshi (1956:362) listed *P. canaliculatus* among the commercial prawns of Pakistan. Jones (1967:1333) mentioned that this species "contributes to a very small percentage in the fishery along the Madras coast especially in Pulicat Lake and in small numbers in Bombay and other places". Ramamurthy (1967:1426) stated its presence in commercial catches in Kutch (N.W. India). Kurian & Sebastian (1976:99) listed the species among the Indian prawns of commercial importance, but indicated that it was "got only in small numbers". Tham (1968:211) reported *P. canaliculatus* as important in Pakistan and the Philippines. Ahmad (1957:5) ranged the species among those that are fished for in Bangladesh. For Indonesia there is a record by Djajadiredjo & Sachlan (1956: 370,372) and for the Philippines by Domantay (1956:363) and Delmendo & Rabanal (1956:424). Uncertainty as to the correct identity of the present species existed until Pérez-Farfante (1976:23) made its true position clear. Many of the pre-1976 records of *P. canaliculatus* may actually pertain to other, more or less closely related species (e.g., *Penaeus japonicus*). Therefore all records concerning the commercial value of *Penaeus canaliculatus* have to be treated with the utmost reserve.

| *Penaeus (Melicertus) kerathurus* (Forskål, 1775) | PEN Pen 1 |

Cancer kerathurus Forskål, 1775, Descriptiones Animalium, 95

Synonymy: *Palaemon sulcatus* Olivier, 1811; *Alpheus trisulcatus* Leach, 1814; *Melicertus tigrinus* Rafinesque, 1814; *Penaeus trisulcatus* - Leach, 1815; *Alpheus caramote* Risso, 1816; *Peneus mars* Risso, 1816; *Penaeus caramote* - Latreille, 1817; *Penaeus sulcatus* - Lamarck, 1818; *Alpheus punctulatus* Risso, 1822; *Peneus cristatus* Risso, 1827; *Pandalus punctulatus* - Risso, 1827; *Pelias punctulata* - Roux, 1831; *Ephyra punctulata* - H. Milne Edwards, 1837; *Penaeus fasciatus* Hope, 1851 (nomen nudum); *Miersia punctulata* - Carus, 1885.

FAO Names: Caramote prawn (En), Caramote (Fr), Camarón langostino español (Sp).

Local Names: Camarão (Portugal), Langostino (official Spanish name), Llangosti (Spain), Caramote (also Caramot or Caramota), Crevette du Maroc, Gros Ligubam (France), Gambaru grossu (Monaco), Spannocchio, Gambero impériale, Mazzancolla (Italy; Palombi & Santarelli, 1961:358, list a great number of local names for the species used in various Italian districts), Mekušica (Jugoslavia), Garída (Greece), Karides, Tèke (Turkey), Penon telat-harizi (Israel), Gambri kbir, Gambli malaki, Grosse crevette, Crevette royale (Tunisia), Gamba rodché, Crevette grise, Caramote (Algeria), Furchenkrebs (Germany), Tiger shrimp, Striped shrimp (West Africa).

Distribution: Eastern Atlantic: from the south coast of England to Angola, and the entire Mediterranean.

Habitat: Depth 5 to 40 m, seldom to 75 m. Bottom muddy sand. Marine and estuarine.

Size: Maximum total length up to 180 mm (♂), 225 mm (♀); the average length is 110 to 140 mm (♂), 130 to 170 mm (♀).

Interest to Fishery: This species is fished for all along the Mediterranean coasts and is an important product of the inshore fishery, because of its large size and excellent taste. Along the West African coast the species is of minor importance. Crosnier & De Bondy (1967:4,5) mentioned the presence of a small fishery in Dahomey and Nigeria.

Penaeus (Melicertus) latisulcatus Kishinouye, 1896	PEN Pen 21

Penaeus latisulcatus Kishinouye, 1896, <u>Zool.Mag., Tokyo</u>, 8:372

FAO Names: Western king prawn (En), Crevette royale occidentale (Fr), Camarón real (Sp).

Local Names: Hutomizo ebi, Futomizo ebi (Japan), Kung luang hangsipha (Thailand), Western king prawn, Blue-legged king prawn (Australia).

Distribution: Indo-West Pacific: Red Sea and S.E. Africa to Korea, Japan, the Malay Archipelago and Australia. Burkenroad (1959:80) distinguished two subspecies, a western, *P. latisulcatus hathor* Burkenroad, 1959, inhabiting the area from the Red Sea and S.E. Africa to the Western Indian Ocean and the typical subspecies occupying the eastern part of the range of the species. A more extensive study has to make out whether or not two species are involved here.

Habitat: Depth 0 to 80 m. Bottom sandy mud, or with stones. Marine.

Size: Maximum total length 137 mm ($\male$), 190 mm ($\female$); maximum carapace length 40 mm ($\male$), 46 mm ($\female$).

Interest to Fishery: According to Longhurst (1970:279,280) the present species is of secondary commercial importance in Mozambique and in the southern Red Sea. It is also reported as of some economic value in Somalia, the Gulf of Aden and the Persian Gulf. Kurian & Sebastian (1976:100) listed the species among the Indian prawns of commercial importance, but indicate that it is obtained in "stray catches only". Racek (1957:12) indicated that this is the only species of commercial value in South Australia, and that it might become of economic importance in Western Australia. Slack-Smith (1969:717) showed that the Western Australian prawn industry is now based on the present species and *P. esculentus*. In Japan the species seems, especially compared to *P. japonicus*, to be of little importance; that it has some commercial value is shown by that Balss (1914:13) reported some specimens from the Nagasaki fishmarket. Experimental aquaculture of this species has started in Thailand.

Penaeus (Melicertus) longistylus Kubo, 1943	PEN Pen 22

Penaeus longistylus Kubo, 1943, <u>Suisan Kenkyusi</u>, 38:200

Synonymy: *Penaeus jejunus* Hall, 1956; *Penaeus caesius* Dall, 1957.

FAO Names: Redspot king prawn (En), Crevette royale à taches rouges (Fr), Camarón real manchado (Sp).

Local Names: Red-spot king prawn, Red-spotted prawn (Australia).

Distribution: Indo-West Pacific: South China Sea; Malaysia, N.W.; N. and N.E. Australia; Lord Howe Island.

Habitat: Depth 35 to 55 m. Bottom sand and reefs. Marine.

Size: Maximum total length 148 mm ($\male$), 151 mm ($\female$); maximum carapace length 40 mm ($\male$), 44 mm ($\female$). Shigueno (1975:144) gave the total length of adults as 130 to 160 mm, and their weight (in 5 to 6 months) as 25 to 35 g.

Interest to Fishery: The species is listed by Harrison, Kesteven & Setter (1965:8) among the commercial species of the Gulf of Carpentaria, N. Queensland. Racek & Dall (1965:15) were of the opinion "that this species is restricted to reef areas unsuitable for bottom trawling gear", and probably will never become of high commercial value, if at all.

Penaeus (Melicertus) marginatus Randall, 1840   PEN Pen 23

Penaeus marginatus Randall, 1840, J.Acad.Nat.Sci.Phila., 8:146

Synonymy: Penaeus teraoi Kubo, 1949; Penaeus (Melicertus) teraoi - Burukovsky, 1972.

FAO Names: Aloha prawn (En), Crevette aloha (Fr), Camarón aloha (Sp).

Distribution: Indo-West Pacific: E. Africa and Madagascar to Singapore, Indonesia, Japan, Cocos Islands, and Hawaiian Islands.

Habitat: Depth 0 to 300 m (the juveniles in shallow, the adults in deeper water). Bottom sand, or mud and sand. Marine.

Size: Maximum total length 205 mm.

Interest to Fishery: Crosnier & Jouannic (1973:10) listed this species as "éventuellement commercialisable" on the continental shelf of Madagascar, and off Tanzania and Kenya. M.J. Rathbun (1906:902,903) reported upon material from the Honolulu fishmarkets. Edmondson (1946:246) remarked that this "is one of the larger Hawaiian shrimps and is of considerable importance as food". Yoshida (1972:257) named this species "the most promising for the development of a commercial fishery" in Hawaiian waters. Bardach et al. (1972:598) mentioned the species among those playing a role in the pond culture in Taiwan.

Penaeus (Melicertus) plebejus Hess, 1865   PEN Pen 24

Penaeus plebejus Hess, 1865, Arch.Naturgesch., Berlin, 31(1):168

Synonymy: Penaeus canaliculatus australiensis Bate, 1888; Penaeus maccullochi Schmitt, 1926.

FAO Names: Eastern king prawn (En), Crevette royale orientale (Fr), Camarón real oriental (Sp).

Local Names: Eastern king prawn King prawn, Sand prawn (Australia).

Literature: Kirkegaard & Walker, 1970.

Distribution: Indo-West Pacific: E. Australia from S. Queensland to Victoria.

Habitat: Depth 2 to 160 m. Bottom sand. Marine (adults) and estuarine (juveniles).

Size: Maximum total length 190 mm ($\male$), 300 mm ($\female$).

Interest to Fishery: The species is fished for in the larger part of its range (25° to 38°S), both inshore (2 to 4 m) for juveniles, and offshore for adults. In Queensland it constitutes more than half of the total prawn catch. "Attempts to introduce this prawn by liberation in our New Zealand waters were made in the 1890's" (Richardson & Yaldwyn, 1958:24), but evidently did not succeed.

Penaeus (Penaeus) esculentus Haswell, 1879   PEN Pen 25

Penaeus esculentus Haswell, 1879, Proc.Linn.Soc.N.S.W., 4:38

FAO Names: Brown tiger prawn (En), Crevette tigrée brune (Fr), Camarón tigre marrón (Sp).

Local Names: Brown tiger prawn, Tiger prawn, Common tiger prawn (Australia).

Literature: Kirkegaard & Walker (1969).

Distribution: Indo-West Pacific: W., N. and E. Australia from Shark Bay to central New South Wales. There is a doubtful record from Borneo.

Habitat: Depth 16 to 22 m. Marine.

Size: Maximum total length 145 mm (♂), 155 mm (♀).

Interest to Fishery: Of commercial importance in Western Australia (Slack-Smith, 1969:717), where the prawn industry is based on this species and *P. latisulcatus*. Harrison, Kesteven & Setter (1965:8) listed it among the commercial species of the Gulf of Carpentaria. And Dall reported that it is "trawled commercially in Queensland, and appearing sporadically in commercial quantities off Evans Head", New South Wales. Longhurst (1970:290) reported that the species is caught in the Philippines, but this probably is based on an incorrect identification.

Penaeus (Penaeus) monodon Fabricius, 1798	**PEN Pen 26**

Penaeus monodon Fabricius, 1798, Suppl.Ent.Syst., 408

Synonymy: *Penaeus carinatus* Dana, 1852; *Penaeus tahitensis* Heller, 1862; *Penaeus semisulcatus exsulcatus* Hilgendorf, 1879; *Penaeus coeruleus* Stebbing, 1905; *Penaeus bubulus* Kubo, 1949; *Penaeus monodon monodon* Burkenroad, 1959. In older literature often confused with *P. semisulcatus*.

FAO Names: Giant tiger prawn (En), Crevette géante tigrée (Fr), Camarón tigre gigante (Sp).

Local Names: Tiger prawn (S. and E. Africa), Kamba, Kamba ndogo (Swahili language, Kenya; Kamba is used for the adults, Kamba ndogo for the small ones, these names are used for all commercial Penaeidae), Kalri (Pakistan; also used for other species of similar size), Jinga (Bombay, India), Kara chemmeen (Kerala, India), Yera (Madras, India), Bagda chingri (Calcutta, India), Ushi-ebi (Japan), Grass shrimp (Taiwan), Ghost prawn (Hong Kong), Sugpo, Jumbo tiger shrimp (Philippines), Udang windu, Udang pantjet (Indonesia), Jumbo tiger prawn, Giant tiger prawn, Black tiger prawn, Blue tiger prawn, Leader prawn, Panda prawn (Australia).

Literature: Mohamed, 1970.

Distribution: Indo-West Pacific: E. and S.E. Africa and Pakistan to Japan, the Malay Archipelago and northern Australia.

Habitat: Depth 0 to 110 m. Bottom mud, sand. Estuarine (juveniles) and marine (adults).

Size: Maximum total length 336 mm. Weight 60 to 130 g.

Interest to Fishery: In S.E. and E. Africa (Natal to Somalia, including Madagascar) the species is of minor or moderate commercial importance, it is used for bait and food. In Pakistan it is likewise of minor importance. Jones (1967:1333) indicated that it is more common in prawn catches on the east coast of India than on the west coast. According to Chopra (1939:222) "This is the commonest large-sized penaeid of Calcutta, and is sold in our markets in enormous quantities". Kurian & Sebastian (1976:100) cited it as an important commercial species in India, especially on the east coast (Bengal and Orissa); juveniles being caught in estuaries. Also in Bangladesh it is of considerable commercial importance. In Malaya and Thailand *Penaeus monodon* is fished in offshore waters. It is obtained both by pond fishing and inshore fishing in Malaya, Singapore, Indonesia, the Philippines and Taiwan; because of its large size the species is quite important economically. Domantay (1956:363) indicated that "among the commercially important prawns in the Philippines, *Penaeus monodon* Fabricius stands foremost". In Japan and Korea it seems to be of minor importance; Yoshida (1941) remarked that it was sold on the Fusan market in Korea. Also in Australia the species is of commercial interest: Harrison, Kesteven & Setter (1965:8) listed it among the commercial species of the Gulf of Carpentaria, while Racek (1957:12) mentioned it as the last of the six most important species of New South Wales, and as the fourth in importance of the species taken in offshore waters of Queensland. Rapson & McIntosh (1971:17) reported it as constituting about 7% of the commercial catches in New Guinea (mainly in the Gulf of Papua).

Penaeus (Penaeus) semisulcatus De Haan, 1844   PEN Pen 27

Penaeus semisulcatus De Haan, In Von Siebold, Fauna Japonica, Crustacea (6/7):Pl. 46, Fig. 1

Synonymy: Penaeus ashiaka Kishinouye, 1900; Penaeus semisulcatus paucidentatus Parisi, 1919; Penaeus monodon manillensis Villaluz & Arriola, 1938. The name semisulcatus has been used incorrectly by some older authors for Penaeus monodon, which has caused considerable confusion.

FAO Names: Green tiger prawn (En), Crevette tigrée verte (Fr), Camarón tigre verde (Sp).

Local Names: Green prawn (South Africa), Tiger prawn (English, Kenya), Kamba (for the larger), Kamba ndogo (for the smaller specimens) (Swahili language, Kenya; these names used for all commercial penaeids),Rebian (Arabian), Kalri (Pakistan, used also for other species of about the same size), Kuma-ebi (Japan), Fa ha, Flower prawn, Bamboo node prawn (Hong Kong), Kung kula lai (Thailand), Grooved tiger prawn, Northern tiger prawn, Green tiger prawn (Australia); Kastanie (Israel).

Distribution: Indo-West Pacific: Red Sea, E. and S.E. Africa to Japan, Korea, the Malay Archipelago and northern Australia. Eastern Atlantic: The species has reached the eastern Mediterranean through the Suez Canal; it is now found all along the coasts of Egypt, Israel, Lebanon, Syria and southern Turkey.

Habitat: Depth 2 to 130 m. Bottom mud, sand. Marine (adults) and estuarine (juveniles).

Size: Maximum total length 180 mm (♂), 228 mm (♀).

Interest to Fishery: The species is of minor to moderate importance in Madagascar, S.E. and E. Africa (Mozambique to Somalia) and the Red Sea. In the Gulf of Aden, the Persian Gulf and in Pakistan it is of major importance in the offshore fishery; in Pakistan it is exported frozen or canned, and also used for shrimp meal and paste (Tirmizi, in Litt.). In India it is more common on the east than on the west coast, but it is not as important commercially as P. monodon is there (Jones, 1967:1333; Kurian & Sebastian, 1976:100). It plays a role in the ricefield shrimp farming in the Ganges delta. According to Longhurst (1970:282,283) the species is likely to be of economic importance in Sri Lanka, Singapore and the Philippines. Lai-shing (1972:287) mentioned that it is caught by trawlers in the Hong Kong area. In the Inland Sea of Japan it is also commercially important (Yasuda, 1956; in table VI Yasuda evidently indicated the species by mistake with the name P. monodon). Yoshida (1941:10) listed the species among the shrimps of economic importance in Korea. In the eastern Mediterranean Penaeus semisulcatus is caught by Turkish, Israeli and Egyptian trawlers. Aquaculture experiments with this species are carried out in Taiwan and Thailand.

Protrachypene precipua Burkenroad, 1934   PEN Prot 1

Protrachypene precipua Burkenroad, 1934, Bull.Bingham Oceanogr.Collect., Yale Univ., 4(7):44

FAO Names: Titi shrimp (En), Crevette titi (Fr), Camarón titi (Sp).

Local Names: Camaroncillo (Nicaragua, also used for other species), Titi (Panama, used also for Xiphopenaeus), Camarón pomada (Ecuador).

Distribution: Eastern Pacific: Nicaragua to Ecuador.

Habitat: Depth less than 15 m. Marine.

Size: Maximum total length 75 mm (♂), 88 mm (♀); maximum carapace length 13.8 mm (♂), 15.3 mm (♀).

Interest to Fishery: The species is of secondary commercial importance throughout its range.

| *Trachypenaeus anchoralis* (Bate, 1881) | PEN Trachyp 3 |

Penaeus anchoralis Bate, 1881, Ann.Mag.Nat.Hist., (5)8:181

Synonymy: *Parapenaeus anchoralis* - Pearson, 1905.

FAO Names: Hardback shrimp (En), Crevette os (Fr), Camarón huesudo (Sp).

Local Names: Hardback prawn, Northern rough prawn (Australia).

Literature: Schmitt, 1926:348, Pl. 62, Figs. 1-3, Pl. 68, Fig. 3; Dall, 1957:203, 209, Fig. 24; Racek & Dall, 1965:93, Pl. 7, Fig. 10, Pl. 12, Fig. 8.

Distribution: Indo-West Pacific: Northern Australia from the northern part of Western Australia east to about Keppel Bay. Queensland; very rare in New South Wales.

Habitat: Depth 12.5 to 52 m. Marine.

Size: Total length 38 to 104 mm.

Interest to Fishery: Very limited; possibly of economic importance in the future. Tham (1968:212) and Domantay (1956:363) listed the species as occurring in commercial catches in Australia and the Philippines. The latter record obviously is erroneous as the species does not occur in the Philippines. Harrison, Kesteven & Setter (1965:8) cited *T. anchoralis* among the non-commercial species of the Gulf of Carpentaria.

| *Trachypenaeus byrdi* Burkenroad, 1934 | PEN Trachyp 4 |

Trachypenaeus (Trachysalambria) byrdi Burkenroad, 1934, Bull.Bingham Oceanogr.Collect., Yale Univ., 4(7):51

FAO Names: Carabali shrimp (En), Crevette carabali (Fr), Camarón carabalí (Sp).

Local Names: Tigre (Panama, Colombia, Ecuador), Cebra, Indio, Carabalí (Panama, Ecuador), Camaroncillo (Nicaragua, a name used for this and similar species alike).

Literature: Burkenroad, 1934; Loesch & Avila, 1964.

Distribution: Eastern Pacific: from Mexico to N. Peru.

Habitat: Depth 3.5 to 20 m. Bottom soft mud. Marine or brackish.

Size: Maximum total length 189 mm; maximum length abdomen 110 mm.

Interest to Fishery: Minor. According to Lindner (1957:145) the species is caught together with commercial species in Peru, but is discarded because of its small size. In Ecuador and Colombia the species is of minor importance and the tails are used only locally, sold fresh, frozen or cooked, whole or peeled, sometimes canned.

| *Trachypenaeus constrictus* (Stimpson, 1874) | PEN Trachyp 1 |

Penaeus constrictus Stimpson, 1874, Ann.Lyc.Nat.Hist.New York, 10:135

Synonymy: *Parapenaeus constrictus* - Smith, 1885; *Penaeopsis agassizii* Bouvier, 1905; *Trachypenaeus (Trachysalambria) constrictus* - Anderson & Lindner, 1945.

FAO Names: Roughneck shrimp (En), Crevette gambri (Fr), Camarón fijador (Sp).

Local Names: Camarão branco (N.E. Brazil; a name also used for *Penaeus* species), Camarão ferrinho (S.E. Brazil, near Santos), Roughneck shrimp (U.S.A.).

Literature: Williams, 1965:31, Fig. 21; Neiva & Mistakidis, 1966.

Distribution: Western Atlantic: from Virginia (U.S.A.) and Bermuda to Estado do Santa Catarina, Brazil.

Habitat: Depth, shallow water to 71 m. Bottom sand or mud and shells. Marine.

Size: Maximum total length 92 mm; length usually between 60 and 80 mm.

Interest to Fishery: The commercial value of this species is insignificant in N.E. Brazil (Fausto Filho, 1968:27). In Florida it is used as bait, and "commercial production is more accidental than intentional" but in the future it "may become commercially important for canning" (Joyce & Eldred, 1966:25). In S.E. Brazil it is found in small numbers in commercial catches of other species (FAO, 1964:9,11).

Trachypenaeus curvirostris (Stimpson, 1860)	PEN Trachyp 5

Penaeus curvirostris Stimpson, 1860, Proc.Acad.Nat.Sci.Phila., 1860:44

Synonymy: *Penaeus longipes* Paulson, 1875; *Parapenaeus curvirostris* - M.J. Rathbun, 1902; *Trachypeneus asper* Alcock, 1905; *Metapenaeus curvirostris* Nobili, 1906; *Metapenaeus palaestinensis* Steinitz, 1932; *Trachypenaeus curvirostris malaiana* Balss, 1933; *Trachypeneus (Trachysalambria) curvirostris* - Burkenroad, 1934; *Trachypeneus (Trachysalambria) curvirostris malaiana* - Burkenroad, 1959; *Trachypeneus (Trachysalambria) curvirostris palaestinensis* - Burkenroad, 1950.

FAO Names: Southern rough shrimp (En), Crevette gambri archée (Fr), Camarón fijador arquero (Sp).

Local Names: Saru ebi (Japan), Sui lim har (Hong Kong; also used for other species of the genus), Hardback prawn, Southern rough prawn (Australia).

Literature: Kubo, 1949:393, Figures; Dall, 1957:203; Burkenroad, 1959:90, Fig. 17; Hall, 1961: 98; Racek & Dall, 1965:89.

Distribution: Indo-West Pacific: Red Sea, East Africa and Madagascar to China, Japan and Australia. Eastern Atlantic: the species entered the eastern Mediterranean through the Suez Canal and has been reported from Egypt, Israel and Turkey.

Habitat: Depth 13 to 150 m. Marine.

Size: Maximum total length 81 mm (♂), 98 mm (♀); maximum carapace length 22 mm (♂), 30 mm (♀).

Interest to Fishery: Because of the small size of the animals, the commercial importance of this species is usually minor. Longhurst (1970:280) reported a fishery for this and other species in the Red Sea, the Gulf of Aden and the Arabian Sea. In Madagascar it is caught in small quantities. Kurian & Sebastian (1976:101), although listing the species among the Indian prawns of commercial importance, remarked that in India it is "not found in large numbers to contribute to a fishery". Liu (1955:14) listed it among the economic shrimps of N. China. In Japan the species is offered at the fish markets (Balss, 1914:11; Kubo, 1949:394). Yasuda (1949:180) cited it as "an important, commercial as well as bait shrimp" in the Ise and Mikawa Bay areas of Japan. In Australia the species, although abundant in New South Wales, Queensland and Western Australia, is rendered commercially unimportant by its small size (Racek, 1957:12).

Trachypenaeus faoe Obarrio, 1954   PEN Trachyp 6

Trachypenaeus faoe Obarrio, 1954, In Segundo Centro Latinoamericano de Capacitación Pesquera (= II CLACP), 41:3 [a]

Synonymy: *Trachypeneus (Trachysalambria) faoe* - Eldred & Hutton, 1960; *Trachypeneus faoea* - Loesch & Avila, 1964.

FAO Names: Indio shrimp (En), Crevette gambri indienne (Fr), Camarón fijador indio (Sp).

Local Names: Chacalín (El Salvador), Indio (Panama), Cebra (Panama, Colombia, Ecuador), Tigre, Carabalí (Panama, Ecuador). These names are also used for other, similar species.

Literature: Loesch & Avila, 1964; Pérez-Farfante, 1971:642, Figs. 3B,4G,5B.

Distribution: Eastern Pacific: Panama to Ecuador. Possibly from Mexico to northern Peru, but records of this species from west of Panama and from northern Peru may pertain to *T. fuscina* (see there).

Habitat: Depth 9 to 24 m. Marine.

Size: Total length of neotype ♀ 100 mm, carapace length 28 mm.

Interest to Fishery: The species is, because of its relatively small size, of minor commercial importance. Lindner (1957:145) stated that in N. Peru specimens are "caught by the fishermen but discarded because of their small size". In most of the rest of its area this species, together with other similarly small species, is sold locally, fresh, cooked, frozen or salted, peeled or whole.

Remarks: Dr. Martin D. Burkenroad, when working with FAO in Panama, discovered the present species to be new and provisionally named it *Trachypenaeus faoae*, but did not publish the name or a description of the species. As a manuscript name it gained acceptance among fishery workers, who even used it in print, be it in a variety of spellings (like *faoe*, *faoea*, etc.). The first publication that made the name available is the one by Obarrio (1954), who, in a mimeographed publication, not only cited the name (as *Trachypenaeus faoe*) but also gave a short description: "Se distingue por tener 3 espinitas, sensibles al tacto, una en cada parte posterior de cada uno de los tres últimos segmentos del abdomen. En el telson no tiene espinas. El telico no se encuentra cubierto y su parte anterior termina en forma puntiaguda". Obarrio first cited the name as *Trachypenaeus face*; that *face* is an error for *faoe*, is clear from his statement: "Especie nueva y que el técnico nombró *faoe* en honor de la FAO". It is clear therefore that the specific name has to be spelled *faoe* and that Obarrio (1954) is its author. Before the rediscovery of Obarrio's paper it was thought that Loesch & Avila (1964) were the first to have validly published the species.

Some of the records of *T. faoe* may pertain to *T. fuscina* Pérez-Farfante (see there).

Trachypenaeus fulvus Dall, 1957   PEN Trachyp 7

Trachypenaeus fulvus Dall, 1957, Aust.J.Mar.Freshwat.Res., 8:203,206

Synonymy: *Trachypenaeus unicus* Hall, 1961.

FAO Names: Brown rough shrimp (En), Crevette gambri brune (Fr), Camarón fijador marrón (Sp).

Local Names: Brown rough prawn (Australia).

Literature: Dall, 1957:203,206, Fig. 23; Hall, 1962:29, Fig. 112; Racek & Dall, 1965:93.

Distribution: Indo-West Pacific: The Philippines; Malaysia; Indonesia; Australia.

Habitat: Depth about 60 m. Marine.

Size: Total length 47 to 63 mm ($\eth$), 32 to 103 mm ($\female$); carapace length 12.5 mm ($\eth$), 23 mm ($\female$).

Interest to Fishery: Slight. Dall (1957:208) remarked that this species was "approaching commercial abundance in Moreton Bay", Queensland. Tham (1968:212) reported that the species occurred in commercial catches in Malaysia. Harrison, Kesteven & Setter (1965:8) listed it among the non-commercial species of the Gulf of Carpentaria.

Trachypenaeus fuscina Pérez-Farfante, 1971	PEN Trachyp 8

Trachypenaeus fuscina Pérez-Farfante, 1971, <u>Fish.Bull.USFWS,</u> 69(3):637

FAO Names: Pinto shrimp (En), Crevette pinto (Fr), Camarón pinto (Sp).

Local Names: Pinto, Cebra, Tigre (Mexico, also used for other, similar species).

Distribution: Eastern Pacific: Mexico to northern Peru.

Habitat: Depth 7 to 70 m. Marine.

Size: Maximum total length 108 mm ($\eth$), 150 mm ($\female$); maximum carapace length 26 mm ($\eth$) 40.5 mm ($\female$).

Interest to Fishery: As until 1971 the present species has not been distinguished from *T. faoe*, the records under the latter name may partly or entirely pertain to the present species (see Pérez-Farfante, 1971).

Trachypenaeus gonospinifer Racek & Dall, 1965	PEN Trachyp 9

Trachypenaeus gonospinifer Racek & Dall, 1965, <u>Verh.K.Ned.Akad.Wet.(Natuurkd.),</u> (2)56(3):89

FAO Names: Northern rough shrimp (En), Crevette gambri nordique (Fr), Camarón fijador norteño (Sp).

Local Names: Hardback prawn, Rough prawn (Australia; both names also used for other species of the genus).

Distribution: Indo-West Pacific: Indonesia; New Guinea; N. Australia.

Habitat: Depth 13 to 52 m. Bottom mud. Marine.

Size: Total length 45 mm ($\eth$), 34 to 74 mm ($\female$); carapace length 12 to 13 mm ($\eth$), 15 to 16 mm ($\female$).

Interest to Fishery: Probably nil. Motoh (1977:1,7) listed this species among the "penaeid shrimps with commercial value" and referred to Munro (1968:14), who, however, ranged it among the "smaller species regarded as having no commercial value".

Trachypenaeus granulosus (Haswell, 1879)	PEN Trachyp 10

Penaeus granulosus Haswell, 1879, <u>Proc.Linn.Soc.N.S.W.,</u> 4:41

Synonymy: *Trachypeneus salaco* De Man, 1907; *Trachypeneus pescadoreensis* Schmitt, 1931; *Trachypeneus furcilla* Hall, 1961.

FAO Names: Coarse shrimp (En), Crevette gambri grenue (Fr), Camarón fijador de granos (Sp).

Local Names: Hardback prawn, Haswell's rough prawn (Australia); Sui lim har (Hong Kong; name used also for other species of the genus).

Literature: De Man, 1911:90-92, Pls. 8,9, Fig. 28 (as *T. salaco*); Hall, 1961:102, Pl.20, Figs. 16,17 (as *T. furcilla*); Racek & Dall, 1965:94, Pl.3, Fig. 4, Pl. 7, Fig. 9, Pl. 13, Fig. 1.

Distribution: Indo-West Pacific: Kuwait; Sri Lanka; Malaya; Indonesia; Taiwan; Australia.

Habitat: Depth 9 to 81 m. Bottom mud. Marine.

Size: Total length 36 to 51 mm (δ), 53 to 90 mm ($\female$); carapace length 12 to 14.5 mm (δ), 18 to 22 mm ($\female$).

Interest to Fishery: Practically nil. Racek & Dall (1965:94) reported the "first discovery in commercial trawl" in Princesse Charlotte Bay, Queensland. Harrison, Kesteven & Setter (1965:8) range the species among the non-commercial species of the Gulf of Carpentaria (N. Australia). Longhurst (1970:282,283) indicated the species (under the name *T. salaco*) as abundant in Sri Lanka waters, and thus possibly as of some potential commercial importance. Kurian & Sebastian (1976:101; under *T. pescadoreensis*) listed it among the Indian prawns of commercial importance, indicating, however, that it is taken "in stray catches only". Muthu (1971:148) found the species in commercial shrimp catches off the east coast of India (Kakinada).

Trachypenaeus pacificus Burkenroad, 1934	PEN Trachyp 11

Trachypenaeus (Trachysalambria) similis pacificus Burkenroad, 1934, Bull.Bingham Oceanogr. Collect., Yale Univ., 4(7):50

FAO Names: Zebra shrimp (En), Crevette zèbre (Fr), Camarón cebra (Sp).

Local Names: Coloradito (Mexico), Tigre, Cebra, Carabalí (Ecuador, also used for other similar species).

Literature: Loesch & Avila, 1964:5,7,25,26, Fig. 8C.

Distribution: Eastern Pacific: Mexico to N. Peru.

Habitat: Depth 22 to 43 m. Marine.

Size: Total length 27 to 50 mm (δ), 36 to 99 mm ($\female$); carapace length 6 to 11 mm (δ), 8 to 25 mm ($\female$).

Interest to Fishery: Not very great. Cobo & Loesch (1966:4) ranged the species among the commercially exploited shrimps of Ecuador, but remark that they are landed in small quantities. They are used locally and are sold peeled and deveined. Longhurst (1970:293) also listed the species (as *T. similis*) among the prawn resources of the American west coast.

Trachypenaeus sedili Hall, 1961	PEN Trachyp 12

Trachypeneus sedili Hall, 1961, Bull.Raffles Mus., 26:100

FAO Names: Malayan rough shrimp (En), Crevette gambri malaise (Fr), Camarón fijador malayo (Sp).

Literature: Thomas, 1971:192, Fig. 1 E-K.

Distribution: Indo-West Pacific: India; Sri Lanka; Malaya.

Habitat: Depth 2 to 44 m. Bottom mud. Marine.

Size: Maximum total length 60 mm; carapace length 8.5 to 12.5 mm (♂), 11 to 19 mm (♀).

Interest to Fishery: Minor if any. Kurian & Sebastian (1976:101) listed the species among the Indian prawns of commercial importance, but indicated that it is obtained only in stray catches from the Bay of Bengal (e.g., from off Visakhapatnam).

| *Trachypenaeus similis* (Smith, 1885) | PEN Trachyp 2 |

Parapenaeus constrictus similis Smith, 1885, <u>Proc.U.S.Natl.Mus.</u>, 8:175

Synonymy: *Parapenaeus constrictus similis* M.J. Rathbun, 1902; *Trachypeneus (Trachysalambria) similis* Burkenroad, 1934.

FAO Names: Yellow roughneck shrimp (En), Crevette gambri jaune (Fr), Camarón fijador amarillo (Sp).

Local Names: Camarón fijador (Cuba).

Literature: Burkenroad, 1934:96, Figs. 10,11; Davant, 1963:25,40,81,96, Figs. 25,26.

Distribution: Western Atlantic: Florida to N. Brazil.

Habitat: Depth 2 to 99 m. Bottom mud and sand. Marine.

Size: Maximum total length 101 mm.

Interest to Fishery: Very minor. It is sometimes found mixed in with the catches of larger species like *Penaeus duorarum* and sold with these. Joyce & Eldred (1966:25) state that "only the largest individuals of *T. similis* occasionally enter the commercial catch in the Tortuga area", and "current commercial production is more accidental than intentional", "because of their small size they are usually discarded". But in the future it may become more important commercially for canning. In N. Brazil the species is fished for in the area of the mouth of the Amazon River, but is of secondary importance and only used locally (P. Alves Coelho, in Litt.).

| *Xiphopenaeus kroyeri* (Heller, 1862) | PEN Xiphop 1 |

Penaeus kroyeri Heller, 1862, <u>S.B.Akad.Wiss.Wien</u>, 45(1):425

Synonymy: *Xiphopeneus hartii* Smith, 1869.

FAO Names: Atlantic seabob (En), Crevette seabob (de l'Atlantique) (Fr), Camarón siete barbas (Sp).

Local Names: Seabob (U.S.A.), Camarón blanco (Venezuela), Coarse shrimp, Large prawn (Guyana), Redi sara-sara, Bigi sara-sara (Surinam), Camarão chifrudo (N. Brazil), Camarão sete barbas (Brazil).

Literature: Williamson, 1965:30, Figs. 18-20; Chace & Hobbs, 1969:55, Figs. 6,7e.

Distribution: Western Atlantic: North Carolina (U.S.A.) to Estado de Santa Catarina (Brazil).

Habitat: Depth 1 to 70 m, usually less than 27 m. Bottom mud or sand. Marine, brackish, exceptionally fresh; most plentiful in areas near river estuaries.

Size: Total length of adult specimens 70 to 140 mm; maximum total length of males 115 mm.

Interest to Fishery: In the United States it is by far the most important commercial species from Pensacola (N.W. Florida) to Texas. The annual catch in the United States (in metric tons) amounted to 2 100 (in 1973), 2 994 (in 1974), 3 182 (in 1975) and 514 (in 1976). In Mexico it is "also taken at times near Ciudad del Carmen, but is not of commercial significance" (Lindner, 1957: 83). Longhurst (1970:275) reports commercial concentrations also off Nicaragua, off eastern Venezuela and off Trinidad. Mistakidis (1972) cited the following fishing grounds for this species: Honduras, Nicaragua, Costa Rica, Colombia. In Venezuela it "is of commercial importance but its capture is not done intensively except locally" (Davant, 1963:95). In the Guianas it is the most common commercial shrimp in local fisheries. It is caught by local fishermen, sold fresh, dried, or frozen and is exported (Holthuis, 1959:72,73). Also in Brazil the species forms the subject of an important fishery, especially in N. Brazil but also as far south as Santa Catarina (see FAO, 1964 and Mistakidis, 1972); it is used mostly locally.

Xiphopenaeus riveti Bouvier, 1907	PEN Xiphop 2

Xiphopeneus riveti Bouvier, 1907, Bull.Mus.Hist.Nat.Paris, 13:113

Synonymy: *Xiphopenaeus kroyeri riveti* - Rioja, 1942.

FAO Names: Pacific seabob (En), Crevette seabob (du Pacifique) (Fr), Camarón botalón (Sp).

Local Names: Botalón (Mexico), Tití (Ecuador, Colombia, Panama), Chacalín (El Salvador, name also used for other small species).

Literature: Bouvier, 1907:113, Fig. 1; Rioja, 1942:630, Figs. 6-11; Loesch & Avila, 1964:5,6, 8,18,22,25,26,28, Figs. 10,14b.

Distribution: Eastern Pacific: Mexico to N. Peru.

Habitat: Depth 3.5 to 18 m. Bottom soft mud. Marine and brackish, estuarine.

Size: Maximum total length 170 mm.

Interest to Fishery: In Mexico the species is of no commercial importance (Lindner, 1957:81). In most of the area from El Salvador to Ecuador the species is caught and sold fresh or peeled and deveined on the local markets (Lindner, 1957; Cobo & Loesch, 1966). In Colombia it is of moderate importance and used locally; the tails are sold, fresh or cooked, frozen, peeled or unpeeled (Squires, in Litt.). In Peru the species is "also caught but discarded because of its small size" (Lindner, 1957:145); however, the type specimens (170 mm long) were bought at the market of Paita, Peru.

FAMILY SICYONIIDAE Ortmann, 1898

Sicyoninae Ortmann, 1898, Bronn's Klass.Ordn.Thierreichs, (ed. 1) 5(2) (2) (50-52):1121

The family consists of only a single genus, six species of which are of (minor) commercial importance.

Sicyonia brevirostris Stimpson, 1874	SICYON Sicyon 1

Sicyonia brevirostris Stimpson, 1874, Ann.Lyc.Nat.Hist., New York, 10:132

Synonymy: *Eusicyonia brevirostris* - Burkenroad, 1934.

FAO Names: Rock shrimp (En), Boucot ovetgernade (Fr), Camarón de piedra (Sp).

Local Names: Rock shrimp (U.S.A., name used also for other species of the genus), Camarón de piedra (Mexico).

Literature: Williams, 1965:35, Figs. 25,26.

Distribution: Western Atlantic: coast of U.S.A. from Virginia to Texas; Bahama Islands; Cuba; Mexico (Yucatán). Eastern Pacific: S. Mexico.

Habitat: Depth shallow water to over 180 m, rarely as deep as 330 m. Bottom white shelly sand. Marine.

Size: Maximum total length 153 mm.

Interest to Fishery: The species has "a limited commercial usage" in North Carolina (Williams, 1965:36). Joyce & Eldred (1966:25) remarked that "*Sicyonia brevirostris* is the only species [of *Sicyonia*] which does occasionally enter the commercial catches" in Florida; they state that it is excellent eating and that the way may be opened for large scale commercial utilization of it in certain areas. Kennedy et al. (1977:1) described the increase in commercial value of the Rock shrimp in Florida: in 1974, 1 683 218 pounds (heads-off) with a value of U.S.$ 908 619, having been landed in Florida. The annual catch of the species in the U.S.A. amounted (in metric tons) to 600 (in 1973), 1 361 (in 1974), 909 (in 1975) and 856 (in 1976). The species is now also exploited off the north coast of Quintana Roo (Mexico).

| *Sicyonia burkenroadi* Cobb, 1971 | see *S. stimpsoni* |

| *Sicyonia carinata* (Brünnich, 1768) | SICYON Sicyon 2 |

Cancer carinatus Brünnich, 1768, Ichthyol.Massiliens., 102

Synonymy: *Cancer pulchellus* Herbst, 1796; *Sicyonia sculpta* H. Milne Edwards, 1830; *Peneus sculptus* H. Milne Edwards, 1830; *Ruvulus sculptus* - Cocco, 1832; *Eusicyonia carinata* - Balss, 1925; *Sicyonia foresti* Rossignol, 1962.

FAO Names: Mediterranean rock shrimp (En), Boucot méditerranéen (Fr), Camarón de piedra mediterráneo (Sp).

Local Names: Camarão da costa (Portugal), Sicionia (Italy), Scurzune (Campania, Italy), Ammiru cani di terra (Sicily, Italy), Bargouth bharr (Tunisia).

Literature: Pesta, 1918:47, Figs. 10-12; Zariquiey Alvarez, 1968:57, Fig. 28.

Distribution: Eastern Atlantic: Portugal to W. Africa (Congo), including the entire Mediterranean.

Habitat: Depth 3 to 35 m, usually less than 5 m. Bottom sand, or slightly muddy sand, often with eelgrass. Marine.

Size: Maximum total length 62.5 mm; maximum carapace length 23.5 mm.

Interest to Fishery: Minor. Heldt (1938:42) reported that in Tunisia the species "ne présente pas un grand intérêt du point de vue économique, bien qu'elle soit comestible et de goût très fin". Palombi & Santarelli (1961:360) ranged the species among the edible shrimps of Italy and stated that the very good gastronomic quality of the species is hampered by the fact that the shell is very hard. They also indicated that the species is used as fish bait.

| Sicyonia cristata (De Haan, 1844) | SICYON Sicyon 3 |

Hippolyte cristata De Haan, 1844, In Von Siebold, Fauna Japonica, Crustacea, (6/7):Pl 45, Fig. 10.

Synonymy: *Eusicyonia cristata* - Kubo, 1949.

FAO Names: Ridgeback rock shrimp (En), Boucot balafré (Fr), Camarón de piedra costurón (Sp).

Local Names: Tiger prawn (Hong Kong; also used for other species of the genus).

Literature: Kubo, 1949:446, Figures.

Distribution: Indo-West Pacific: Japan; Hong Kong.

Habitat: Depth 46 to 350 m. Marine.

Size: Total length 23 to 42 mm (δ), 22 to 57 mm ($\female$); carapace length 7 to 11 mm (δ), 7 to 18 mm ($\female$).

Interest to Fishery: Evidently of minor commercial value. Kubo (1949:477) mentioned a specimen obtained at the fish market at Simonoseki, Japan.

| Sicyonia dorsalis Kingsley, 1878 | SICYON Sicyon 4 |

Sicyonia dorsalis Kingsley, 1878, Proc.Acad.Nat.Sci.Phila., 1878:97

Synonymy: *Eusicyonia dorsalis* - Burkenroad, 1934.

FAO Names: Lesser rock shrimp (En), Boucot nain (Fr), Camaroncito de piedra (Sp).

Local Names: Rock shrimp (U.S.A.), Camarão da pedra, Camarão muído (Brazil).

Literature: Williams, 1965:37, Fig. 28.

Distribution: Western Atlantic: North Carolina (U.S.A.) to Central Brazil, including the entire Caribbean Sea.

Habitat: Depth 5.5 to 160 m, rarely 420 m. Bottom mud and sand. Marine.

Size: Maximum total length 63 mm (δ), 75 mm ($\female$).

Interest to Fishery: Little if any. Joyce & Eldred (1966:24) commented that the species was "too small to be commercially productive at this time" in Florida. Neiva & Mistakidis (1966:5) mentioned the presence of this species in commercial catches in the south central part of the Brazilian coast.

| Sicyonia galeata Holthuis, 1952 | SICYON Sicyon 5 |

Sicyonia galeata Holthuis, 1952, Résult.Sci.Expéd.Océanogr.Belge Eaux Côt.Afr.Atl.Sud, 3(2):84

FAO Names: Tufted rock shrimp (En), Sicyonie huppée (Fr), Camarón penachudo (Sp).

Distribution: Eastern Atlantic: West Africa from Rio de Oro to Angola.

Habitat: Depth 15 to 70 m. Bottom mud and sandy mud.

Size: Maximum total length 62 mm.

Interest to Fishery: Minor if at all. The species is fished in the coastal area from Senegal to Angola and sold fresh. It is too small and not enough abundant to form the subject of a special fishery.

| *Sicyonia ingentis* (Burkenroad, 1938) | SICYON Sicyon 5 |

Eusicyonia ingentis Burkenroad, 1938, Zoologica(New York), 23:88

FAO Names: Pacific rock shrimp (En), Boucot du Pacifique (Fr), Camarón de piedra del Pacifico (Sp).

Distribution: Eastern Pacific: California (U.S.A.) and Baja California (Mexico).

Habitat: Depth 68 to 108 m. Marine.

Size: Total length 20 to 86 mm ($\male$), 30 to 105 mm ($\female$); carapace length 5 to 22 mm ($\male$), 7 to 27 mm ($\female$).

Interest to Fishery: Longhurst (1970:272) remarked that "a potential exists for development of a small trawl fishery for *Sicyonia ingentis* off Santa Barbara", California, U.S.A.

| *Sicyonia lancifera* (Olivier, 1811) | SICYON Sicyon 6 |

Palaemon lancifer Olivier, 1811, Encycl.Méthod.Hist.Nat.(Ins.), 8:664

Synonymy: *Eusicyonia lancifer* - Kubo, 1949.

FAO Names: Knight rock shrimp (En), Boucot chevalier (Fr), Camarón de piedra lanzón (Sp).

Distribution: Indo-West Pacific: Red Sea and Madagascar to the Malay Archipelago and Japan.

Habitat: Depth 22 to 55 m. Bottom sand and mud. Marine.

Size: Total length 18 to 40 mm ($\male$), 30 to 53 mm ($\female$); carapace length 7 to 16 mm ($\male$), 6 to 16 mm ($\female$). Kurian & Sebastian (1976:99) gave the maximum length of the species as 80 mm.

Interest to Fishery: Minor if at all. Kurian & Sebastian (1976:101) listed the species among the Indian prawns of commercial importance, but remarked that "only very small numbers reported from Arabian Sea". Motho (1977:7) listed *Sicyonia lancifer japonica* Balss among the "penaeid shrimps with commercial value" (Motho, 1977:1) and referred to Cheung (1960:3), who listed the subspecies from Hong Kong, without indicating, however, that it is of commercial importance there.

Remarks: The spelling *lancifera* of the specific name should be used in combination with the feminine generic name *Sicyonia*; lancifer is the masculine form of the adjective.

| *Sicyonia stimpsoni* Bouvier, 1905 | SICYON Sicyon 7 |

Sicyonia stimpsoni Bouvier, 1905, C.R.Hebd.Séances Acad.Sci., Paris, 141:748

Synonymy: *Eusicyonia stimpsoni* - Burkenroad, 1939.

FAO Names: Eyespot rock shrimp (En), Boucot ocellé (Fr), Camarón ocelado (Sp).

Distribution: Western Atlantic: North Carolina (U.S.A.) to Panama and Colombia; West Indies.

Habitat: Depth 73 to 411 m. Bottom predominantly mud. Marine.

Size: Maximum carapace length 10.4 mm (♂), 12.4 mm (♀).

Interest to Fishery: Ewald (1969:771) mentioned the species from commercial catches in Venezuela, but it does not occur there in commercially attractive quantities.

Remarks: Cobb (1971) showed that two species have been confused under the name *S. stimpsoni*; it is very likely that Ewald's above cited specimens from Venezuela do not belong to the true *S. stimpsoni*, but to *S. burkenroadi* Cobb, 1971, which has about the same range (North Carolina to Panama and French Guiana), but occurs less deep (33 to 118 m) and predominantly on mud, mud-shell, or mud-sand bottoms.

Sicyonia typica (Boeck, 1864)	SICYON Sicyon 8

Synhimantites typicus Boeck, 1864, Forh.Videnskabsselsk.Krist., 1863:189

Synonymy: *Penaeus carinatus* Olivier, 1811 (not *Cancer carinatus* Brünnich, 1764); *Sicyonia carinata* - H. Milne Edwards, 1830; *Sicyonia edwardsii* Miers, 1881; *Eusicyonia edwardsi* - Boone, 1930.

FAO Names: Kinglet rock shrimp (En), Boucot roitelet (Fr), Camarón reyecito (Sp).

Local Names: Camarão da pedra (Brazil; also used for other species of the genus), Rock shrimp (U.S.A.; also used for other species of the genus), Camarón reyecito (Cuba).

Literature: Williams, 1965:36, Fig. 27.

Distribution: Western Atlantic: North Carolina (U.S.A.) to Rio de Janeiro (Brazil).

Habitat: Depth 0 to 67 m. Bottom rocks, mud, and algae. Marine.

Size: Maximum total length 74 mm.

Interest to Fishery: Minor. Hildebrand (1954:270) mentioned that the species is fished commercially in the Gulf of Batabanó, S.W. Cuba, and that it occurs in commercial quantities in the Gulf of Campeche. In N. Brazil it is of secondary economic importance, and only sold locally for direct consumption. In S.E. Brazil the species is found in small numbers in commercial catches of other shrimp species (FAO, 1964:9).

SUPERFAMILY SERGESTOIDEA Dana, 1852

This superfamily consists of two families: Sergestidae and Luciferidae.

FAMILY SERGESTIDAE Dana, 1852

Sergestidae Dana, 1852, Proc.Acad.Nat.Sci.Phila., 6:18

The family contains two genera of economic importance: *Acetes* H. Milne Edwards, 1830, and *Sergestes* H. Milne Edwards, 1830.

Acetes americanus Ortmann, 1893   SERG Ac 1

Acetes americanus Ortmann, 1893, Ergeb.Plankton-Exped., 2(Gb):39

Synonymy: *Acetes brasiliensis* Hansen, 1919; *Acetes carolinae* Hansen, 1933; *Acetes americanus limonensis* Burkenroad, 1934; *Acetes americanus louisianensis* Burkenroad, 1934.

FAO Names: Aviu shrimp (En), Chevrette aviu (Fr), Camarón aviu (Sp).

Local Names: Net clinger (U.S.A.)

Literature: Omori, 1975:21, Figs. 7,8.

Distribution: Western Atlantic: North Carolina (U.S.A.) to S. Brazil, including Gulf of Mexico and Caribbean.

Habitat: Shallow coastal waters, mostly estuarine.

Size: Total length 10 to 17 mm ($\eth$), 14 to 26 mm ($\female$).

Interest to Fishery: Minor if at all. Holthuis (1959:49) mentioned specimens obtained at the fish markets of Paramaribo (Surinam) and Cayenne (French Guiana); the specimens may have formed an admixture to catches of other species.

Acetes australis Colefax, 1940   SERG Ac 2

Acetes australis Colefax, 1940, Rec.Aust.Mus., 20:341

FAO Names: Australian paste shrimp (En), Chevrette australienne (Fr), Camarón de pasta australiano (Sp).

Literature: Omori, 1975:63 (as *Acetes sibogae australis*).

Distribution: Indo-West Pacific: east coast of Australia from Townsville (Queensland) to Port Hacking (New South Wales).

Habitat: Shallow coastal waters. Marine and brackish.

Size: Total length 18 to 25 mm ($\eth$), 18 to 34 mm ($\female$); maximum carapace length 8 mm.

Interest to Fishery: According to Tham (1968:212) the species has been reported in commercial catches in Australia.

Acetes chinensis Hansen, 1919   SERG Ac 3

Acetes chinensis Hansen, 1919, Siboga Exped.Mon., 38:33,35,41

FAO Names: Northern mauxia shrimp (En), Chevrette mauxia nordique (Fr), Camaroncillo mauxia norteño (Sp).

Local Names: Penicillated shrimp (China), Maoxia (China), Baek ha (Korea).

Literature: Omori, 1975:29, Figs. 11,12.

Distribution: Indo-West Pacific: Korea; China; Taiwan; Japan, as far north as 40°50'N.

Habitat: Shallow coastal waters. Marine.

Size: Total length 20 to 35 mm (♂), 25 to 42 mm (♀).

Interest to Fishery: "This shrimp has long been recognized as one of the most important marine products in North China. The fresh material is usually dried or fermented for food in various ways and it is distinguished for its taste and nourishment" (Liu, 1956:39). Omori (1975:71,73,77) reported on the fishery for this species in Northeast China, Korea and Taiwan.

Acetes erythraeus Nobili, 1905	SERG Ac 4

Acetes erythraeus Nobili, 1905, <u>Bull.Mus.Hist.Nat.Paris</u>, 11:393

· FAO Names: Tsivakihini paste shrimp (En), Chevrette tsivakihini (Fr), Camaroncillo tsivakihini (Sp).

Local Names: Tsivakihiny (Madagascar), Kwei kung (Thailand), Alamang (Philippines), Bubok (W. Borneo).

Literature: Omori, 1975:32, Figs. 13,14.

Distribution: Indo-West Pacific: Red Sea and S.E. Africa to China, Thailand, Indonesia and N.E. Australia.

Habitat: Depth 0 to 55 m; fished for in the intertidal zone. Bottom mud or sand. Marine or brackish, usually brackish.

Size: Total length 16 to 33 mm, rarely up to 48 mm.

Interest to Fishery: In Madagascar the species is of moderate economic importance; although several tons are exported to Reunion, the consumption is mostly local. It is also fished for in Mozambique, Tanzania and Kenya (Omori, 1975:80). Together with *A. serrulatus* this species is also of commercial importance in India, especially in Madras and Kerala (Chopra, 1943:5; Nataraj, 1949:139; Jones, 1967:1338; Omori, 1975:32,80). Kurian & Sebastian (1976:102) mentioned for this species a "fairly good fishery in Bengal, Orissa and Madras. In Trivandrum coast got in large quantities from December to April". Also in Malaysia the species is of economic importance (Longhurst, 1970:285; Johnson, 1965:8; Johnson, 1966:279). Omori (1975:33,71-79) reported it from fishmarkets in Hong Kong and Sabah (Borneo) and mentioned that it is exploited along the south coast of China, in the Philippines, Thailand and W. Borneo.

Acetes indicus H. Milne Edwards, 1830	SERG Ac 5

Acetes indicus H. Milne Edwards, 1830, <u>Ann.Sci.Nat.Paris</u>, (1)19:351

Synonymy: *Acetes spiniger* Hansen, 1919.

FAO Names: Jawla paste shrimp (En), Chevrette jawla (Fr), Camaroncillo javlá (Sp).

Local Names: Con ruốc (Viet Nam), Kwei kung (Thailand), Udang gragok (Malaysia), Jawla (Marathi, India).

Literature: Omori, 1975:36, Figs. 12,15.

Distribution: Indo-West Pacific: west coast of India to Thailand and Indonesia.

Habitat: Shallow, sometimes brackish coastal waters. The species usually swims in mid water or near the surface.

Size: Total length 15 to 25 mm (♂), 23 to 40 mm (♀).

Interest to Fishery: The species "contributes to a good percentage of the fishery in the inshore waters of Bombay in certain months and also along the Bengal and Madras coasts" (Jones, 1967:1338). It is the second important shrimp species at the Maharashtra coast (west coast of India). Kurian & Sebastian (1976:102) stated of this species: "good fishery in N.W. Coast and East Coast [of India]. In Bombay contributes to 20% of prawn fishery". Also in Malaya it is of some importance (Johnson, 1966:279; Longhurst, 1970:285). Suvatti (1950:136) remarked that in Thailand the species is used for the preparation of shrimp paste. Omori (1975:77-80) mentioned its fishery in Viet Nam, Thailand, Malaysia, Burma and India.

| *Acetes intermedius* Omori, 1975 | SERG Ac 6 |

Acetes intermedius Omori, 1975, Bull.Ocean Res.Inst.Univ.Tokyo, 7:40

FAO Names: Taiwan mauxia shrimp (En), Chevrette mauxia de Formose (Fr), Camaroncillo mauxia de Formosa (Sp).

Local Names: Alamang (Philippines).

Distribution: Indo-West Pacific: Taiwan; Philippines; Indonesia.

Habitat: Marine.

Size: Total length 17 to 24 mm (♂), 20 to 26 mm (♀).

Interest to Fishery: Omori (1975) reported the species from commercial catches made in Taiwan, the Philippines (Iloilo) and Indonesia. No data are available on commercial value of the species.

| *Acetes japonicus* Kishinouye, 1905 | SERG Ac 7 |

Acetes japonicus Kishinouye, 1905, Annot.Zool.Jap., 5:167

Synonymy: *Acetes dispar* Hansen, 1919; *Acetes cochinensis* Rao, 1968.

FAO Names: Akiami paste shrimp (En), Chevrette akiami (Fr), Camaroncillo akiami (Sp).

Local Names: Aki ami, Hon ami (Japan), Baek ha (Korea), Con ruốc (Viet Nam), Kwei kung (Thailand), Udang gragok (Malaysia).

Literature: Omori, 1975:43, Figs. 12,18.

Distribution: Indo-West Pacific: west coast of India to Korea, Japan, China and Indonesia.

Habitat: Shallow waters over a muddy bottom. Marine.

Size: Total length 11 to 24 mm (♂), 15 to 30 mm (♀).

Interest to Fishery: Liu (1955:22) ranged the species among the economically important shrimps of North China and Yoshida (1941:18) included it among those of Korea. Kemp (1918:296), Kishinouye (1928:125) and Harada (1968:82) stated that the species is caught commercially in Japan. Omori (1975:71-78) reported that it is fished for along the Yellow Sea coasts of Korea and China, and in Viet Nam, Thailand and Malaysia; he gave extensive details of its fishery in Japan. Also Longhurst (1970:285) reported it from commercial catches made in Malaya. According to Nataraj (1949:139) this species together with other species of the genus is "of considerable commercial importance" in Travancore, S.W. India. Kurian & Sebastian (1976:102, under *A. cochinensis* and *A. japonicus*) stated that the species usually occurs in small numbers in Indian waters, but that off Trivandrum it is taken in great quantities in July.

| *Acetes serrulatus* (Kröyer, 1859) | SERG Ac 8 |

Sergestes serrulatus Kröyer, 1859, K.Dan.Vidensk.Selsk.Skr., (5)4:268

Synonymy: *Acetes insularis* Kemp, 1917.

FAO Names: Southern mauxia shrimp (En), Chevrette mauxia méridionale (Fr), Camaroncillo mauxia sureño (Sp).

Literature: Omori, 1975:59, Figs. 20,26.

Distribution: Indo-West Pacific: Leichou Peninsula (S. China) to Indonesia.

Habitat: Shallow coastal water.

Size: Total length 12 to 17 mm (♂), 15 to 21 mm (♀).

Interest to Fishery: Longhurst (1970:285) indicated that in Malaya the species is of some importance locally or seasonally. Omori (1975:59,71) reported on material obtained from the fish market at Jakarta (Indonesia) and also mentioned its fishery along the southern coast of China. Chopra (1943:5), Nataraj (1949:139), Jones (1967:1338), and Kurian & Sebastian (1976:102) indicated that this species, together with *A. erythraeus* is of commercial importance especially along the Madras and Kerala coasts of S. India, being the subject there of an important fishery; as, however, Omori (1975) in his revision of the genus intimated that there are no certain records of *A. serrulatus* from India, it is doubtful whether the material so named from India actually does belong to *A. serrulatus*.

| *Acetes sibogae* Hansen, 1919 | SERG Ac 9 |

Acetes sibogae Hansen, 1919, Siboga Exped.Mon., 38:35,38

FAO Names: Alamang shrimp (En), Chevrette alamang (Fr), Camaroncillo alamang (Sp).

Local Names: Kwei kung (Thailand), Bubok (W. Borneo), Alamang (Philippines).

Literature: Omori, 1975:61, Figs. 27,29.

Distribution: Indo-West Pacific: west coast of India to Philippines and Indonesia.

Habitat: Depth 0 to 55 m. Bottom mud. Marine and estuarine.

Size: Total length 13 to 20 mm (♂), 14 to 27 mm (♀).

Interest to Fishery: Nataraj (1949:139) remarked that this species, together with other species of *Acetes* is of considerable commercial importance in Travancore, S.W. India. But Kurian & Sebastian (1976:102), in their list of Indian prawns of commercial importance, listed this species with the remark: "Only stray records off Quilon in S.W. coast". According to Longhurst (1970:285) *Acetes sibogae* is important in the north of Malaysia. Omori (1975:77-79) listed its fishery in the Philippines (Manila Bay and Iloilo), W. Borneo and along the Andaman Sea coast of Thailand.

| *Acetes vulgaris* Hansen, 1919 | SERG Ac 10 |

Acetes vulgaris Hansen, 1919, Siboga Exped.Mon., 38:35

FAO Names: Jembret shrimp (En), Chevrette jembre (Fr), Camaroncillo jembre (Sp).

Local Names: Kwei kung (Thailand), Rebon, Djembret (Indonesia; names used for a mixture of *Acetes*, penaeid larvae and Mysidacea).

Literature: Omori, 1975:69, Figs. 14,30.

Distribution: Indo-West Pacific: south coast of China to Malaya, Singapore and Indonesia.

Habitat: Depth 9 to 55 m, possibly also shallower. Bottom mud and sand. Marine.

Size: Total length 17 to 26 mm (δ), 20 to 34 mm ($\stackrel{o}{+}$).

Interest to Fishery: Omori (1975:69) reported the species from the fish market in Jakarta (Indonesia) and also mentioned it as one of the species of the genus fished commercially in Thailand and Singapore.

Sergestes lucens Hansen, 1922	SERG Serg 1

Sergestes lucens Hansen, 1922, Result.Campagne Sci.Prince Albert I, 64:38,121

Synonymy: *Sergestes kishinouyei* Nakazawa & Terao, 1915; *Sergestes phosphoreus* Kishinouye, 1925.

FAO Names: Sakura shrimp (En), Chevrette sakura (Fr), Camarón sakura (Sp).

Local Names: Sakura ebi (Japan) [Niboshi ebi for the dried product].

Literature: Gordon, 1935:310, Figs. 1c,3a,4,5,6a,b,7; Omori, 1969:1-83, textfigs. 1-40, col. Pl. 1.

Distribution: Indo-West Pacific: so far only known from Japan (Tokyo, Sagami and Suruga Bays).

Habitat: In shallow coastal waters. Planktonic. Marine.

Size: Maximum total length 35 to 43 mm (δ), 37 to 48 mm ($\stackrel{o}{+}$).

Interest to Fishery: Notwithstanding the restricted area of the species, it "is one of the commercially important shrimps in Japan, and is one of the few planktonic organisms which [are] utilized by Man directly" (Omori, 1969:1); the annual landing around 1969 was 4 000 to 7 000 t. The animals are boiled in salt water and dried. They are consumed locally and are exported.

INFRAORDER CARIDEA Dana, 1852

Caridea Dana, 1852, U.S.Explor.Exped., 13:501,528

The Caridea are divided into ten superfamilies, all but two of which contain species that are of greater or smaller economic importance.

SUPERFAMILY OPLOPHOROIDEA Dana, 1852

Hoplophoroida Alcock, 1901, Descr.Catal.Indian Deep Sea Crust.Macr.Anom., 55

This superfamily consists of three families, two of which (Oplophoridae and Nematocarcinidae) are deep-sea forms, and so far have not been commercially exploited (although *Nematocarcinus* species are sometimes caught in great quantities). The remaining family, the Atyidae, inhabits almost exclusively fresh water and in various areas is of commercial importance.

FAMILY NEMATOCARCINIDAE Smith, 1884

Nematocarcininae   Smith, 1884, Rep.U.S.Fish Comm., 10:368

Nematocarcinus africanus Crosnier & Forest, 1973

NEMAT Nemat 1

Nematocarcinus africanus Crosnier & Forest, 1973, Faune Trop., 19:114

Synonymy: Crosnier & Forest (1973) showed that under the name *Nematocarcinus cursor* A. Milne Edwards, 1881, several species were confused. The true *N. cursor* is restricted to the western Atlantic, the West African specimens until then assigned to *N. cursor* proved to belong to *N. africanus*.

FAO Names: African spider shrimp (En), Crevette araignée d'Afrique (Fr), Camarón araña africano (Sp).

Distribution: Eastern Atlantic: West Africa from Senegal to Angola.

Habitat: Depth 200 to 700 m, most common between 300 to 600 m. Bottom soft mud.

Size: Maximum total length 104 mm.

Interest to Fishery: So far nil. When caught, the species usually occurs in great numbers and for that reason a fishery might seem promising. The great depth at which the species occurs and the fact that the specimens are rather soft, while the long legs and antennae form large entangled masses, reduce the interest for it as a commercial species.

FAMILY ATYIDAE De Haan, 1849

Atyadea De Haan, 1849, In Von Siebold, Fauna Japonica, Crustacea, (6):168,184

Only two genera of this family are known to be of commercial importance, viz. *Atya* Leach and *Caridina* H. Milne Edwards.

The atyid species, especially those of *Caridina*, are quite numerous and are difficult to distinguish. In the literature, therefore, in several instances the economic importance of the family or a genus, but not of separate species is given. So Blanco (1935:29) in the introduction to his paper on Philippine Atyidae stated that in the Philippines the Atyidae "are abundant in large freshwater lakes, especially Laguna de Bay and Taal Lake, where they are caught in large quantities by means of scissors-nets....... This crustacean is eaten fresh, or salted and made into a fermented product called alamang. It is also simply dried and sold as dry prawn. When the supply is abundant, it is prepared as protein feed for ducks and chickens or converted into some form of fertilizer", and Shen (1948:120,121) remarked in his paper on *Caridina* from S.W. China: "They can be caught by dip nets or scissor nets. Heretofore they seems to have little commercial value, although they sometimes can be found in the market in fresh or dried form. Only the local inhabitants occasionally use them in various ways as a subsidary food article. It may be eaten fresh, or dried or salted and made into a fermented product, or powdered and mixed with some other food stuffs as those sold at certain places of Yunnan. While in the lower Yangtze Valley, when the supply becomes abundant, the villagers usually collect this sort of crustacea to feed the domestic fowl as a protein food, which may effectively increase the flesh and egg- (p.120:) production, or it may be converted into some form of fertilizer as they do in the Philippines". Johnson (1966:280) stated that "in parts of Madagascar, Celebes and the Ganges delta area such prawns [i.e. *Caridina* species] are of considerable economic importance. Though several species are abundant in Malaysia, especially in slightly saline water, they are never used for food here". Dartevelle (1959a:24) mentioned about the *Caridina* species of Zaire, W. Africa: "Les indigènes les pêchent et les font sécher au soleil sur les rochers avant de les vendre".

Of the following species I did find information about their commercial value.

Atya gabonensis Giebel, 1875   ATY Aty 1

Atya gabonensis Giebel, 1875, Z.Gesamte Naturwiss., 45:52

FAO Names: Gabon shrimp (En), Saltarelle gabonaise (Fr), Camarón gabonés (Sp).

Local Names: Osa (Ghana), Mobèngomô (Duala, Cameroon), Bomingomô (Batanga, Cameroon), Dikuta (Bassa Bania, Cameroon), Ekusa (Soubou, Cameroon); these names are also used for *Atya sulcatipes*.

Literature: Bouvier, 1925:317, Figs. 707,708.

Distribution: West Africa: Senegal to Gabon.

Habitat: Fresh water of streams with rocky bottom.

Size: Maximum total length 124 mm ($\male$), 92 mm ($\female$).

Interest to Fishery: Minor. Irvine (1947:306) mentioned the species as edible in his book on the Fisheries of Ghana. Monod (1928:205; 1966:176) listed it among the species fished for in Cameroon.

Atya innocous (Herbst, 1792)   ATY Aty 2

Cancer (Astacus) innocous Herbst, 1792, Vers.Naturgesch.Krabben Krebse, 2:62

Synonymy: *Astacus nasoscopus* Meuschen, 1778 (unavailable name); *Atya occidentalis* Newport, 1847; *Atya robusta* A. Milne Edwards, 1864.

FAO Names: Basket shrimp (En), Saltarelle panier (Fr), Camarón cestillo (Sp).

Literature: Chace & Hobbs, 1969:57, Figs. 8,10a-c,14a,b.

Distribution: Atlantic America: Nicaragua to Panama; West Indies (Cuba to St. Vincent, Curaçao).

Habitat: Fresh waters; small streams; among rocks.

Size: Maximum carapace length 33.7 mm ($\male$), 20.6 mm ($\female$).

Interest to Fishery: Minor. Hart (1961:73) mentioned that in Jamaica the species is "collected locally by holding baskets made of reeds in the swift waters and then turning over rocks a few feet up-streams".

Atya pilipes Newport, 1847   ATY Aty 3

Atya pilipes Newport, 1847, Ann.Mag.Nat.Hist., (1)19:160

Synonymy: *Atyoida tahitensis* Stimpson, 1860; *Atya serrata* Bate, 1888; *Atya brevirostris* De Man, 1892; *Atya brevirostris demani* Nobili, 1900; *Ortmannia alluaudi* Bouvier, 1905; *Pseudatya beauforti* Roux, 1928; *Vanderbiltia rosamondae* Boone, 1935.

FAO Names: Koros shrimp (En), Saltarelle koros (Fr), Camarón koros (Sp).

Local Names: Udang grago (Indonesia), Apta, Yapyap (Tagalog language, Philippines), Daliw daliw, Koros (Hocaco language, Philippines). In all cases the names are also used for other species of the genus or even family.

Literature: Bouvier, 1925:294, Figs. 611-615,630-633 (as *A. serrata*).

Distribution: Indo-West Pacific: Madagascar and the Seychelles east to the Philippines, Micronesia and Polynesia.

Habitat: Fresh water, juveniles are found in water with higher salinity.

Size: Total length 20 to 45 mm.

Interest to Fishery: The species was indicated by Djajadiredja & Sachlan (1956:370) as being economically important in the Lesser Sunda Islands, Indonesia. Blanco (1935:29) indicated the commercial importance of Atyidae in general in the Philippines, but did not specify which species are so. Among the Philippine Atyidae Blanco (1935:31) also listed the present species. Both in Indonesia and the Philippines the Atyidae are usually sold fresh, sometimes they are dried and used for food both for men and animals, or for fertilizer.

| *Atya scabra* (Leach, 1815) | ATY Aty 4 |

Atys scaber Leach, 1815, <u>Trans.Linn.Soc.Lond.</u>, 11:345

Synonymy: *Astacus (Atya) scabra* - Voigt, 1836; *Atya mexicana* Wiegmann, 1836; *Atya margaritacea* A. Milne Edwards, 1864; *Atya punctata* Kingsley, 1878.

FAO Names: Camacuto shrimp (En), Saltarelle camacuto (Fr), Camarón camacuto (Sp).

Local Names: Chacales (Mexico), Camacuto (Venezuela), Conca, Camarão da pedra (N. Brazil), Curuca, Coruca, Cruca (Pernambuco, Brazil), Guaricuru (Brazil, after Marcgraf, 1648), Guàbara (Puerto Rico), Bouc (Martinique), Cacador (Guadeloupe).

Literature: Bouvier, 1925:314, Figs. 55-67,703-706; Villalobos, 1943; Chace & Hobbs, 1969:63, Figs. 9,10d-f,14d-e.

Distribution: Atlantic America: Mexico to Saõ Paulo (Brazil); West Indies (Cuba to Trinidad, Curaçao). The West African material brought to this species in most cases belongs to *A. sulcatipes*, the Western American to *A. rivalis*.

Habitat: Fresh water, usually small, often fast flowing streams, under stones.

Size: Maximum total length 98 mm (δ), 65 mm ($\female$); average 70 mm (δ) and 50 mm ($\female$); maximum carapace length 39 mm (δ), average 30 mm (δ), 19 mm ($\female$).

Interest to Fishery: Villalobos (1943:12) indicated that the species is caught and used as food in Vera Cruz, Mexico. Davant (1963:98) described it as of local economic importance in Venezuela. Fausto Filho (1968:28) listed the species as of moderate commercial importance in N.E. Brazil. Also Oliveira (1945:177) cited it as being used as food by the inhabitants of the interior of Pernambuco State, Brazil, where it, if well prepared, "constitue um prato saboroso". Coelho (in Litt.) indicated that the species is sold on the markets in Recife, Brazil, where it is of "importancia comercal considerável para as populaçoes ribeirinhos". Gundlach (1887:131) and M.J. Rathbun (1901:119) both reported the species as being sold on the market of San Juan, Puerto Rico.

Atya spinipes Newport, 1847   ATY Aty 5

Atya spinipes Newport, 1847, <u>Ann.Mag.Nat.Hist.</u>, (1)19:159

Synonymy: *Atya moluccensis* De Haan, 1849; *Atya armata* A. Milne Edwards, 1864; *Atya gustavi* Ortmann, 1890; *Atya dentirostris* Thallwitz, 1891.

FAO Names: Soldier brush shrimp (En), Saltarelle soldat (Fr), Camarón soldado (Sp).

Local Names: see under *A. pilipes*.

Literature: Bouvier, 1925:299, Figs. 672-681; Johnson, 1961:145, Figs. 38-42.

Distribution: Indo-West Pacific: Madagascar to the Ryukyu Islands and Polynesia.

Habitat: Fresh water, usually in fast flowing streams; among rocks.

Size: Maximum total length 84 mm (♂), 77 mm (♀).

Interest to Fishery: Of minor importance. Johnson (1966:280) reported that it is collected and used for food by riverside dwellers in Malaya and (1968:235) that it is the object of a very small scale subsistence fishery in a few areas there. Djajadiredja & Sachlan (1956:368,370) enumerated it among the economically important shrimps of Sumatra, Borneo, Java, Celebes and the Lesser Sunda Islands. Blanco (1935:29,30) dealt with the Atyidae in general as being edible and caught for food in the Philippines, and listed the present species without precise indication of its role in the economy of the country.

Atya sulcatipes Newport, 1847   ATY Aty 6

Atya sulcatipes Newport, 1847, <u>Ann.Mag.Nat.Hist.</u>, (1)19:159

Synonymy: *Atya margaritacea claviger* Aurivillius, 1898. Specimens from West Africa referred to in the literature as *Atya scabra* do not belong to that species, but in practically all instances are *A. sulcatipes*.

FAO Names: Ekusa shrimp (En), Saltarelle·ekusa (Fr), Camarón ecusa (Sp).

Local Names: Mobèngomô (Douala, Cameroon), Ekusa (Soubou, Cameroon), Crevette gros-doigt (French, Cameroon), Bomingomô (Batanga, Cameroon), Dikuta (Bassa Bania, Cameroon). These names also are used for *A. gabonensis*.

Literature: Holthuis, 1966:232, Fig. 4.

Distribution: West Africa: Liberia; Cameroon; Zaire; N. Angola; Cape Verde Islands; Fernando Poo; Ilha do Principe; São Thomé; Annobon.

Habitat: Fresh water streams; among rocks.

Size: Maximum total length 69 mm (♂), 49 mm (♀); maximum carapace length 29 mm (♂), 18 mm (♀).

Interest to Fishery: Minor. The species is listed by Monod (1928:121,205 as *Atya scabra*) among the edible species of Cameroon. Monod (1967:176) spoke about "une pêche traditionelle aux crevettes assez active" in Cameroon, and included among the shrimps also *Atya*.

Caridina africana Kingsley, 1882	ATY Cari 1

Caridina africana Kingsley, 1882, <u>Bull.Essex Inst.</u>, 14:127

Synonymy: *Caridina togoensis* Hilgendorf, 1893; *Caridina togoensis stuhlmanni* Hilgendorf, 1898; *Caridina togoensis decorsei* Bouvier, 1904; *Caridina togoensis breviatus* Lenz, 1910; *Caridina africana* (with forms *typica, natalensis, aegyptiaca, roubaudi, togoensis, decorsei* and *stuhlmanni*) - Bouvier, 1925; *Caridina togoensis* (with vars. *stuhlmanni, decorsei, breviatus, kasaiensis kwamouthensis*, and *schoutedeni*) - De Man, 1925.

FAO Names: African caridina (En), Saltarelle africaine (Fr), Caridina africana (Sp).

Literature: Bouvier, 1925:212, Figs. 470-477; Schmitt, 1926a:11, Figs. 1-62; Roth-Woltereck, 1942:293, Figs. 15-18.

Distribution: Africa: Nile basin; Great Lakes area; S.E. Africa; Western Africa from Sahara, Lake Tchad basin and French Guinea south to Angola.

Habitat: Fresh water.

Size: Maximum total length 30 mm; maximum carapace length (without rostrum) 5.5 mm.

Interest to Fishery: Minor. Although very much has been written about this species, there is very little information as to its economic importance. Dartevelle (1950:43; 1950a:24) reported that near Leopoldville (Kinshasa) "les indigenes pêchent" this species and dry the specimens in the sun before selling them.

Caridina denticulata (De Haan, 1844)	ATY Cari 2

Hippolyte denticulata De Haan, 1844, <u>In</u> Von Siebold, Fauna Japonica, Crustacea (6/7):Pl. 45, Fig. 8

Synonymy: *Caridina davidi* Bouvier, 1904; *Caridina denticulata sinensis* Kemp, 1918; *Neocaridina denticulata* - Kubo, 1938; *Neocaridina denticulata sinensis* - Kubo, 1938; *Neocaridina denticulata koreana* Kubo, 1938. The status of the various subspecies proposed is not certain, for the time being they are all synonymized here.

FAO Names: Sawtooth caridina (En), Saltarelle scie (Fr), Caridina sierra (Sp).

Literature: Bouvier, 1925:234, Figs. 533-537; Kubo, 1938:73-82, Figs. 5-12.

Distribution: Indo-West Pacific: Korea; China; Japan; Taiwan.

Habitat: Fresh water from near the sea coast to an altitude of 400 to 500 m.

Size: Maximum total length 20 mm (♂), 30 mm (♀).

Interest to Fishery: Minor. Sowerby (1925:133) mentioned the species from Fukien and Shanghai, China and indicated that it is eaten, being dried and used as flavouring in food. Ping (1931:183) mentioned that near Nanking the species is "of economic importance" and is "sought by people for food". Liu (1955:25) also ranged the species among the economic shrimps of North China. Kamita (1954:33) remarked that in Japan the species is used as bait for fishing. In Taiwan the species does not seem to be regarded as food, as Tang (1961:44) stated that this "is an inedible species of very small size"; actually the species forms a pest in the pond culture of *Penaeus monodon* in Taiwan, where it acts both as a predator on the juvenile *Penaeus* and as a food competitor (Chen, 1976:117, Fig. 70).

Caridina edulis Bouvier, 1904

Caridina edulis Bouvier, 1904, <u>Bull.Mus.Hist.Nat.Paris</u>, 10:135

FAO Names: Malagasy caridina (En), Saltarelle malgache (Fr), Caridina malgacha (Sp).

Literature: Bouvier, 1925:208, Figs. 458-463.

Distribution: Indo-West Pacific: Madagascar.

Habitat: Fresh water.

Size: Not mentioned. Judging by Bouvier's (1905,1925) figures, the carapace length is about 9 mm (inclusive of the rostrum).

Interest to Fishery: The original description was based on "très nombreux exemplaires cuits, visiblement préparés pour la vente sur le marché".

Caridina gracilirostris De Man, 1892

Caridina gracilirostris De Man, 1892, <u>In</u> M. Weber, <u>Zool.Ergeb.Reise Niederl.Ost Indien</u>, 2:399

Synonymy: *Caridina nilotica gracilirostris* - Roux, 1919.

FAO Names: Needlenose caridina (En), Saltarelle aiguille (Fr), Caridina aguja (Sp).

Literature: Bouvier, 1925:142, Figs. 305-307; Holthuis, 1965:23, Fig. 7.

Distribution: Indo-West Pacific: Madagascar and India to Indonesia, Australia and Palau.

Habitat: Fresh or slightly brackish water.

Size: Maximum total length 37 mm.

Interest to Fishery: Minor. Menon (1955:132) mentioned this species as one of those obtained in the paddy field prawn fishery in Travancore and Cochin, India; however, it proved to be very rare in the catches. Djajadiredja & Sachlan (1956:368,370) listed the species as being economically important in Sumatra, Celebes, the Lesser Sunda Islands and the Moluccas. This is the only atyid species mentioned by Blanco (1935:32) from Laguna de Bay, Luzon, where according to the same author (:29) atyids "are caught in large quantities" and used for food. Johnson (1968:235) indicated this species (together with a few others of the same genus) as a potential basis for a culture fishery in Malaysia.

Caridina laevis Heller, 1862

Caridina laevis Heller, 1862, <u>S.B.Akad.Wiss.Wien</u>, 40 (1):411

FAO Names: Smooth caridina (En), Saltarelle glabre (Fr), Caridina lisa (Sp).

Literature: Bouvier, 1925:183, Figs. 382-385.

Distribution: Indo-West Pacific: India to Thailand, the Philippines and Indonesia.

Habitat: Fresh water.

Size: Maximum total length 26 mm.

Interest to Fishery: Minor. Djajadiredja & Sachlan (1956:368,370) listed the species as of economic importance in Indonesia (Java, Celebes).

The *Caridina nilotica* (P. Roux, 1833) complex

ATY Cari 6

Pelias niloticus P. Roux, 1833, Ann.Sci.Nat.Paris, (1)28:73

Species, subspecies and synonymy: *Caridina longirostris* H. Milne Edwards, 1837; *Caridina grandirostris* Stimpson, 1858; *Caridina leucosticta* Stimpson, 1858; *Atya wyckii* Hickson, 1888; *Caridina wyckii gracilipes* De Man, 1892; *Caridina wyckii paucipara* De Man, 1898; *Caridina modiglianii* Nobili, 1900; *Caridina nilotica minahassae* De Man, 1902; *Caridina simoni* Bouvier, 1904; *Caridina nilotica* (with subspecies *bengalensis, brachydactyla, gracilipes, natalensis, paucipara, wyckii*) - De Man, 1908; *Caridina nilotica aruensis* J. Roux, 1911; *Caridina brachydactyla* - Bouvier, 1913; *Caridina brachydactyla peninsularis* Kemp, 1918; *Caridina nilotica macrophora* Kemp, 1918; *Caridina alphonsi* Bouvier, 1919; *Caridina nilotica brevidactyla* J. Roux, 1919; *Caridina nilotica simoni* - Bouvier, 1925; *Caridina nilotica meridionalis* J. Roux, 1926; *Caridina nilotica brachydactyla peninsularis* - Edmondson, 1935; *Caridina gracilipes* - Chopra, 1939; *Caridina nilotica chauhani* Chopra & Tiwari, 1949; *Caridina nilotica zeylanica* Arudpragasam & Costa, 1962; *Caridina nilotica veliensis* Pillai, 1964; *Caridina simoni peninsularis* - Johnson, 1965; *Caridina b. brachydactyla* - Tiwari & Pillai, 1971. The status of the numerous species and subspecies of this complex are still under debate. Until a thorough systematic revision of it has been made it seems best to treat this complex as a single unit.

FAO Names: Common caridina (En), Saltarelle commune (Fr), Caridina común (Sp).

Local Names: Ghusha chingri (Calcutta, India; Bangladesh), Sunka chingri (Bangladesh).

Distribution: Indo-West Pacific: the taxonomic status of the various forms assigned to this complex have not yet been satisfactorily straightened out, but the complex as a whole occupies the entire eastern part of Africa (Cairo to Natal) and goes eastward as far as southern Japan, Australia and Polynesia.

Habitat: The species inhabit fresh, sometimes slightly brackish, water.

Size: Maximum total length about 35 mm.

Interest to Fishery: Bouvier (1905:92) remarked that the form, which he indicated with the name *Caridina wyckii* var. *paucipara*, is sold on the market in Madagascar: "dans un panier remis au Musée ethnographique, plusieurs centaines d'individus de cette forme se trouvaient réunis pour la vente, sans trace de melange avec une autre espèce". Chopra (1939:223) mentioned *Caridina gracilipes* as being eaten in Calcutta and in different other parts of India. Qureshi (1956:362) listed the same form under the shrimps fished for in Bangladesh in estuarine waters. Liu (1955:27) had the species as *Caridina nilotica gracilipes* enumerated among the economic shrimps and prawns of North China. Djajadiredja & Sachlan (1956:368,370) listed *Caridina wyckii* as of economic importance in Indonesia (Celebes and Lesser Sunda Islands). Hickson (1888:357) when describing his new species *Atya wyckii*, mentioned that he first saw the animals "prepared rather for use [as food] than for observation" when he took his midday meal at Kelelonde, N. Celebes, and later (1889:224) stated that "as an article of food these small prawns are much prized by the natives, and the Dutchman is very glad to add the kleine garnalen to his list of comestibles at the rijsttafel". Blanco (1935:33,34) mentioned *Caridina nilotica brachydactyla* and *C. modiglianii* from the Philippines, but did not specifically indicate them as commercially important.

Caridina propinqua De Man, 1908

ATY Cari 7

Caridina propinqua De Man, 1908, Rec.Indian Mus., 2:227

FAO Names: Bengal caridina (En), Saltarelle bengalaise (Fr), Caridina bengalí (Sp).

Local Names: Ghusa chingri, Choanicha (Bangladesh).

Literature: Bouvier, 1925:181, Figs. 375,381; Johnson, 1961:131, Figs. 12-15.

Distribution: Indo-West Pacific: Bay of Bengal from Chilka Lake to Chittagong, Malay Peninsula, Thailand.

Habitat: Fresh and brackish water.

Size: Maximum total length 20 mm.

Interest to Fishery: Minor. Qureshi (1956:362) listed the present species as found in commercial catches brought to the market in Bangladesh (incorrectly spelled *Caridina propinea*). Tham (1969: 212) in a table marked *C. propinqua* as present in commercial catches in Pakistan (probably Bangladesh is meant) and Malaysia. Johnson (1966:280) stated that species of *Caridina* "are never used for food" in Malaysia. The same author later (Johnson, 1968:235) thought it possible that this and other species of the genus could form the basis of a culture fishery.

Caridina tonkinensis Bouvier, 1919

ATY Cari 8

Caridina tonkinensis Bouvier, 1919, Bull.Mus.Hist.Nat.Paris, 25:331

FAO Names: Tonkin caridina (En), Saltarelle tonkinoise (Fr), Caridina tonkinesa (Sp).

Literature: Bouvier, 1925:223, Figs. 494-496; Johnson, 1961:133, Figs. 16-20.

Distribution: Indo-West Pacific: Viet Nam and Malaysia.

Habitat: Fresh water.

Size: Maximum total length 19 mm.

Interest to Fishery: So far not known, but Johnson (1968:235) mentioned this species (with two others of this genus) as a possible basis of a culture fishery in Malaysia).

Caridina weberi De Man, 1892

ATY Cari 9

Caridina weberi De Man, 1892, In M. Weber, Zool.Ergeb.Reise Niederl.Ost Indien, 2:371

Synonymy: *Caridina weberi typica* Bouvier, 1925.

FAO Names: Pugnose caridina (En), Saltarelle nez-camus (Fr), Caridina ñata (Sp).

Literature: Bouvier, 1925:242, Figs. 562-571.

Distribution: Indo-West Pacific: India to Viet Nam, Palau and Polynesia.

Habitat: Fresh water.

Size: Maximum total length 30 mm.

Interest to Fishery: The species was listed by Djajadiredja & Sachlan (1956:370) as being economically important in Celebes and the Lesser Sunda Islands, Indonesia.

| *Paratya compressa* (De Haan, 1844) | ATY Para 1 |

Ephyra compressa De Haan, 1844, <u>In</u> Von Siebold, Fauna Japonica, Crustacea, (6/7):Pl.46, Fig. 7.

Synonymy: *Miersia compressa* - Kingsley, 1879; *Atyaephyra compressa* - Miers, 1882; *Xiphocaris compressa* - Ortmann, 1894; *Xiphocaridina compressa* - Bouvier, 1909.

FAO Names: Nuka shrimp (En), Saltarelle nuca (Fr), Camarón nuca (Sp).

Local Names: Nuka ebi (Japan).

Literature: Kubo, 1938:68, Figures; Kamita, 1961:11, Figs. 1-5.

Distribution: Indo-West Pacific: Korea; Japan.

Habitat: Fresh water.

Size: Maximum total length 26 mm ($\male$), 37 mm ($\female$).

Interest to Fishery: Kamita (1954:33) indicated that in Tottori Prefecture, Japan, this species, together with *Caridina denticulata* is used as bait for hook and line fishing.

SUPERFAMILY PASIPHAEOIDEA Dana, 1852

Pasiphaeoida Alcock, 1901, <u>Descr.Catal.Indian Deep Sea Crust.Macr.Anom.</u>, 55

This superfamily contains a single family

| FAMILY PASIPHAEIDAE Dana, 1852 |

Pasiphaeidae - Dana, 1852, <u>Proc.Acad.Nat.Sci.Phila.</u>, 6:13,18

Only three genera of this family are known to be of some commercial importance, but none of the species is of outstanding value.

| Glyphus marsupialis Filhol, 1884 | PASI Gly 1 |

Glyphus marsupialis Filhol, 1884, Nature(Paris), 12:231,328

FAO Names: Kangaroo shrimp (En), Sivade kangourou (Fr), Camarón canguro (Sp).

Literature: Crosnier & Forest, 1973:144, Figs. 42,43.

Distribution: Eastern Atlantic: West Africa from off Rio de Oro (25°39'N) to off Angola (13°30'S).

Habitat: Depth 500 to 1 000 m. Bottom mud or sandy mud. Marine.

Size: Maximum total length about 160 mm; carapace length 13 to 61 mm (♂), 23 to 59 mm (♀), 58 and 59 mm (ovigerous ♀).

Interest to Fishery: Longhurst (1970:278) mentioned this species among the prawn resources of the eastern central Atlantic region. Crosnier & de Bondy (1967:42) reported that the species is not found in important quantities and fishing trials for it "n'ont pas donné de rendements supérieurs à 2 kg/h".

| Leptochela gracilis Stimpson, 1860 | PASI Lep 1 |

Leptochela gracilis Stimpson, 1860, Proc.Acad.Nat.Sci.Phila., 1860:42

Synonymy: Leptochela pellucida Boone, 1935.

FAO Names: Lesser glass shrimp (En), Sivade cristal (Fr), Camaroncito cristal (Sp).

Literature: Chace, 1976:11, Figs. 8-10.

Distribution: Indo-West Pacific: Japan; Korea; China; Singapore.

Habitat: Depth to 194 m. Marine.

Size: Maximum total length about 45 mm; carapace length 7 to 8.8 mm (♂), 8 to 9.6 mm (ovigerous (♀).

Interest to Fishery: Kemp (1925:252) reported on material from the market in Amoy, S. China. Liu (1955:23) listed the species among the economically important shrimps and prawns of N. China, and Yoshida (1941:21) mentioned it as of economic interest in Korea.

| Pasiphaea japonica Omori, 1976 | PASI Pasi 1 |

Pasiphaea japonica Omori, 1976, Bull.Natl.Sci.Mus.Tokyo, (A)2(4):249

Synonymy: Formerly incorrectly identified with Pasiphaea sivado (Risso).

FAO Names: Japanese glass shrimp (En), Sivade japonais (Fr), Camarón cristal japonés (Sp).

Local Names: Shira ebi (Japan).

Literature: Omori, 1976:249,250, Figs. 1,2.

Distribution: Indo-West Pacific: Japan (Toyama Bay and Suruga Bay).

Habitat: Depth between 0 to 80 and 0 to 300 m. Bottom mud. Marine.

Size: Total length 48 to 70 mm (♂), 50 to 75 mm (♀); carapace length 14 to 21 mm (♂), 14 to 22 mm (♀).

Interest to Fishery: Since 1953 annual catches of 142 to 220 metric tons are made in Toyama Bay, Japan. Fishing (by boat seine) is regulated by law, and is carried out from 1 April to 30 November.

Pasiphaea multidentata Esmark, 1866	PASI Pasi 2

Pasiphaea multidentata Esmark, 1866, Forh.Videnskabsselsk.Krist., 1865:259,314-316

Synonymy: *Pasiphaea norvegica* M. Sars, 1866; *Pasiphaea (Phye) sicula* Riggio, 1896; *Pasiphaea multidentata sicula* - Zariquiey Alvarez, 1946.

FAO Names: Pink glass shrimp (En), Sivade rose (Fr), Camarón cristal rosado (Sp).

Literature: Sivertsen & Holthuis, 1956:27, Figs. 19-21; Zariquiey Alvarez, 1968:73, Figs. 8a, 10a,31.

Distribution: North Atlantic: N. Norway to the eastern Mediterranean; Iceland; Greenland; Massachusetts, U.S.A.

Habitat: Depth 10 to 2 000 m, most common around 400 m depth. Marine.

Size: Maximum total length 105 mm.

Interest to Fishery: Minor. The species is found mixed in with other deep-sea shrimps obtained at the fish markets of N.E. Spain (cf. Zariquiey Alvarez, 1946:60, who mentioned that they are caught by Spanish trawlers) and Italy (Brian, 1941:24 reported their presence at the Genoa fish markets). The species, however, is only met with accidentally, and is even far scarcer there than *P. sivado* (Risso). Dieuzeide (1952:38) listed this species among those which present "un intérêt pour la pêche" in Algeria.

Pasiphaea sivado (Risso, 1816)	PASI Pasi 3

Alpheus sivado Risso, 1816, Hist.Nat.Crust.Nice, 93

Synonymy: *Astacus (Pasiphaea) sivado* - Voigt, 1836; *Pasiphaea savignyi* H. Milne Edwards, 1837; *Pasiphaea brevirostris* H. Milne Edwards, 1837; *Pasiphaea neapolitana* Hope, 1851.

FAO Names: White glass shrimp (En), Sivade blanc (Fr), Camarón cristal blanco (Sp).

Local Names: Ghost prawn (English, vid. Kemp, 1910:38), Glass-shrimp (English, vid.Sund, 1913:1; Yonge, 1949:288), Glassreke (Norwegian, vid.Sund 1942:138,140), Glasreje (Danish, vid. Stephensen, 1910:114). These names probably also used for other species of the genus.

Literature: Kemp, 1910:37, Pl. 4, Fig. 12; Zariquiey Alvarez, 1968:70, Figs. 6a,30.

Distribution: Eastern Atlantic: Norway and Scotland south to the eastern Mediterranean. Also reported from the Red Sea and India, but these records are probably based on other species. The species reported from Japan under the name *P. sivado* proved to be *P. japonica* Omori (see there).

Habitat: Depth 0 to 550 m, most frequent between 100 and 300 m. Marine.

Size: Total length adult specimens 50 to 80 mm; maximum carapace length 21.5 mm.

Interest to Fishery: Minor. Zariquiey Alvarez (1946:59) stated that the species is "cogida con grandísima frecuencia por las "vacas" [commercial trawlers operating off the north-east coast of Spain]"; these specimens are brought with the economically more important shrimp to the markets of Barcelona and Rosas; the *Pasiphaea* form a negligible part of the catch and are sold only when mixed in with the other species. Brian (1941:22) reported that species from the fish market at Genoa, Italy, and stated that "la specie è piuttosto rara nel nostro mercato e non ha importanza economica". Dieuzeide (1952:38) ranged *Pasiphaea sivado* among "les crevettes de nos côtes méditerranéennes nord-africaines qui présentent un intérêt pour la pêche et la conserverie".

SUPERFAMILY BRESILOIDEA Calman, 1896

Bresiloida Holthuis, 1955, Zool.Verh.Leiden, 26:36

Only one family contains commercially important species.

FAMILY RHYNCHOCINETIDAE Ortmann, 1890

Rhynchocinetidae Ortmann, 1890, Zool.Jahrb.(Syst.Geogr.Biol.Thiere), 5:459

One species has been reported as being of commercial value.

| *Rhynchocinetes typus* H. Milne Edwards, 1837 | RHYN Rhyn 1 |

Rhynchocinetes typus H. Milne Edwards, 1837, Hist.Nat.Crust., 2:383

Synonymy: *Rhynchocinetes typicus* - Dana, 1852.

FAO Names: Rabbitnose shrimp (En), Sauté des plages (Fr), Camarón de playa (Sp).

Local Names: Camarón de playa, Camarón de mar (Chile).

Literature: Gordon, 1936:83, Figs. 5a,d,6a,b; Bahamonde & Lopez, 1967:121.

Distribution: Eastern Pacific: Peru; Chile.

Habitat: Depth less than 20 m, usually in shallow coastal waters among rocks. Marine.

Size: Maximum total length 87 mm; maximum carapace length (without rostrum) 29.3 mm (♂), 24.8 mm (♀).

Interest to Fishery: Secondary. Until 1953 this species formed the majority of the shrimp catch in Chile. Longhurst (1970:303) indicated that *Heterocarpus reedi* and *Rhynchocinetes typus* were the most important commercial shrimps of Chile and Peru, the total catch being annually 11 000 t in Chile and 500 t in Peru.

Lipkius holthuisi Yaldwyn, 1960 — RHYN Lip 1

Lipkius holthuisi Yaldwyn, 1960, Bull.N.Z.Dep.Sci.Ind.Res., 139:16

FAO Names: Wellington shrimp (En), Sauté Wellington (Fr), Camarón Wellington (Sp).

Literature: Yaldwyn, 1960:16, Fig. 1.

Distribution: Indo-West Pacific: New Zealand area 41°39'-44°4'S.

Habitat: Depth 360 to 470 m. Bottom mud. Marine.

Size: Maximum carapace length 16.5 mm.

Interest to Fishery: The New Zealand Marine Department (Anon. 1964:9, Fig. 3) listed this species as a commercial prawn, but probably is meant that it is potentially commercial.

SUPERFAMILY PALAEMONOIDEA Rafinesque, 1815

Palaemoninea Dana, 1852, Proc.Acad.Nat.Sci.Phila., 6:13,15

Two families in this superfamily are dealt with here. The first (Campylonotidae) contains a species which has been considered to be of potential commercial value, the other (Palaemonidae) contains a great number of species that are of various interests commercially.

FAMILY CAMPYLONOTIDAE Sollaud, 1913

Campylonotidae Sollaud, 1913, Bull.Mus.Hist.Nat.Paris, 19:184

Campylonotus rathbunae Schmitt, 1926 — CAMP Camp 1

Campylonotus rathbunae Schmitt, 1926, Biol.Results Fisher.Exped.F.I.S.Endeavour, 1909-14, 5:373

FAO Names: Sabre prawn (En), Raguié sabre (Fr), Camarón sable (Sp).

Local Names: Sabre prawn (New Zealand).

| PALAEM Exo 1

Literature: Yaldwyn, 1960:20, Figs. 2-4.

Distribution: Indo-West Pacific: Australia, New Zealand.

Habitat: Depth 280 to 810 m. Bottom mud. Marine.

Size: Maximum carapace length 24 mm (♂), 28 mm (♀).

Interest to Fishery: The New Zealand Marine Department published a paper (Anon., 1964) in which on p. 9, Fig. 3 the present species is indicated as a commercial prawn. Evidently it is considered potentially commercial for New Zealand.

FAMILY PALAEMONIDAE Rafinesque, 1815

Palemonia Rafinesque, 1815, Analyse de la Nature, 98

This family, containing the true "prawns", is rich in genera and species that are of some commercial importance.

| *Cryphiops caementarius* (Molina, 1782) | PALAEM Cry 1

Cancer caementarius Molina, 1782, Saggio Stor.Nat.Chili, 208

Synonymy: *Astacus caementarius* - Molina, 1810; *Palaemon caementarius* - Poeppig, 1836; *Palaemon gaudichaudii* H. Milne Edwards, 1837; *Cryphiops spinulosomanus* Dana, 1852; *Bithynis longimana* Philippi, 1860; *Macrobrachium africanum* Bate, 1868; *Palaemon gaudichaudii caementarius* - Miers, 1877; *Bithynis gaudichaudii* - Ortmann, 1891; *Bithynis caementarius gaudichaudii* - M.J. Rathbun, 1910.

FAO Names: Changallo shrimp (En), Bouquet changallo (Fr), Camarón changallo (Sp).

Local Names: Camarón de rio (Peru, Chile), Camarón de rio del norte de Chile (Chile), Changallo (Chile, only used for the male).

Literature: Holthuis, 1952:137, Pls. 33-35; Hartmann, 1957:117-124, Pl. 31.

Distribution: Eastern Pacific: Peru and Chile.

Habitat: Fresh water. The females migrate to the sea to spawn. The larvae hatch in the sea and migrate up the rivers.

Size: Maximum total length 185 mm.

Interest to Fishery: Secondary. The species is sold fresh and peeled locally. In Chile, because of the heavy exploitation due to its high price on the local market, the fishery for this species is closed. Hernandéz (1967:682) indicated that in two rivers in Peru about 100 000 kg of this species were caught annually, he also described the various methods for capture of the shrimps. In Peru experiments for the cultivation of the species are in progress, similar experiments are planned in Chile.

Exopalaemon annandalei (Kemp, 1917)   PALAEM Exo 1

Leander annandalei Kemp, 1917, Rec.Indian Mus., 13:211

Synonymy: *Palaemon (Leander) annandalei* - Gee, 1925; *Leander annandalei stylirostris* Yu, 1930; *Palaemon (Exopalaemon) annandalei* - Holthuis, 1950.

FAO Names: Cipango prawn (En), Bouquet cipango (Fr), Camarón cipango (Sp).

Literature: Kemp, 1917:211, Figs. 1-4; Kemp, 1925:289.

Distribution: Indo-West Pacific: Korea; China.

Habitat: Depth 5.5 to 7.5 m. Fresh water.

Size: Maximum total length 63 mm.

Interest to Fishery: Liu (1955:49) treated this species among the economic important prawns and shrimps of North China. The extent of the commercial use is not known to me.

Exopalaemon carinicauda (Holthuis, 1950)   PALAEM Exo 2

Palaemon (Exopalaemon) carinicauda Holthuis, 1950, Siboga Exped.Mon., 39(a 9):48

Synonymy: *Leander longirostris carinatus* Ortmann, 1890; *Leander carinatus* - Doflein, 1902; *Leander styliferus carinatus* - Balss, 1914; *Palaemon (Leander) carinatus* - Gee, 1925.

FAO Names: Ridgetail prawn (En), Bouquet quille (Fr), Camarón quilla (Sp).

Literature: Kemp, 1917:219, Figs. 6c,d; Holthuis, 1950:48, Fig. 9.

Distribution: Indo-West Pacific: Korea and China.

Habitat: Probably brackish water.

Size: Maximum total length 97 mm (δ), 95 mm ($\female$).

Interest to Fishery: Liu (1955:48) listed this species among the economically important prawns of N. China, and Yoshida (1941:23) mentioned it in the same way for Korea. Sowerby (1925:133) referred to it as one of the edible prawns of China. Ivanov (1967:41) mentioned it as being "of marked commercial value in the fisheries of the Yellow and East China Seas".

Exopalaemon mani (Sollaud, 1914)   PALAEM Exo 3

Leander mani Sollaud, 1914, Bull.Soc.Zool.Fr., 39:315

FAO Names: Mamtom prawn (En), Bouquet mamtom (Fr), Camarón mamtom (Sp).

Local Names: Con tôm gao (Tonkin, Viet Nam).

Distribution: Indo-West Pacific: Viet Nam.

Habitat: Fresh water.

Size: Maximum total length 54 mm.

Interest to Fishery: In the original description Sollaud (1914:314,315) indicated that this is one of the species "les plus communément pêchées dans le delta du fleuve Rouge", and is used for the preparation of a famous native paste "mam tôm".

Exopalaemon modestus (Heller, 1862)	PALAEM Exo 4

Leander modestus Heller, 1862, <u>Verh.Zool.-Bot.Ges.Wien</u>, 12:527

Synonymy: *Leander czerniavskyi* Brashnikov, 1907; *Leander modestus sibirica* Brashnikov, 1907; *Palaemon (Leander) modestus* - Gee, 1925; *Leander czerniavskyi lacustris* Buldovsky, 1933.

FAO Names: Siberian prawn (En), Bouquet sibérien (Fr), Camarón siberiano (Sp).

Literature: Kemp, 1917:221, Pl. 9, Fig. 1.

Distribution: Indo-West Pacific: Siberia (Amur and Ussur basins); Manchuria; Korea; China; Taiwan.

Habitat: Depth 5.5 to 7.5 m. Fresh water.

Size: Maximum total length 60 mm.

Interest to Fishery: Liu (1955:50) listed this species among the "Economic Shrimps and Prawns of North China". Also Sowerby (1925:133) mentioned it as being "caught and eaten by the Chinese", and Kemp (1917:203) stated that it is fished for in Kiangsu Province, China, especially in Tai Hu Lake. Ling & Costello (1976:2) listed this species, under the incorrect name *Macrobrachium modestus*, among the species on which aquaculture experiments were carried out in Japan.

Exopalaemon orientis (Holthuis, 1950)	PALAEM Exo 5

Palaemon (Exopalaemon) orientis Holthuis, 1950, <u>Siboga Exped.Mon.</u>, 39(a 9):49

Synonymy: *Leander longirostris japonicus* Ortmann, 1890; *Palaemon japonicus* - M.J. Rathbun, 1902; *Leander japonicus* - Balss, 1914.

FAO Names: Oriental prawn (En), Bouquet oriental (Fr), Camarón oriental (Sp).

Local Names: Tsunonagashiro ebi (Japan).

Literature: Kubo, 1942:57, Figures.

Distribution: Indo-West Pacific: Japan; Korea; China; Taiwan.

Habitat: Marine and fresh water (?).

Size: Maximum total length 46 mm (δ), 68 mm ($\female$).

Interest to Fishery: Yoshida (1941:28) listed this species among the economic shrimps of Korea. Yasuda (1957:174,196) mentioned that the species in Japan is used as bait shrimp.

Exopalaemon styliferus (H. Milne Edwards, 1840) — PALAEM Exo 6

Palaemon styliferus H. Milne Edwards, 1840, Hist.Nat.Crust., 3:638

Synonymy: *Palaemon longirostris* H. Milne Edwards, 1837:394 (not *Palaemon longirostris* H. Milne Edwards, 1837:392); *Leander styliferus* - Kemp, 1915.

FAO Names: Roshna prawn (En), Bouquet rosna (Fr), Camarón rosna (Sp).

Local Names: Roshna (West Bengal, India), Ghora chingri (West Bengal, India; Bangladesh), Gara icha (Bangladesh).

Literature: Kemp, 1917:214, textfigs. 5,6ab, Pl. 8, Fig. 2.

Distribution: Indo-West Pacific: Pakistan and India to Thailand and Indonesia.

Habitat: Shallow coastal waters. In sea or brackish, occasionally fresh water.

Size: Maximum total length 90 mm; ovigerous females 68 to 86 mm.

Interest to Fishery: Major. Rai (1933:885), Chopra (1943:5) and Panikkar & Menon (1956:329) mentioned this species as important in the Bombay area, west coast of India. Rai listed the species among the most important and abundant there, while Panikkar & Menon stated it to be the subject of a sea fishery. Kunju (1967:1 385), however, pointed out that near Bombay this species occurs only to a limited extent, and that *Nematopalaemon tenuipes* is the most important species there. Kunju listed both species as occurring in the fishery. This is confirmed by Kagwade (1967:1 379). The species is of "considerable commercial value" in the Gangetic delta region of West Bengal (Kunju, 1956:404) as was also pointed out by Kemp (1917:203), Chopra (1939:223; 1943:5), Panikkar & Menon (1956:329) and Kurian & Sebastian (1976:92). In the Gangetic delta it also plays a role in the rice field shrimp farming. In Bangladesh it is of some importance (Qureshi, 1956:362; Ahmad, 1957:17). Field and laboratory experiments for aquaculture of the species have been carried out in India.

Leptocarpus fluminicola (Kemp, 1917) — PALAEM Lep 1

Leander fluminicola Kemp, 1917, Rec.Indian Mus., 13:223

FAO Names: Ganges delta prawn (En), Bouquet du bas Gange (Fr), Camarón estuarino del Ganges (Sp).

Literature: Kemp, 1917:223, Pl. 9, Fig. 2.

Distribution: Indo-West Pacific: Bay of Bengal area of India and Birma.

Habitat: Fresh and slightly brackish water.

Size: Maximum total length 47 mm.

Interest to Fishery: Jones (1967:1 337) listed the species among the crustacean fishery resources of India, remarking that it is caught in very large numbers in the Gangetic delta.

Leptocarpus potamiscus (Kemp, 1917) — PALAEM Lep 2

Leander potamiscus Kemp, 1917, Rec.Indian Mus., 13:225

Synonymy: *Palaemon potamiscus* - Suvatti, 1937.

FAO Names: Bombay prawn (En), Bouquet bombay (Fr), Camarón de Bombay (Sp).

Literature: Kemp, 1917:225, Fig. 7.

Distribution: Indo-West Pacific: Bombay, India to Thailand and Indonesia.

Habitat: Brackish or marine habitats. Shallow water.

Size: Maximum total length 59 mm.

Interest to Fishery: The only record of the commercial importance of this species known to me is by Rai (1933:886) who listed the species among the prawns obtained by the fisheries near Bombay, India, where it occurs in large numbers.

Macrobrachium Bate, 1868

The genus *Macrobrachium* occurs throughout the tropics and in several subtropical areas. Almost all species pass at least part of their life in fresh water, in several the juveniles are found in brackish or salt water. Many of the species (there are about 125 known at present) are of good size and it is likely that most will be used as food wherever they occur. The present list only enumerates those species of which there are positive indications of their importance as food, and therefore of necessity must be quite incomplete.

Macrobrachium acanthurus (Wiegmann, 1836)   PALAEM Macro 1

Palaemon acanthurus Wiegmann, 1836, Arch.Naturgesch.Berlin, 2 (1):150

Synonymy: *Palaemon forceps* H. Milne Edwards, 1837; *Palaemon swainsonii* White, 1847; *Palaemon mexicanus* De Saussure, 1857; *Macrobrachium longidigitum* Bate, 1868; *Palaemon dasydactylus* Streets, 1871; *Palaemon sexdentatus* Streets, 1871; *Palaemon potiete* Müller, 1892; *Bithynis acanthurus* - M.J. Rathbun, 1900; *Bithynis forceps* - Young, 1900; *Palaemon (Eupalaemon) acanthurus* - De Man, 1912.

FAO Names: Cinnamon river prawn (En), Bouquet cannelle (Fr), Camarón canela (Sp).

Local Names: Langostino, Camarón prieto, Acamaya, Camarón de río (Mexico), Camarón de río, Camarón brazo largo (Venezuela), Camarão do rio (Pernambuco, Brazil), Camarão canela (N.E. Brazil).

Literature: Holthuis, 1952:45, Pl. 8, Fig. a,b; Chace & Hobbs, 1969:89, Figs. 20,25a,g.

Distribution: Atlantic America: from N. Carolina (U.S.A.) to S. Brazil and the West Indies.

Habitat: Fresh or brackish water (mesohaline and oligohaline), usually on muddy bottoms.

Size: Maximum total length 166 mm (δ), 110 mm ($\female$); maximum carapace length 36.5 mm (δ), 20.6 mm ($\female$).

Interest to Fishery: In Mexico the species is of secondary importance commercially. It is sold fresh as food. According to Carillo (1968:417) in 1966, 150 t of this species were caught in Veracruz State by a single fishing cooperative. In Venezuela "because of its size, it is without doubt of economic value" (Davant, 1963:108). Ewald (1969:771) indicated that this species has been found in commercial catches in Lake Maracaibo, Venezuela; Croker (1967:81) stated it to be of little commercial importance in Venezuela. In N.E. Brazil the species is of moderate importance as shown by Fausto Filho (1968:27). Locally it is of considerable importance there for the people living along the rivers. It is eaten as such or as part of regional dishes. In his assessment of shrimp resources of S.E. Brazil, FAO (1964:11) pointed to the presence of small numbers of this species near Florianopolis (Santa Catarina). Aquaculture experiments with this species were undertaken in the U.S.A. and Mexico.

| *Macrobrachium aemulum* (Nobili, 1906) | PÀLAEM Macro 2 |

Palaemon (Parapalaemon) aemulus Nobili, 1906, <u>Bull.Mus.Hist.Nat.Paris</u>, 12:258

FAO Names: Nouméa river prawn (En), Bouquet nouméa (Fr), Camarón de Numea (Sp).

Literature: J. Roux, 1926:221, Figs.47-51.

Distribution: Indo-West Pacific: New Caledonia.

Habitat: Depth 0 to 15 m. Fresh water.

Size: Maximum total length 83 mm (δ); maximum carapace length 33 mm (δ).

Interest to Fishery: Kamita (1967:8) dealt with specimens bought at the fish market at Nouméa, but the extent of the commercial importance of the species is not known. Kamita reported that "the fresh prawns are procurable from the fish market to which they are carried out from the localities near Nouméa city".

| *Macrobrachium amazonicum* (Heller, 1862) | PALAEM Macro 3 |

Palaemon amazonicus Heller, 1862, <u>S.B.Akad.Wiss.Wien</u>, 45 (1):418

Synonymy: *Palaemon ensiculus* Smith, 1869; *Palaemon dieperinkii* De Man, 1879; *Bithynis ensiculus* - Young, 1900; *Palaemon (Eupalaemon) amazonicus* - Nobili, 1901; *Bithynis amazonicus* - Moreira, 1912.

FAO Names: Amazon river prawn (En), Bouquet amazone (Fr), Camarón amazónico (Sp).

Local Names: Camaroncito de río (Venezuela), Camarão sossêgo (N.E. Brazil).

Literature: Holthuis, 1952:18, Pl. 2, Figs. a-h.

Distribution: Atlantic drainage of South America from Venezuela to Paraguay.

Habitat: Fresh water.

Size: Maximum total length 150 mm.

Interest to Fishery: Longhurst (1970:296) remarked that less important stocks of this species are present in Guyana, Surinam and N. Brazil. Ewald (1967:773) as well as Davant (1963:44), Pericchi (1965:25) and Croker (1967:81) mentioned the species as of some economic importance in Venezuela. Fausto Filho (1968:27) listed it among the species that in N.E. Brazil are of moderate commercial importance. Laboratory aquaculture experiments with this species have been carried out in Brazil.

Macrobrachium americanum Bate, 1868 | PALAEM Macro 4

Macrobrachium americanum Bate, 1868, <u>Proc.Zool.Soc.Lond.</u>, 1868:363

Synonymy: *Palaemon americanus* - Thallwitz, 1891.

FAO Names: Cauque river prawn (En), Bouquet cauque (Fr), Camarón cauque (Sp).

Local Names: Langostino, Langostino del Pacifico, Camarón de agua dulce (Mexico), Cauque, Acamaya (Sonora and Sinaloa States, Mexico).

Literature: Holthuis, 1952:128, Pl. 31, Figs. d,e.

Distribution: Pacific slope of America between Baja California (Mexico) and N. Peru; also at Cocos and Galapagos Islands.

Habitat: Fresh water; part of the development is passed in brackish or salt water. Bottom sand or stones.

Size: Maximum total length 250 mm (♂), 193 mm (♀).

Interest to Fishery: In Mexico the commercial importance of the species is considerable, although it is exploited on a limited scale. It is considered a good possibility for artificial cultivation. It is sold fresh and frozen. According to Bate (1868:364) "a considerable number [of this species] are procured [from Lake Amatitlan, Guatemala] and brought to the markets in Guatemala". Holthuis (1954:10) mentioned a specimen bought (as a curio) by Dr. M. Boeseman on the market of San Salvador, El Salvador. Sanchez (1976:1) reported that the present species and *M. tenellum* are the only *Macrobrachium* that are of commercial importance in El Salvador.

Macrobrachium australe (Guérin, 1838) | PALAEM Macro 5

Palaemon australis Guérin, 1838, <u>In</u> Duperrey, Voyage Coquille, Zool., 2(2):37

Synonymy: *Palaemon sundaicus* Heller, 1862; *Palaemon danae* Heller, 1865; *Palaemon dispar* von Martens, 1868; *Palaemon alphonsianus* Hoffmann, 1874; *Palaemon parvus* Hoffmann, 1874; *Palaemon maillardi* Richters, 1880; *Palaemon (Eupalaemon) dispar* - De Man, 1892; *Palaemon (Eupalaemon) ustulatus* Nobili 1899; *Palaemon (Eupalaemon) danae* - Coutière, 1900; *Leander lepidus* De Man, 1915; *"Palaemon sundaicus"* of most authors refers to *Macrobrachium equidens* (Dana).

FAO Names: Koua river prawn (En), Bouquet koua (Fr), Camarón kúa (Sp).

Local Names: Orana, Camarón (Madagascar; general name for *Macrobrachium* species), Koua (Marquesas; general name for *Macrobrachium* species), Ainehu (Fatuhiva, Marquesas).

Literature: Holthuis, 1950:124, Figs. 27-30.

Distribution: Indo-West Pacific: Madagascar and the Seychelles to Polynesia.

Habitat: Fresh water, part of the early development is passed in salt and brackish water.

Size: Maximum total length 105 mm (♂), 77 mm (♀).

Interest to Fishery: Longhurst (1970:288) indicated that in Fiji fishing for this and other *Macrobrachium* species is quite heavy; the fishery there is a subsistence fishery. Adamson (1935:18) listed three species of *Macrobrachium* (among which the present) as being caught by the natives of the Marquesas Islands "with nets and spears, usually with a light at night". Louvel (1930:19) mentioned some *Macrobrachium* species (including the present) that are fished for as food in Madagascar by the natives.

Macrobrachium birmanicum (Schenkel, 1902) | PALAEM Macro 6

Palaemon spinipes birmanicus Schenkel, 1902, Verh.Naturforsch.Ges.Basel, 13:503

Synonymy: *Palaemon choprai birmanicus* - Tiwari, 1955.

FAO Names: Birma river prawn (En), Bouquet birman (Fr), Camarón birmano (Sp).

Local Names: Shul icha, Najari icha (Bangladesh).

Literature: Schenkel, 1902:503, Pl. 9, Fig. 8; Ahmad, 1957:24, Pl. 7, Fig. 20.

Distribution: Indo-West Pacific: Eastern India; Bangladesh; lower Ganges basin and lower Irawaddy basin, Birma.

Habitat: Fresh and brackish water.

Size: Maximum total length 315 mm (♂), 147 mm (♀).

Interest to Fishery: The species is listed by Ahmad (1957:24) among the economic prawns of Bangladesh.

Macrobrachium caledonicum (J. Roux, 1926) | PALAEM Macro 7

Palaemon (Macrobrachium) caledonicus J. Roux, 1926, Nova Caledonia, 4(2):224

FAO Names: New Caledonia river prawn (En), Bouquet néocalédonien (Fr), Camarón de Nueva Caledonia (Sp).

Distribution: Indo-West Pacific: New Caledonia.

Habitat: Fresh-water.

Size: Maximum carapace length 43 mm.

Interest to Fishery: Kamita (1967:6) reported that the species is sold fresh on the Nouméa fish market.

Macrobrachium carcinus (Linnaeus, 1758) | PALAEM Macro 8

Cancer carcinus Linnaeus, 1758, Syst.Nat., (ed. 10)1:631

Synonymy: *Astacus carcinus* - Fabricius, 1775; *Cancer (Astacus) jamaicensis* Herbst, 1792; *Palaemon carcinus* - Weber, 1795; *Palaemon jamaicensis* - Olivier, 1811; *Palaemon brachydactylus* Wiegmann, 1836; *Palaemon punctatus* Randall, 1840; *Palaemon brevicarpus* De Haan, 1849; *Palaemon aztecus* De Saussure, 1857; *Palaemon montezumae* De Saussure, 1857; *Palaemon laminatus* Von Martens, 1869; *Bithynis jamaicensis* - Pocock, 1889; *Bithynis aztecus* - Young, 1900; *Bithynis montezumae* - Young, 1900; *Macrobrachium jamaicense* - Pearse, 1915; *Palaemon ornatus* Torralbas, 1917; *Palaemon (Macroterocheir) jamaicensis* - De Man, 1925; *Periclimenes portoricensis* Schmitt, 1933.

FAO Names: Painted river prawn (En), Bouquet pintade (Fr), Camarón pintado (Sp).

Local Names: Langostino, Camarón de agua dulce, Cauque, Chacal (Mexico), Acamaya (Veracruz, Mexico), Camarón de río, Langostino de río (Venezuela), Stone sara-sara (Surinam), Pitu, Camarão pitu (N.E. Brazil), [Potipema (Recife, Brazil, according to Marcgraf, 1648)], Camarão de rio (S.E. Brazil).

Literature: Holthuis, 1952:114, Pls. 30,31, Figs. a-c.

Distribution: Atlantic America: Florida (U.S.A.) to S.E. Brazil.

Habitat: Fresh water, part of the early development is passed in salt and brackish water. Bottom sand and stones.

Size: Maximum total length 233 mm (δ), 170 mm ($\female$).

Interest to Fishery: In Mexico the species is of considerable importance. It is sold there fresh and frozen. Davant (1963:55) indicated that the species is fished for and highly appreciated as food in Venezuela. Also in Surinam the species is greatly esteemed, because of its size and excellent flavour, but it does not play an important part in the diet of the population (Holthuis, 1959:96). In N.E. Brazil the species is of considerable commercial importance; it is eaten as such by the people living along the rivers or it is used as an ingredient for a regional dish; specimens are also transported to the towns and sold on the market. FAO (1964:11) mentioned the species in his assessment of shrimp resources near Florianopólis (S.E. Brazil). The species is evidently fished for food wherever it occurs, but as large specimens often are not too frequent, the caught animals are mostly used by the fishermen for their own consumption and less frequently sold. Chace & Hobbs (1969:98) described the catching of these animals in Dominica. I myself witnessed this in Curaçao. Gundlach (1887:133) said that in Puerto Rico it was "estimado por su carne". The great size of the adult animals makes the species attractive for aquaculture, and at several places in the U.S.A., Mexico, Puerto Rico and Barbados experiments to this effect are under way.

Macrobrachium choprai (Tiwari, 1949)	PALAEM Macro 9

Palaemon choprai Tiwari, 1949, Rec.Indian Mus., 45:333

Synonymy: Tiwari (1955:233) considered *Palaemon spinipes birmanicus* Schenkel, 1902, a subspecies of the present species. If this is correct, the name of the present form should be *Macrobrachium birmanicus choprai* (Tiwari).

FAO Names: Ganges river prawn (En), Bouquet du haut Gange (Fr), Camarón del río Ganges (Sp).

Literature: Tiwari, 1949:333, Fig. 2.

Distribution: Indo-West Pacific: "The Indo-Gangetic plain in the Ganges and Brahmaputra River systems in the plains of U.P., Bihar & Assam", India (Tiwari, 1955:233).

Habitat: Fresh water.

Size: Maximum total length 188.5 mm (δ), 130.5 mm ($\female$).

Interest to Fishery: Part of the type material was obtained at the fish market in Banaras, India.

Macrobrachium dayanum (Henderson, 1893)	PALAEM Macro 10

Palaemon dayanus Henderson, 1893, Trans.Linnean Soc.London, (Zool.), (2)5:443

FAO Names: Kaira river prawn (En), Bouquet kaira (Fr), Camarón kaira (Sp).

Local Names: Kaira icha, Daiya chingri (Bangladesh).

Literature: Chopra & Tiwari, 1949:215, Fig. 1

Distribution: Indo-West Pacific: Pakistan; India; Bangladesh.

Habitat: Fresh water.

Size: Maximum total length 92 mm (♂), 84 mm (♀).

Interest to Fishery: Listed by Ahmad (1957:20) among the commercial prawns of Bangladesh.

| *Macrobrachium dux* (Lenz, 1910) | PALAEM Macro 11 |

Palaemon (Eupalaemon) dux Lenz, 1910, Wiss.Ergeb.Dtsch.Zentral-Afrika-Exped., 1907-08, 3:129

Synonymy: *Palaemon (Eupalaemon) lenzii* De Man, 1911; *Palaemon (Eupalaemon) dux congoensis* De Man, 1912; *Palaemon (Eupalaemon) dux tenuicarpus* De Man, 1925.

FAO Names: Congo river prawn (En), Bouquet congolais (Fr), Camarón congoleño (Sp).

Literature: Schmitt, 1962a:33,65, Pl. 4, Fig. 2, Pl. 5, Pl. 6, Fig. 1.

Distribution: Eastern Atlantic: West Africa from Rio Muni to Zaire.

Habitat: Fresh water.

Size: Maximum carapace length 55 mm (♂), 30 mm (♀).

Interest to Fishery: Dartevelle (1950a:24) indicated that the species is found "assez rarement ..... au marché de poisson de Léopoldville" [Kinshasa, Zaire].

| *Macrobrachium equidens* (Dana, 1852) | PALAEM Macro 12 |

Palaemon equidens Dana, 1852, Proc.Acad.Nat.Sci.Phila., 6:26

Synonymy: *Palaemon sundaicus bataviana* De Man, 1897; *Palaemon (Eupalaemon) sundaicus brachydactyla* Nobili, 1899; *Palaemon (Eupalaemon) acanthosoma* Nobili, 1899; *Palaemon (Eupalaemon) sundaicus baramensis* De Man, 1902; *Palaemon (Eupalaemon) nasutus* Nobili, 1903; *Palaemon sulcatus* Henderson & Matthai, 1910. In older literature the species usually is (incorrectly) indicated as *"Palaemon sundaicus"*.

FAO Names: Rough river prawn (En), Bouquet chagrin (Fr), Camarón lija (Sp).

Literature: Holthuis, 1950:162, Fig. 36.

Distribution: Indo-West Pacific: Madagascar to S. China, New Britain and New Caledonia.

Habitat: Brackish and fresh water.

Size: Maximum total length 98 mm.

Interest to Fishery: Panikkar (1937:346) mentioned the species among those fished for at the Malabar coast of S.W. India. Kurian & Sebastian (1976:92) listed the species as commercially important in India, but at the same time stated that it is only found in Kerala and in small numbers. Also in Indonesia, especially in Java, the species is fished for (Djajadiredja & Sachlan, 1956:372). It is of secondary importance, usually only found mixed in catches for other species. Domantay (1956:363) listed the species (as *Palaemon sundaicus*) among the commercially important prawns of the Philippines. In Malaya it is "considered to be almost valueless" (Johnson, 1966:279).

| *Macrobrachium esculentum* (Thallwitz, 1891) | PALAEM Macro **13** |

Palaemon esculentus Thallwitz, 1891, Zool.Anz., 14:98

Synonymy: *Palaemon dulcis* Thallwitz, 1891.

FAO Names: Sweet river prawn (En), Bouquet saveur (Fr), Camarón saborete (Sp).

Distribution: Indo-West Pacific: Celebes; Indonesia; Philippines.

Habitat: Fresh water.

Size: Maximum total length 79 mm; maximum carapace length 33 mm.

Interest to Fishery: Domantay (1956:363) listed the species among those that are commercially important in the Philippines. Although Thallwitz (1891) did not explain the derivation of the name "esculentus" it seems obvious that the collector (A.B. Meyer) gave him the information that the species is edible.

| *Macrobrachium formosense* Bate, 1868 | PALAEM Macro **14** |

Macrobrachium formosense Bate, 1868, Proc.Zool.Soc.Lond., 1868:364

Synonymy: *Palemon longipes* De Haan, 1849; *Palaemon formosensis* – Ortmann, 1891; *Palaemon (Eupalaemon) longipes* – De Man, 1897; *Bithynis longipes* – M.J. Rathbun, 1902; *Macrobrachium longipes* – Maki & Tsuchiya, 1923.

FAO Names: Crane river prawn (En), Bouquet grue (Fr), Camarón grulla (Sp).

Distribution: Indo-West Pacific: Japan; Taiwan.

Habitat: Fresh water.

Size: Total length 60 to 106 mm.

Interest to Fishery: Ling & Costello (1976:2) listed this species as being the subject of laboratory experiments for aquaculture in Okinawa, Japan.

| *Macrobrachium geron* Holthuis, 1950 | PALAEM Macro **15** |

Macrobrachium geron Holthuis, 1950, Siboga Exped.Mon., 39(a9):258

Synonymy: *Cryphiops geron* – Johnson, 1966.

FAO Names: Greybeard river prawn (En), Bouquet barbegris (Fr), Camarón barbagris (Sp).

Distribution: Indo-West Pacific: Southern Malaya; Banka (Indonesia).

Habitat: Fresh water.

Size: Maximum total length 61 mm.

Interest to Fishery: Johnson (1966:279) stated that the species is "common in 'tree-country' streams in southern Malaya [and is] sometimes collected and eaten by children and trippers". It is "excellent in flavour; but the productivity of such streams is so low that they can scarcely be regarded as a valuable reserve of food".

Macrobrachium grandimanus (Randall, 1840) — PALAEM Macro 16

Palaemon grandimanus Randall, 1840, J.Acad.Nat.Sci.Phila., 8:142

Synonymy: *Palaemon gracilimanus* Randall, 1840; *Palaemon acutirostris* Dana, 1852; *Bithynis grandimanus* - Bate, 1888.

FAO Names: Hawaii river prawn (En), Bouquet hawaïen (Fr), Camarón hauaiano (Sp).

Local Names: Opae (Hawaii).

Literature: Holthuis, 1950:230.

Distribution: Indo-West Pacific: Hawaiian Archipelago; Ryukyu Islands.

Habitat: Fresh and brackish water.

Size: Maximum total length 67 mm.

Interest to Fishery: The species is sold on the Honolulu market (Bate, 1888:794; M.J. Rathbun, 1906:922). The importance of the fishery is not known to me.

Macrobrachium heterochirus (Wiegmann, 1836) — PALAEM Macro 17

Palaemon heterochirus Wiegmann, 1836, Arch.Naturgesch.Berlin, 2(1):149

Synonymy: *Palaemon appuni* Von Martens, 1869.

FAO Names: Cascade river prawn (En), Bouquet cascade (Fr), Camarón de cascada (Sp).

Literature: Holthuis, 1952:69, Pl. 15, Figs. a,b, Pl. 16, Figs. a-c; Chace & Hobbs, 1969:106, Figs. 24,25e,k.

Distribution: Atlantic America: Mexico to S. Brazil; West Indies.

Habitat: In rapid fresh water streams, riffle areas and low cascades. Bottom sand and stones.

Size: Maximum total length 135 mm (δ), 73 mm ($\female$); maximum carapace length 34 mm (δ), 24 mm ($\female$).

Interest to Fishery: The species is of secondary commercial importance in N. and N.E. Brazil, being mostly used as bait there (Fausto Filho, 1968:28; Coelho & Ramos, 1968:3).

Macrobrachium idae (Heller, 1862) — PALAEM Macro 18

Palaemon idae Heller, 1862, S.B.Akad.Wiss.Wien, 45(1):416

Synonymy: *Palaemon (Eupalaemon) idae* - De Man, 1897; *Palaemon (Eupalaemon) ritsemae* De Man, 1897; *Palaemon (Eupalaemon) idae subinermis* Nobili, 1899; *Palaemon (Eupalaemon) mariae* Coutière, 1900; *Palaemon (Eupalaemon) robustus* De Man, 1902.

FAO Names: Orana river prawn (En), Bouquet orana (Fr), Camarón orana (Sp).

Local Names: Orana, Camaron (Madagascar).

Literature: Holthuis, 1950:142, Fig. 33.

Distribution: Indo-West Pacific: Madagascar to the Philippines, Indonesia and the Admiralty Islands.

Habitat: Fresh and brackish water.

Size: Maximum total length 110 mm.

Interest to Fishery: Louvel (1930:19) mentioned the present species among the species fished for by the local population in Madagascar and stated the species of the genus to be there "très recherchées des européens". Moulhérat & Vincke (1968:178) stated that the present species with *Metapenaeus monoceros* and *Palaemon concinnus* dominate in the fishery in the Madagascar "pangalanes". Jones (1967:1 337) mentioned its fishery in "Kerala backwaters area and other regions" in India. Chopra (1943:5) stated that this species is "of considerable economic importance in South India and especially in Travancore" ..... being ..... "fished extensively in the backwaters of Travancore from September to December".

| *Macrobrachium idella* (Hilgendorf, 1898) | PALAEM Macro 19 |

Palaemon (Eupalaemon) idae idella Hilgendorf, 1898, Deutsch Ost-Afrika, 4(7):29

Synonymy: *Palaemon (Eupalaemon) multidens* Coutière, 1900.

FAO Names: Slender river prawn (En), Bouquet hâve (Fr), Camarón cenceño (Sp).

Literature: Henderson & Matthai, 1910:285, Pl. 15, Fig. 3, Pl. 16, Fig. 3 (as *Palaemon idae*).

Distribution: Indo-West Pacific: East Africa; Madagascar; India.

Habitat: Fresh water.

Size: Total length 42 to 111 mm.

Interest to Fishery: Bailey & Crichton (1971:7) reported this species as being caught for food in Tanzania, but considered it of only sligth economic importance. Kurian & Sebastian (1976:93) mentioned a small fishery for this species in the southwestern region of India and near the east coast.

| *Macrobrachium intermedium* (Stimpson, 1860) | PALAEM Macro 20 |

Leander intermedius Stimpson, 1860, Proc.Acad.Nat.Sci.Phila., 1860:41

Synonymy: *Palaemon (Leander) intermedius* Miers, 1884.

FAO Names: Striped river prawn (En), Bouquet rayé (Fr), Camarón rayado (Sp).

Local Names: Striped prawn (S. Australia).

Literature: Hale, 1927:58, Fig. 53.

Distribution: Indo-West Pacific: Australia (New South Wales, Victoria, Tasmania, S. Australia and W. Australia).

Habitat: Littoral zone and deeper. Marine.

Size: Maximum total length 60 mm.

Interest to Fishery: Minor if at all. Hale (1927:59) stated "that a haul of these prawns taken by a boat belonging to the Fishing Company of South Australia in St. Vincent Gulf in 1885 were boiled in soft water and eaten with relish".

Macrobrachium jaroense (Cowles, 1914)	PALAEM Macro 21

Palaemon jaroensis Cowles, 1914, Philipp.J.Sci., 9(D):385

FAO Names: Jaro river prawn (En), Bouquet jaro (Fr), Camarón jaro (Sp).

Literature: Cowles, 1914:385, Pl. 3, Fig. 8.

Distribution: Indo-West Pacific: Philippines; Indonesia.

Habitat: Fresh water.

Size: Maximum total length 72 mm ($\male$), 62 mm ($\female$).

Interest to Fishery: Domantay (1956:363) listed the species (as *Palaemon jarvensis*) among the commercially important prawns of the Philippines.

Macrobrachium javanicum (Heller, 1862)	PALAEM Macro 22

Palaemon javanicus Heller, 1860, S.B.Akad.Wiss.Wien, 45(1):421

Synonymy: *Palaemon (Parapalaemon) javanicus* - De Man, 1892; *Palaemon (Eupalaemon) neglectus* De Man, 1905; *Macrobrachium neglectus* - Suvatti, 1937.

FAO Names: Java river prawn (En), Bouquet javanais (Fr), Camarón javanés (Sp).

Literature: De Man, 1892:457, Pl. 26, Fig. 38.

Distribution: Indo-West Pacific: India; Birma; Thailand; Malaya; Indonesia (Sumatra, Java, Celebes).

Habitat: Fresh water.

Size: Maximum total length 105 mm.

Interest to Fishery: Kurian & Sebastian (1976:93) mentioned a small fishery for this species in deltaic Bengal, India. Longhurst (1970:285) mentioned the species as forming part of "subsistence fisheries in fresh water" in Malaya. Djajadiredja & Sachlan (1956:370) reported it among the economically important shrimp in Sumatra, Java and Celebes.

Macrobrachium jelskii (Miers, 1877) | PALAEM Macro 23

Palaemon jelskii Miers, 1877, Proc.Zool.Soc.Lond., 1877:661

Synonymy: *Bithynis jelskii* - Young, 1900.

FAO Names: Agar river prawn (En), Bouquet agar (Fr), Camarón agareño (Sp).

Local Names: Camarão-sossêgo (N.E. Brazil).

Literature: Holthuis, 1952:26, Pl. 4, Figs. a-d; Chace & Hobbs, 1969:109, Fig. 25f.

Distribution: Atlantic America: Costa Rica and Venezuela to Brazil; Trinidad.

Habitat: Fresh, occasionally brackish water.

Size: Maximum total length up to 56 mm; maximum carapace length (exclusive of rostrum) 15 mm.

Interest to Fishery: Fausto Filho (1968:27) listed the present species as being of "regular valor comercial" in N.E. Brazil.

Macrobrachium lamarrei (H. Milne Edwards, 1837) | PALAEM Macro 24

Palaemon lamarrei H. Milne Edwards, 1837, Hist.Nat.Crust., 2:397

Synonymy: *Palaemon (Eupalaemon) lamarrei* - De Man, 1908.

FAO Names: Kuncho river prawn (En), Bouquet kuncho (Fr), Camarón kuncho (Sp).

Local Names: Kuncho chingri (Calcutta, India; Bangladesh), Gura ichha (Bangladesh).

Literature: De Man, 1908:222, Pl. 19, Fig. 4; Ahmad, 1957:19, Pl. 5, Fig. 15.

Distribution: Indo-West Pacific: India; Bangladesh.

Habitat: Fresh and brackish water.

Size: Maximum total length 69 mm.

Interest to Fishery: Jones (1967:1 337) reported that in India the species is "caught in small numbers in various estuaries and fresh-water areas". Chopra (1930:223) indicated the species as "familiar to many people in Calcutta". Kurian & Sebastian (1976:93) mentioned a small fishery for this species in N.E. India (Chilka Lake and Bengal). Aquaculture laboratory experiments on this species have been carried out in India. Ahmad (1957:19) listed *M. lamarrei* among the economic important prawns of Bangladesh, being found in "fresh-water ponds throughout" the country.

Macrobrachium lanceifrons (Dana, 1852) | PALAEM Macro 25

Palaemon lanceifrons Dana, 1852, Proc.Acad.Nat.Sci.Phila., 6:26

FAO Names: Philippine river prawn (En), Bouquet philippin (Fr), Camarón filipino (Sp).

Local Names: Hipontagunton (Luzon, Philippines).

Literature: Cowles, 1914:364, Pl. 2, Figs. 4,5;   Rasalan, Delmendo & Reyes, 1969:923-933, Figs. 1-4.

Distribution: Indo-West Pacific: Philippines.

Habitat: Fresh water.

Size: Maximum total length 61 mm.

Interest to Fishery: Rasalan, Delmendo & Reyes (1969:925) indicate this species as "one of the important resources of Laguna de Bay, Philippines. Large specimens are especially esteemed as food by the people in the area", it is there also an important duck food. The fishery for these shrimps is also dealt with by these authors. Domantay (1956:363) also indicated the species and its variety *montalbanensis* (Cowles) among the commercially important Philippines prawns. Aquaculture experiments with this species have been undertaken in the Philippines (Guerrero & Guerrero, 1976).

Macrobrachium lanchesteri (De Man, 1911)	PALAEM Macro 26

Palaemon (Eupalaemon) lanchesteri De Man, 1911, Notes Leyden Mus., 33:264

Synonymy: *Palaemon paucidens* Lanchester, 1901 (non De Haan, 1841); *Cryphiops lanchesteri* - Johnson, 1966.

FAO Names: Riceland prawn (En), Bouquet rizière (Fr), Camarón de arrozal (Sp).

Local Names: Koong voi (Thailand).

Literature: Lanchester, 1902:568, Pl. 33, Fig. 4; Johnson, 1968:233-241.

Distribution: Indo-West Pacific: Thailand; Malaya; India.

Habitat: Fresh or brackish water.

Size: Maximum total length 55 mm.

Interest to Fishery: Longhurst (1970:289) stated that there is a small fishery for this species in Thailand, while Johnson (1966:279) thought the species of great potential importance in Malaya, where it "occurs in immense numbers in riceland ditches and in some ponds. It should be quite satisfactory for tinning or conversion into prawn paste, and indeed prawns of this size are eaten in other parts of the world". Pond culture experiments with this species have been undertaken in the Philippines (Guerrero & Guerrero, 1976) and in Malaysia.

Macrobrachium lar (Fabricius, 1798)	PALAEM Macro 27

Palaemon lar Fabricius, 1798, Suppl.Ent.Syst., 402

Synonymy: *Palaemon ornatus* Olivier, 1811; *Palaemon tridens* White, 1847; *Palaemon vagus* Heller, 1862; *Palaemon spectabilis* Heller, 1862; *Palaemon ruber* Hess, 1865; *Palaemon mayottensis*, Hoffmann, 1874; *Palaemon reunionnensis* Hoffmann, 1874; *Palaemon longimanus* Hoffmann, 1874; *Palaemon madagascariensis* Hoffmann, 1874; *Bithynis lar* - Bate, 1888; *Palaemon (Eupalaemon) lar* - De Man, 1892; *Palaemon (Eupalaemon) vagus* - Nobili, 1899; *Palaemon (Eupalaemon) reunionnensis* - De Man, 1905; *Leander dionyx* Nobili, 1905; *Cancer teatae* Curtiss, 1938.

FAO Names: Monkey river shrimp (En), Bouquet singe (Fr), Camarón mono (Sp).

Local Names: Oura-pape (Tahiti; French Oceania), Paeho, ♀:Hetou, juvenile:Tipu (Nukuhiva, Marquesas), Akae (Fatuhiva, Marquesas), Hakae (Uapou, Marquesas).

Literature: Cowles, 1914:380, Pl. 2, Fig. 7; Holthuis, 1950:176, Fig. 37.

Distribution: Indo-West Pacific: E. Africa to the Ryukyu Islands and the Marquesas, introduced in the Hawaiian Archipelago.

Habitat: Fresh water; juvenile stages in brackish or salt water.

Size: Maximum total length 181 mm.

Interest to Fishery: Being a large sized shrimp, *Macrobrachium lar* probably is fished for wherever it occurs. In Mauritius it is a traditional food, which probably through overfishing, has become scarce. Djajadiredja & Sachlan (1956:370) cited the species as being of economic importance in Indonesia (Java, Celebes, the Lesser Sunda Islands and the Moluccas). I myself saw it fished for as food in Western New Guinea (Irian Barat, Indonesia). Longhurst (1970:284,288,290) also cited it as being fished for in Indonesia, and further in the Philippines (in small quantities) and Tahiti ("a very small fishery"), Fiji (as subsistence fishery), Guam and the Marianas ("a small subsistence fishery"). Also Domantay (1956:363) listed it from the Philippines as commercially important. Aquaculture experiments have been initiated in Malaysia, Taiwan, Hawaii and Tahiti (Ling & Costello, 1976:2).

| *Macrobrachium latidactylus* (Thallwitz, 1891) | PALAEM Macro 28 |

Palaemon latidactylus Thallwitz, 1891, Zool.Anz., 14:97

Synonymy: *Palaemon (Eupalaemon) endehensis* De Man, 1892; *Palaemon (Macrobrachium) lampropus* De Man, 1892.

FAO Names: Scissor river prawn (En), Bouquet cisseaux (Fr), Camarón tijera (Sp).

Literature: Cowles, 1914:392, Pl. 3, Fig. 10; Holthuis, 1950:239, Fig. 50.

Distribution: Indo-West Pacific: Malay Peninsula; Malay Archipelago.

Habitat: Fresh water; possibly part of the life cycle is passed in the sea or brackish water.

Size: Maximum total length 80 mm.

Interest to Fishery: Cowles (1914:397) reported upon some specimens "purchased in a Manila market". Also Tham (1968:213) and Domantay (1956:363) listed it among the economically important prawns of the Philippines.

| *Macrobrachium latimanus* (Von Martens, 1868) | PALAEM Macro 29 |

Palaemon latimanus Von Martens, 1868, Arch.Naturgesch.Berlin, 34(1):44

Synonymy: *Palaemon euryrhynchus* Ortmann, 1891; *Palaemon (Macrobrachium) singalangensis* Nobili, 1900.

FAO Names: Mountain river prawn (En), Bouquet montagne (Fr), Camarón montés (Sp).

Local Names: Kaipimata (Hivaoa, Marquesas), Aipimata (Fatuhiva, Marquesas), Vaeaei (Nukuhiva and Uapou, Marquesas).

Literature: Tiwari, 1961:98, Figs. 1-3.

Distribution: Indo-West Pacific: India and Sri Lanka to the Ryukyu Islands, the Malay Archipelago and the Marquesas.

Habitat: Fresh water; possibly an early part of the life cycle is spent in the sea or in brackish water.

Size: Maximum total length 125 mm.

Interest to Fishery: Adamson (1935:18) wrote that in the Marquesas "these prawns are caught by the Marquesans with nets and spears, usually with a light at night". Longhurst (1970:288) reported a subsistence fishery for this species in Fiji. In both cases *M. lar* and *M. australe* were fished at the same time.

| *Macrobrachium lepidactyloides* (De Man, 1892) | PALAEM Macro 30 |

Palaemon (Macrobrachium) lepidactyloides De Man, 1892, In M. Weber, Zool.Ergeb.Reise.Ost Indien, 2:497

FAO Names: Malayan scale prawn (En), Bouquet malais (Fr), Camarón escamoso malayo (Sp).

Literature: Holthuis, 1952a:210, Pl. 15, Fig. 2.

Distribution: Indo-West Pacific: Malay Archipelago; Fiji.

Habitat: Fresh water.

Size: Maximum total length 87 mm.

Interest to Fishery: Domantay (1956:363) listed the species (as *Palaemon lepidactylus*) among the economically important prawns in the Philippines.

| *Macrobrachium lepidactylus* (Hilgendorf, 1897) | PALAEM Macro 31 |

Palaemon lepidactylus Hilgendorf, 1879, Monatsber.Akad.Wiss.Berlin, 1878:838

Synonymy: *Palaemon (Macrobrachium) hilgendorfi* Coutière, 1899.

FAO Names: Madagascar scale prawn (En), Bouquet malgache (Fr), Camarón escamoso malgache (Sp).

Local Names: Orana, Camaron (Madagascar).

Distribution: Indo-West Pacific: E. and S.E. Africa; Madagascar.

Habitat: Fresh water.

Size: Maximum total length (inclusive of rostrum) 52 mm.

Interest to Fishery: In Madagascar the species is being fished for (Louvel, 1930:19, as *Palaemon hilgendorfi*; Moulherat & Vincke, 1968:133). Bailey & Crichton (1971:7) reported this species as of minor commercial value in Kenya, and probably also in Tanzania.

| *Macrobrachium macrobrachion* (Herklots, 1851) | PALAEM Macro 32 |

Palaemon macrobrachion Herklots, 1851, Addit.Faun.Carcinol.Afr.Occident., 15,25

Synonymy: *Palaemon africanus* Kingsley, 1882; *Palaemon (Eupalaemon) macrobrachion* - De Man, 1904.

FAO Names: Brackish river prawn (En), Bouquet saumâtre (Fr), Camarón salobreño (Sp).

Local Names: Sanson (Soussou language, Guinea), Mesurado shrimp (Liberia).

Distribution: Eastern Atlantic: West Africa (Senegal to N. Angola).

Habitat: Fresh and brackish water.

Size: Maximum total length 78 mm.

Interest to Fishery: Miller (1971) dealt with the fishery and the commercial importance of this species in Liberia. Because of its small size it is of less importance than *M. vollenhovenii* and is mostly eaten by the fishermen themselves. Gruvel (1912:16; 1913:170) listed the species among the edible prawns of Guinea. Monod (1967:174) mentioned it as being "commercialisée à l'état frais" in Benin.

Macrobrachium malcolmsonii (H. Milne Edwards, 1844)	PALAEM Macro 33

Palaemon malcolmsonii H. Milne Edwards, 1844, In Jacquemont Voyage Inde, 4(2):8

FAO Names: Monsoon river prawn (En), Bouquet mousson (Fr), Camarón monzón (Sp).

Literature: Patwardhan, 1958:5, Fig. 1-65; Rajyalakshmi & Ranadhir, 1969:903-921.

Distribution: Indo-West Pacific: Pakistan; India; Bangladesh.

Habitat: Fresh and brackish water.

Size: Maximum total length 230 mm (δ), 200 mm ($\female$).

Interest to Fishery: Qureshi (1956:362) listed this species from commercial catches made in fresh water in Pakistan. Jones (1967:1 337) mentioned that *M. malcolmsonii* in India "is most common in the estuaries and lakes of Madras and Andhra and also in Chilka Lake .... The fishery, although limited, is during the monsoon months". In the Bombay region the species is "only occasionally met with" (Kagwade, 1967:1 380). Rajyalakshmi & Ranadhir (1969:903) noted that "it is the only fresh-water prawn of commercial importance in the River Godavary" (Andhra Pradesh, India), its annual yield there being about 80 t. Chopra (1939:223) stated that it "is very extensively fished in the Chilka Lake". Kurian & Sebastian (1976:93) reported that there is a fairly good fishery for *M. malcolmsonii* in N.E. India in the monsoon months. Ahmad (1957:25) listed the present species among the commercially important prawns of Bangladesh. Aquaculture experiments have been initiated for this species in Pakistan, India, and Bangladesh.

Macrobrachium mammillodactylus (Thallwitz, 1891)	PALAEM Macro 34

Palaemon idae mammillodactylus Thallwitz, 1891, Abh.Ber.Zool.-Anthropol.-Ethnogr.Mus.Dres., 1890-1891 (3):15

Synonymy: *Palaemon (Eupalaemon) wolterstorffi* Nobili, 1900; *Palaemon philippinensis* Cowles, 1914; *Palaemon (Eupalaemon) philippinensis* - J. Roux, 1921; *Palaemon talaverae* Blanco, 1939.

FAO Names: Knobtooth prawn (En), Bouquet meule (Fr), Camarón granuloso (Sp).

Literature: Cowles, 1914:340, Pl. 2, Fig. 2 (as *P. philippinensis*); Holthuis, 1950:148, Fig. 34.

Distribution: Indo-West Pacific: Philippines; Indonesia; New Guinea.

Habitat: Fresh water.

Size: Maximum total length 137 mm.

Interest to Fishery: Domantay (1956:363) listed both *Palaemon philippinensis* and *P. talaverae* among the commercial important prawns in the Philippines. From J. Glucksman, Port Moresby, I received a large sample of this species obtained at the market of Pagui, E. Sepik District, Territory of New Guinea.

| *Macrobrachium mirabile* (Kemp, 1917) | PALAEM Macro 35 |

Palaemon mirabilis Kemp, 1917, <u>Rec.Indian Mus.</u>, 13:227

FAO Names: Shortleg river prawn (En), Bouquet tipattes (Fr), Camarón patojo (Sp).

Local Names: Lotia icha (Bangladesh).

Literature: Kemp, 1917:227, Pl. 10.

Distribution: Indo-West Pacific: Eastern India; Bangladesh; Birma; Thailand; Malaya; Borneo.

Habitat: Fresh and brackish water.

Size: Maximum total length 40 mm (♂), 60 mm (♀).

Interest to Fishery: Jones (1967:1 337) and Kurian & Sebastian (1976:93) indicated that *M. mirabile* is caught in India in small numbers in various estuaries and fresh-water areas. Ahmad (1957:18) listed the species among the commercial prawns of Bangladesh.

| *Macrobrachium nipponense* (De Haan, 1849) | PALAEM Macro 36 |

Palaemon nipponensis De Haan, 1849, <u>In</u> Von Siebold, Fauna Japonica, Crustacea, (6):171

Synonymy: *Palaemon asper* Stimpson, 1860; *Palaemon sinensis* Heller, 1862; *Bithynis nipponensis nipponensis* - M.J. Rathbun, 1902; *Palaemon (Eupalaemon) nipponensis* - Parisi, 1919.

FAO Names: Oriental river prawn (En), Bouquet nippon (Fr), Camarón nipón (Sp).

Local Names: Tenaga ebi (Japan), Ho hsia (Ningpo, China), Con tôm căng (Tonkin, Viet Nam).

Literature: Kubo, 1940:6, textfigs. 1,2, Pl. 1, Fig. f; Kamita, 1961:96, Figs. 40,41, 66u-w, 69,71.

Distribution: Indo-West Pacific: N. China to Annam, Japan and Taiwan.

Habitat: Fresh and brackish water.

Size: Maximum total length 86 mm (♂), 75 mm (♀).

Interest to Fishery: Liu (1955:56) listed the species among the economic prawns and shrimps of N. China. Ping (1931:183) mentioned it from Nanking as being of economic importance. Sowerby (1925: 133) reported the species as common near Shanghai and to be caught and eaten by the Chinese. Dried prawns of this species are exported in cardboard boxes from Hong Kong all over the world. Tanikawa (1971:245) listed the present species as of commercial importance in Japan where it is mostly dried. The species, however, is also canned in Japan for export. Also Harada (1968:83) indicated that the present species is fished for by commercial fishermen in Lake Naka-umi, Honshu, Japan. Kamita (1954:33) stated that fishermen of Lake Koyama and Lake Tôgô, S.W. Honshu, Japan, catch the species by trawling; the prawns are eaten there cooked or fried. Sollaud (1914:315) indicated that this species is "l'objet d'une pêche active au Tonkin [Viet Nam] et se vend en grande quantité sur les marchés d'Hanoï". Aquaculture experiments with this species have been initiated in Japan.

| *Macrobrachium ohione* (Smith, 1874) | PALAEM Macro 37 |

Palaemon ohionis Smith, 1874, <u>Rep.U.S.Fish Comm.</u>, 2:640

Synonymy: *Palaemon sallei* Kingsley, 1882; *Bithynis ohionis* – Cary & Spaulding, 1909.

FAO Names: Ohio river prawn (En), Bouquet ohio (Fr), Camarón de Ohio (Sp).

Local Names: River shrimp (U.S.A.).

Literature: Holthuis, 1952:62, Pl. 14.

Distribution: Western Atlantic: U.S.A. (Virginia to Texas, Mississippi basin).

Habitat: Fresh water, part of the early life history probably in brackish or salt water.

Size: Maximum total length 68 mm (δ), 102 mm ($\female$).

Interest to Fishery: Hedgpeth (1947:183) remarked that at "one time there was a small-scale commercial fishery for this shrimp in Illinois, but that seems to have been abandoned in recent years". McCormick (1933:218) indicated that *M. ohione* "is a staple market article " in Louisiana, he also discussed the fishery for the species in Illinois. Smith (1874) in the original description stated that in Indiana the species "is taken for food". Experiments for its culture have been started in the U.S.A.

| *Macrobrachium olfersii* (Wiegmann, 1836) | PALAEM Macro 38 |

Palaemon olfersii Wiegmann, 1836, <u>Arch.Naturgesch.Berlin</u>, 2(1):150

Synonymy: *Palaemon spinimanus* H. Milne Edwards, 1837; *Palaemon potiporanga* Müller, 1880; *Bithynis olfersii* – M.J. Rathbun, 1902.

FAO Names: Buchura river prawn (En), Bouquet buchura (Fr), Camarón buchura (Sp).

Local Names: Buchura (Venezuela), Aratanha, Camarão aratanha (N.E. Brazil).

Literature: Holthuis, 1952:95, Pls. 24,25, Fig. a,b.

Distribution: Western Atlantic: U.S.A. (Florida to Texas) and Mexico to S. Brazil; not in the West Indies.

Habitat: Fresh water, bottom sand and rocks.

Size: Maximum total length 90 mm.

Interest to Fishery: Davant (1963:106) reported that this species is of local economic value in Venezuela, being a "very abundant species in the Manzanares River and the people living in this area catch them with cast-nets or even by hand". In N.E. Brazil it is of considerable local importance and is used fresh or for the preparation of special dishes.

Macrobrachium patsa (Coutière, 1899)	PALAEM Macro 39

Palaemon (Parapalaemon) patsa Coutière, 1899, Bull.Mus.Hist.Nat.Paris, 5:382

FAO Names: Patsa river prawn (En), Bouquet patsa (Fr), Camarón patsa (Sp).

Local Names: Orana (Madagascar, indig.), Camaron (Madagascar, europ.).

Literature: Coutière, 1901:284, Pl. 11, Fig. 20-22.

Distribution: Indo-West Pacific: Madagascar.

Habitat: Fresh water.

Size: Maximum total length 72 mm.

Interest to Fishery: Louvel (1930:19) listed the species together with others of the same genus as being fished for in Madagascar.

Macrobrachium pilimanus (De Man, 1879)	PALAEM Macro 40

Palaemon pilimanus De Man, 1879, Notes Leyden Mus., 1:181

Synonymy: *Palaemon (Macrobrachium) pilimanus leptodactylus* De Man, 1892; *Palaemon (Macrobrachium) pygmaeus* J. Roux, 1928; *Palaemon (Macrobrachium) pilimanus malayanus* J. Roux, 1935.

FAO Names: Muff prawn (En), Bouquet manchon (Fr), Camarón manguito (Sp).

Literature: De Man, 1892:471, Pls. 27,28, Fig. 44.

Distribution: Indo-West Pacific: Malaya; Sumatra; Java; Borneo.

Habitat: Fresh water.

Size: Maximum total length 59 mm.

Interest to Fishery: Longhurst (1970:284) cited this species as of commercial importance in Indonesia. Djajadiredja & Sachlan (1956:370) listed the species as economically important in Sumatra and Java.

Macrobrachium raridens (Hilgendorf, 1893)	PALAEM Macro 41

Palaemon (Eupalaemon) raridens Hilgendorf, 1893, S.B.Ges.Naturf.Freunde Berlin, 1893:181

Synonymy: *Palaemon (Eupalaemon) paucidens* Hilgendorf, 1893; *Bithynis paucidens* - M.J. Rathbun, 1900.

FAO Names: Volta river prawn (En), Bouquet volta (Fr), Camarón del Volta (Sp).

Local Names: Sanson (Guinea), Ga, Twi, Fante, Nzima, Ewe (Ghana, in various languages).

Distribution: Eastern Atlantic: West Africa from Guinea to Nigeria.

Habitat: Fresh water.

Size: Maximum total length about 150 mm.

Interest to Fishery: Gruvel (1912:16) stated that the species is caught by the natives in Guinea. Irvine (1947:306) mentioned that in Ghana it is caught in fish traps, cooked, eaten whole or peeled and sometimes dried.

| *Macrobrachium rosenbergii* (De Man, 1879) | PALAEM Macro 42 |

Palaemon rosenbergii De Man, 1879, Notes Leyden Mus., 1:167

Synonymy: *Palaemon carcinus rosenbergi* - Ortmann, 1891; *Palaemon whitei* Sharp, 1893; *Palaemon (Eupalaemon) rosenbergii* - Nobili, 1899; *Palaemon spinipes* Schenkel, 1902; *Palaemon dacqueti* Sunier, 1925; *Cryphiops (Macrobrachium) rosenbergii* - Johnson, 1966. In older literature the species is often, but incorrectly, indicated with the name *Palaemon carcinus*.

FAO Names: Giant river prawn (En), Bouquet géant (Fr), Camarón gigante (Sp).

Local Names: Giant freshwater shrimp, Giant freshwater prawn (U.S.A.), Golda chingri, Mocha chingri (Calcutta, India; Bangladesh), Bharo chingri (or Bara chingri), Chooan chingri, Mota chingri, Shala chingri (Bangladesh), Udang satang, Udang duri (Java, Indonesia), Udang galah (Malaya, Borneo, Indonesia), Koong yai (Thailand).

Literature: Cowles, 1914:324, Pl. 1, Fig. 1.

Distribution: Indo-West Pacific: N.W. India to Viet Nam, the Philippines, New Guinea and Northern Australia.

Habitat: Fresh and brackish water, sometimes marine.

Size: Maximum total length 320 mm (♂), 250 mm (♀).

Interest to Fishery: Qureshi (1956:362, under *Palaemon carcinus*) listed the species as recorded from commercial catches of prawns brought to the market in Pakistan. Jones (1967:1 1337, Fig. 5) indicated a regular fishery for the species in the following regions of India: Bombay area, Kerala, and the northern half of the coast of the Bay of Bengal; in other areas of the Indian coast the fishery was either "occasional" or "stray", the species also "contributes to a fairly good freezing industry in the Kerala backwaters". Longhurst (1970:281) stated that in S.W. India *M. rosenbergii* is caught in very limited quantities in certain areas only. Raman (1967:649-669) dealt extensively with the fishery and biology of the species on the Kerala coast of India. Kurian & Sebastian (1976: 93) stated that there is an intensive fishery in Kerala, India, during the monsoon and post-monsoon months, but that the harvest has diminished owing to indiscriminate fishing. Ahmad (1957:23, as *Palaemon carcinus*) mentioned that the species "is exploited throughout the year in the estuaries in [Bangladesh] and during the winter months from beels and rivers"; it "is much relished by everybody". In Malaysia and Indonesia the species is economically exploited on a considerable scale (Johnson, 1968:235; Longhurst, 1970:284,285). Djajadiredja & Sachlan (1956:370) indicated it as economically important in the Indonesian islands of Sumatra, Java, Borneo, Celebes and the Lesser Sunda Islands. Figures given for the annual catch of this species in Indonesia are (in metric tons): 4 300 (in 1973), 3 065 (in 1974), 2 516 (in 1975), 2 530 (in 1976). In New Guinea the species is fished for by the population throughout the western part of the island. In Papua it is obtained from the Fly River. In the Philippines Cowles (1914:325 under *Palaemon carcinus*) called it "the most important species from a commercial point of view in the Philippines Islands". Longhurst (1970:289) indicated that there is a small fishery for this species in Thailand.

The great size of this species and its excellent taste ("in my view, shared by many people, it is superior to the best of the penaeid prawns", Johnson, 1966:279), made this species fished for wherever it occurs. Also it has become the subject of intensive efforts to cultivate it. Ling (1969:589-619), in Malaysia was the first to manage to raise the species through complete metamorphosis and showed that it can be successfully cultivated in ponds. Also in other areas of South and East Asia (e.g., India, Sri Lanka, Bangladesh, Birma, Indonesia, Thailand, Cambodia, Viet Nam, Japan, Taiwan, Philippines) experiments on a larger or smaller scale have been started to investigate the possibility of raising this species in ponds for commercial purposes. Similar experiments are under way, in Hawaii, Palau, Tahiti, Australia, Africa (Malawi, Mauritius, Seychelles), in various countries in America (U.S.A., Mexico, Puerto Rico, Honduras, Colombia) and even in England.

| *Macrobrachium rude* (Heller, 1862) | PALAEM Macro 43 |

Palaemon rudis Heller, 1862, Verh.Zool.-Bot.Ges.Wien, 12:527

Synonymy: *Palaemon mossambicus* Hilgendorf, 1879; *Palaemon (Eupalaemon) rudis* - Coutière, 1900; *Palaemon (Eupalaemon) alcocki* Nobili, 1903; *Palaemon delagoae* Stebbing, 1915; *Urocaridella borradailei* Stebbing, 1923.

FAO Names: Hairy river prawn (En), Bouquet velu (Fr), Camarón de cerda (Sp).

Local Names: Goda chingri (Bengal, India; Bangladesh), Paitta ichha (Bangladesh).

Literature: Henderson & Matthai, 1910:291, Pl. 17, Fig. 5.

Distribution: Indo-West Pacific: East Africa; Madagascar; India; Bangladesh.

Habitat: Fresh and brackish water.

Size: Maximum total length about 130 mm.

Interest to Fishery: Bailey & Crichton (1971:7) mentioned this species as being of minor commercial value in Tanzania and in Kenya. According to Jones (1967:1 337, Fig. 5) there is a regular fishery for this species in India in the following areas: Bombay region, Kerala, and the northern half of the coast of the Bay of Bengal; elsewhere on the west coast there is a stray fishery. Chopra (1943:4) indicated that the species "is common in Bengal from August to October, when large numbers of egg-bearing females are brought to the markets. In the Chilka Lake this is the commonest *Palaemon* fished in large quantities from September to November". Kurian & Sebastian (1976:93) reported that the species is the subject of a good seasonal fishery in Bengal and Orissa, India. Qureshi (1956:362) and Ahmad (1957:26) mentioned that there is a fishery for this species in Bangladesh. Aquaculture experiments with *M. rude* have been initiated in Thailand (Ling & Costello, 1976:3).

| *Macrobrachium scabriculum* (Heller, 1862) | PALAEM Macro 44 |

Palaemon scabriculus Heller, 1862, Verh.Zool.-Bot.Ges.Wien, 12:527

Synonymy: *Palaemon dolichodactylus* Hilgendorf, 1879; *Palaemon (Parapalaemon) scabriculus* - De Man, 1897; *Palaemon (Parapalaemon) dolichodactylus* - Hilgendorf, 1898; *Palaemon dubius* Henderson & Matthai, 1910; *Palaemon (Macrobrachium) dolichodactylus* - J. Roux, 1934.

FAO Names: Goda river prawn (En), Bouquet goda (Fr), Camarón goda (Sp).

Local Names: Goda chingri (Bangladesh).

Distribution: Indo-West Pacific: East Africa and Madagascar to India, Sri Lanka, Bangladesh and Sumatra.

Habitat: Fresh and brackish water.

Size: Maximum total length 70 mm (♂), 62 mm (♀).

Interest to Fishery: Bailey & Crichton (1971:7) reported this species as of minor commercial value in Kenya, and probably also in Tanzania. Jones (1967:1 337) and Kurian & Sebastian (1976:94) stated that the species is of minor economical importance in India. Ahmad (1957:21) listed it among the prawns that are fished for in Bangladesh.

| *Macrobrachium sintangense* (De Man, 1898) | PALAEM Macro 45 |

Palaemon (Eupalaemon) sintangensis De Man, 1898, Notes Leyden Mus., 20:138

Synonymy: *Palaemon (Eupalaemon) elegans* De Man, 1892; *Bithynis (Eupalaemon) elegans* - M.J. Rathbun, 1910; *Macrobrachium elegans* - Suvatti, 1937.

FAO Names: Sunda river prawn (En), Bouquet krakatoa (Fr), Camarón krakatoa (Sp).

Literature: De Man, 1892:440, Pl. 26, Fig. 36.

Distribution: Indo-West Pacific: S. Thailand; Malaya; Indonesia (Sumatra, Java, Borneo).

Habitat: Fresh water.

Size: Maximum total length 66 mm.

Interest to Fishery: Johnson (1968:236) remarked that in Malaysia this species "appears to have potential economic value". Longhurst (1970:285) stated that in Malaysia there is an unrecorded subsistence fishery in freshwater for a number of prawn species, including the present. Djajadiredja & Sachlan (1956:370) reported the present species to be of economic importance in Java.

| *Macrobrachium tenellum* (Smith, 1871) | PALAEM Macro 46 |

Palaemon tenellus Smith, 1871, Rep.Peabody Acad.Sci., 1869:98

Synonymy: *Palaemon longipes* Lockington, 1878.

FAO Names: Longarm river prawn (En), Bouquet brasolargue (Fr), Camarón brazolargo (sp).

Local Names: Chacal, Langostino (Mexico), Molla (southern Sinaloa, Mexico), Camarón del río (El Salvador).

Literature: Holthuis, 1952:54, Pls. 10,11, Figs. a,b.

Distribution: Eastern Pacific: Lower California, Mexico to N. Peru.

Habitat: Fresh water, sometimes brackish. Bottom rocks, sand and mud.

Size: Maximum total length 150 mm; maximum carapace length 48 mm.

Interest to Fishery: In Mexico and El Salvador the species is of secondary commercial importance. It is consumed directly, fresh or cooked (Dr. Y.L. Cifuentes, in Litt.). It is fished locally in El Salvador.

| *Macrobrachium trompii* (De Man, 1898) | PALAEM Macro 47 |

Palaemon (Parapalaemon) trompii De Man, 1898, <u>Notes Leyden Mus.</u>, 20:144

Synonymy: *Palaemon (Parapalaemon) thienemanni* J. Roux, 1898; *Palaemon (Parapalaemon) trompi armatus* J. Roux, 1936.

FAO Names: Forest river prawn (En), Bouquet forestier (Fr), Camarón guardabosque (Sp).

Literature: Holthuis, 1950:211.

Distribution: Indo-West Pacific: Malay Peninsula; Sumatra; Borneo.

Habitat: Fresh water.

Size: Maximum total length 72 mm.

Interest to Fishery: Longhurst (1970:285) included this species among those for which there are unrecorded subsistence fisheries in fresh water in Malaysia. Johnson (1968:236) stated that the species is abundant in forest streams in Malaysia and is of excellent flavour; but the waters of its natural habitat tend to be unproductive so that it is unlikely that the species will ever be exploited on a large scale.

| *Macrobrachium villosimanus* (Tiwari, 1949) | PALAEM Macro 48 |

Palaemon villosimanus Tiwari, 1949, <u>Rec.Indian Mus.</u>, 45:329

FAO Names: Dimua river prawn (En), Bouquet dimua (Fr), Camarón dimúa (Sp).

Local Names: Dimua ichha (Bangladesh).

Distribution: Indo-West Pacific: N.E. India; Bangladesh.

Habitat: Fresh water.

Size: Maximum total length 146 mm (δ), 117 mm ($\female$).

Interest to Fishery: The species is listed by Kurian & Sebastian (1976:94) among the commercial prawns of India, but they state that it is found in small numbers only near Calcutta and Chittagong. Ahmad (1957:22) ranged the species among the prawns fished for in Bangladesh.

| *Macrobrachium vollenhovenii* (Herklots, 1857) | PALAEM Macro 49 |

Palaemon vollenhovenii Herklots, 1857, <u>Tijdschr.Entomol.</u>, 1:96

Synonymy: *Palaemon jamaicensis africanus* Bouvier, 1895; *Palaemon (Bithynis) jamaicensis vollenhovenii* - Lönnberg, 1903; *Palaemon (Macrobrachium) jamaicensis angolensis* De Man, 1904; *Palaemon (Parapalaemon) vollenhovenii* - De Man, 1912; *Palaemon (Macrobrachium) jamaicensis herklotsii* De Man, 1912; *Palaemon (Macroterocheir) jamaicensis herklotsii* - De Man, 1925.

FAO Names: African river prawn (En), Bouquet africain (Fr), Camarón africano (Sp).

Local Names: Sipa sipa (Ouolof language, Senegal), Sanfoui (Soussou language, Guinea), Sanzaket (Appollonia language, Ivory Coast), Abitan (Abouré language, Ivory Coast), Otana (Gabon), Kossa (Congo).

Literature: Schmitt, 1926a:37,65, Pl. 6, Fig. 2, Pl. 7; Holthuis, 1951:150; Miller, 1971:5-11.

Distribution: Eastern Atlantic: West Africa from the Cape Verde Islands and Senegal to S. Angola.

Habitat: Fresh, brackish and sometimes salt water.

Size: Maximum total length 182 mm.

Interest to Fishery: Gruvel (1908:159) reported the fishery for this species in Senegal and later (Gruvel, 1912:14-16), that in French Guinea, Ivory Coast, Gabon and Congo (Zaire). Miller (1971)very extensively dealt with the fishery of this species in Liberia. The large size of the specimens of this species and their excellent taste, make it likely that it is caught throughout its range. But the fishery, due to the fact that the species does not seem to occur in large quantities, probably everywhere is of a local nature.

Nematopalaemon hastatus (Aurivillius, 1898)	PALAEM Nemat 2

Palaemon (Leander) hastatus Aurivillius, 1898, Bih.K.Sven.Vetenskapsakad.Handl., 24(4) (1):27

FAO Names: Estuarine prawn (En), Bouquet étier (Fr), Camarón estuarino (Sp).

Literature: Holthuis, 1951:142.

Distribution: Eastern Atlantic: West Africa from Senegal to Angola.

Habitat: Depth 1 to 50 m. Bottom sand and mud. Marine and estuarine.

Size: Maximum total length 74 mm.

Interest to Fishery: The species forms the subject of local fisheries, usually with seines (Monod, 1967:136; Longhurst, 1970:278). Bassindale (1961:485) reported it from Ghana as "to be sufficiently abundant in the sub-littoral to be fished and marketed". In Nigeria *N. hastatus* is caught during the rainy season "en quantités parfois importantes", it is "sechée ou fumée et uniquement vendue sur place" (Crosnier & de Bondy, 1967:3). Holthuis (1952b:57) listed specimens from Moanda, Zaire obtained by "pêcherie indigène". Gruvel (1912:16) when dealing with the occurrence of the species in the mouth of the Congo stated: "ce palaemonide est bien une forme comestible, mais, en fait, il n'est que très rarement utilisé par les rares Européens qui, à l'aide d'engins perfectionnés, peuvent se livrer à sa pêche".

Nematopalaemon schmitti (Holthuis, 1950)	PALAEM Nemat 1

Palaemon schmitti Holthuis, 1950, Proc.K.Ned.Akad.Wet., 53:97

FAO Names: Whitebelly prawn (En), Bouquet covac (Fr), Camarón cuac (Sp).

Local Names: Fine shrimp, White bellies (Guyana), Witti bere (Surinam), Crevette couac (French Guyane).

Literature: Holthuis, 1952:169, Pl. 43.

Distribution: Western Atlantic: north coast of S. America from Venezuela to N.E. Brazil.

Habitat: Depth 5 to 75 m. Bottom mud or sand. Marine and estuarine.

Size: Maximum total length 80 mm.

Interest to Fishery: Lindner (1957:21) described the present species together with *Exhippolysmata oplophoroides* as "in British Guiana the most abundant commercial forms", where they are either sold on the local market or exported in a dried state. In Surinam it is also of great commercial importance and next to *Xiphopenaeus* it is the most important species fished for locally; here too the dried product is exported, the fresh and also dried shrimp is sold at the local markets. In French Guiana, however, the species is "parfois utilisée dans l'alimentation, elle n'est que peu appréciée (Durand, 1961:33). In N.E. Brazil *Nematopalaemon schmitti* is of considerable commercial importance and either used directly or in local dishes (P.A. Coelho and M. de Araujo Ramos, in Litt.).

Nematopalaemon tenuipes (Henderson, 1893)	PALAEM Nemat 3

Leander tenuipes Henderson, 1893, Trans.Linn.Soc.Lond., (Zool.), (2)5:440

Synonymy: *Palaemon luzonensis* Blanco, 1939; *Palaemon (Nematopalaemon) tenuipes* - Holthuis, 1950.

FAO Names: Spider prawn (En), Bouquet araignée (Fr), Camarón araña (Sp).

Local Names: Aramang (Philippines).

Literature: Kemp, 1917:206, Pl. 8, Fig. 1.

Distribution: Indo-West Pacific: India; Burma; Philippines.

Habitat: Shallow water to 17 m. Brackish and marine.

Size: Maximum total length 70 mm.

Interest to Fishery: According to Jones (1967:1 337, Fig. 5) in India there is an occasional fishery for the species in the Bombay area and in the Gangetic delta. Kunju (1967:1394) said this "to be the most important species from the point of view of its abundance" in the fishery off the Maharashtra coast near Bombay, India. Kemp (1917:203) and Chopra (1943:5) indicated that the present species (together with *Exopalaemon styliferus*) "is extremely common in the Gangetic delta and vast quantities are sold in the markets mostly frequented by the poorer sections of the population". According to Kurian & Sebastian (1976:92) it forms the subject of "one of the most important fisheries in Bombay and Gangetic Delta". Blanco (1939:201) described the fishery of this species in northern Luzon, where it is of considerable importance; the product is dried or salted and shipped to other parts of the Philippines.

Palaemon adspersus Rathke, 1837	PALAEM Palaem 2

Palaemon adspersus Rathke, 1837, Mém.Acad.Imp.Sci.St. Pétersb., (6B) 3:368

Synonymy: *Cancer squilla* Linnaeus, 1758; *Palaemon communis* Anslijn, 1826; *Palaemon fabricii* Rathke, 1843; *Palaemon rectirostris* Zaddach, 1844; *Palaemon leachii* Bell, 1851; *Palaemon imbellis* Fischer, 1872; *Palaemon rectirostris octodentatus* Neumann, 1878; *Leander rectirostris transitans* Czerniavsky,1884; *Leander rectirostris typica* Czerniavsky, 1884; *Leander brandti* Czerniavsky, 1884; *Palaemon (Leander) brandti* - Thallwitz, 1892; *Leander adspersus* - Ortmann, 1894; *Leander adspersus fabricii* - De Man, 1915; *Leander rectirostris octodentatus* - Bolivar, 1916; *Leander imbellis* - Kemp, 1925.

FAO Names: Baltic prawn (En), Bouquet balte (Fr), Camarón báltico (Sp).

Local Names: Räka, Allmän räka (Sweden), Roskildereje, Almindelige reje (Denmark), Strandreke (Norway), Ostseegarnele, Ostseekrabbe (Germany), Gambaretto (Venice, Italy), Creveta de iarbă; Garida (Romania), Черноморская травяная креветка, Европейская креветка (U.S.S.R).

Literature: Kemp, 1910:131, Pl. 20, Figs. 2a,e.

Distribution: Eastern Atlantic: Baltic from S.W. Finland and Sweden south; S. Norway and British Islands to the Mediterranean and Black Sea; Caspian Sea.

Habitat: Depth 1 to 10 m, seldom deeper, bottom mud and algae. Brackish or salt water.

Size: Maximum total length 70 or 80 mm.

Interest to Fishery: In Sweden there is a small fishery for this species (in 1938 8.4 t was caught). In Denmark, however, it is far more important: between 1915 and 1964 the annual catch varied from 100 to 300 t. Also in Norway the species is fished, but evidently on a minor scale. In 1900 Wollebaek (1900:20) stated this to be the only species of shrimp, besides *Pandalus borealis*, that is fished in Norway. In the British Isles there is no special fishery for this species, although specimens may occur in catches of other prawns. So Bell (1851:307) stated that in Poole Harbour in Dorsetshire, this species, *P. elegans* and young *P. serratus* are sold as "cup-shrimps". In Germany it is fished on the coast of the Baltic, but the fishery is localized and on a restricted scale; the species is used as bait, but also for local human consumption (Scheer, 1967). Along the Atlantic and Mediterranean coasts of Europe, the species is not very important economically, although it is sold on fish markets, probably often as an admixture to other species. Fischer (1872:420-422) reported it as offered for sale in the markets of S.W. France ("on en mange en plus grande quantité"). Brian (1942:32) reported it from the fish market of Genoa "in quantitá discreta", while Paolucci (1909:252) encountered it on the Adriatic coast of Italy "sul mercato con maggiore frequenza". Giordani Soika (1948:25) reported it from the Venice fish market. In the Black Sea the species is of considerable importance: along the northwest coast it is fished for on a fairly large scale (Bacescu, 1967:106), being economically the most important prawn there. Heldt & Heldt (1954:12) included it among the edible shrimps of Tunisia. Gruvel (1926:128) indicated that in Algeria (in Bône) "on vend ... sur le marché, mais en bien moins grande quantité [que *Penaeus kerathurus*], une autre crevette ... que l'on capture l'été, à l'embouchure et dans la Seybouse même (partie saumâtre), c'est le *Palaemon (Leander) adspersus*, Rath.". Also on the Atlantic coast of Morocco (near Mehdiya) the species is caught and used as food by the Europeans (Gruvel, 1923:84). Longhurst (1970:267,268) indicated the present species as of economic importance in the Mediterranean and Black Sea, but as nowhere taken in large quantities: the largest production of *Palaemon* and *Crangon* "appears to be that reported by Bulgaria".

Palaemon concinnus Dana, 1852	PALAEM Palaem 3

Palaemon concinnus Dana, 1852, Proc.Acad.Nat.Sci.Phila., 6:26

Synonymy: *Palaemon exilimanus* Dana, 1852; *Leander longicarpus* Stimpson, 1860; *Palaemon (Leander) concinnus* - Hilgendorf, 1879; *Palaemon (Leander) longicarpus* - Gee, 1925; *Leander exilimanus* - Kemp, 1925; *Palaemon lagdaoensis* Blanco, 1939; *Leander lagdaoensis* - Tiwari, 1950.

FAO Names: Mangrove prawn (En), Bouquet mangrove (Fr), Camarón de manglar (Sp).

Local Names: Lagdao (Philippines).

Literature: Holthuis, 1950:61, Fig. 12.

Distribution: Indo-West Pacific: E. Africa to Hong Kong, the Philippines and Polynesia.

Habitat: Fresh, brackish and salt water, shallow.

Size: Maximum total length 66 mm.

Interest to Fishery: Moulherat & Vincke (1963:178) indicated that in the shrimp fishery in the "pangalanes" along the east coast of Madagascar *Macrobrachium idae*, *Metapenaeus monoceros* and *Palaemon concinnus* dominate. However, the importance of the present species cannot be very great, due to its small size. Domantay (1956:363) listed the species among the economically important prawns of the Philippines without giving further data.

Palaemon elegans Rathke, 1837

Palaemon elegans Rathke, 1837, Mém.Acad.Imp.Sci.St.Pétersb., (6B)3:370

Synonymy: *Palaemon minans* Norman, 1861; *Palaemonella gracilis* Paulson, 1875; *Leander squilla prototypa* Czerniavsky, 1884; *Leander squilla brevidigitata* Czerniavsky, 1884; *Leander squilla typica* Czerniavsky, 1884; *Palaemon (Leander) minans* - Thallwitz, 1892; *Leander squilla intermedia* De Man, 1915; *Leander squilla elegans* - De Man, 1915; *Palaemon (Palaeander) elegans* - Holthuis, 1950. Most records of *Leander squilla* pertain to this species, and not to *P. adspersus*.

FAO Names: Rockpool prawn (En), Bouquet flaque (Fr), Camarón de poza (Sp).

Local Names: Tångräka (Sweden), Strandreje (Denmark), Strandreke (Norway), Steingarnele (Germany), Prawn, White prawn (British Isles), Gamberetto (Italy), Creveta, Garida de piatra (Romania), Европейская - Африканская Креветка (U.S.S.R.); usually not distinguished from *P. adspersus*.

Literature: Kemp, 1910:132, Pl. 20, Fig. 3a-e.

Distribution: Eastern Atlantic: from W. Norway, W. Sweden and Denmark to S.W. Africa; Mediterranean; Black Sea; Caspian Sea.

Habitat: Usually inhabiting rockpools and the shallow sublittoral zone. Marine.

Size: Maximum total length about 60 mm.

Interest to Fishery: Longhurst (1970:267,268) listed the present species among the economically important shrimps of the Mediterranean and Black Sea, and indicated specifically that in Greece it forms about 50% of the catch together with *Penaeus kerathurus* and *Parapenaeus longirostris*. As the present species and *P. adspersus* have been confused with one another, both taxonomically and nomenclaturally, it is possible that, at least part of, the above records are based on *P. adspersus*. If *P. elegans* is of commercial importance, this probably is quite minor; it may form an admixture with other species of prawns (see also under *P. adspersus*), or may be fished locally for bait. Fischer (1872:420) indicated, rather casually, that it is "portée sur les marchés" (of S.W. France) together with *P. serratus* and *P. adspersus*. Heldt & Heldt (1954:12) listed the species among the edible shrimps of Tunisia. Paolucci (1909:248,249, Pl. 3, Figs. 37,38) described and figured a species from the Adriatic near Ancona, Italy, which he identified as "*Anchistia amethystea* Heller". However, his material is neither *Periclimenes amethysteus* (Risso), nor, as Pesta (1918:124-126) supposed, *Periclimenes scriptus* (Risso). The shape of the rostrum, the colour pattern of the carapace, the arrangement of the spines on the posterior margin of the telson, as well as the other characters mentioned by Paolucci, including the habitat, make it clear that his specimens belong to *Palaemon elegans*. After describing the way of capture of these shrimps, usually by children with small round nets called "nichessino", Paolucci continued "serve come esca in varie pesche alla lenza ed è anche assai buona a mangiarsi".

Palaemon gravieri (Yu, 1930)

Leander gravieri Yu, 1930, Bull.Soc.Zool.France, 55:564

FAO Names: Chinese ditch prawn (En), Bouquet chinois des canaux (Fr), Camarón chino de acequia (Sp).

Local Names: Aka ebi (Korea).

Literature: Kubo, 1942:48, Figures.

Distribution: Indo-West Pacific: Korea; N. China.

Habitat: Marine.

Size: Maximum total length 58 mm.

Interest to Fishery: Liu (1955:51) listed the species in his paper on the economically important Decapoda of N. China, while Yoshida (1941:26, under the incorrect name *Leander macrodactylus*) mentioned it in his list of important marine shrimps of Korea. Ivanov (1967:41) reported it as being of marked commercial importance in China, being fished in the Yellow and East China Seas.

Palaemon longirostris H. Milne Edwards, 1837	PALAEM Palaem 6

Palaemon longirostris H. Milne Edwards, 1837, Hist.Nat.Crust., 2:392

Synonymy: *Palaemon edwardsii* Heller, 1863; *Palaemon longipes* Fischer, 1872; *Leander edwardsii* (with vars. *brevidigitata, intermedia, prototypa, simplicior* and *similis*) - Czerniavsky, 1884; *Leander longirostris* - De Man, 1915; *Leander longirostris robusta* De Man, 1924.

FAO Names: Delta prawn (En), Bouquet delta (Fr), Camarón delta (Sp).

Local Names: White prawn (British Isles), Dorngarnele (Germany), Steurkrab (Netherlands), Crevette blanche, Esquille, Esquirre, Squille, Santé (S.W. France).

Literature: De Man, 1915:149, Pl. 12, Fig. 3; Holthuis, 1950:59, Fig. 3,5a,20.

Distribution: Eastern Atlantic: N.W. Germany, British Isles and the Netherlands to the Mediterranean and possibly Black Sea.

Habitat: Brackish water of estuaries.

Size: Maximum total length 70 mm.

Interest to Fishery: In the Netherlands the species is fished for and sold as bait (Holthuis, 1950a:61). Also in S.W. France, in the estuary of the Gironde near Bordeaux it is fished, as indicated by Fischer (1872:421), who in his turn also referred to Rondelet (1554).

Palaemon macrodactylus M.J. Rathbun, 1902	PALAEM Palaem 7

Palaemon macrodactylus M.J. Rathbun, 1902, Proc.U.S.Natl.Mus., 26:52

FAO Names: Migrant prawn (En), Bouquet migrateur (Fr), Camarón emigrante (Sp).

Literature: Kubo, 1942:36, Figures; Newman, 1963:119-132, Figs. 1-3.

Distribution: Originally Indo-West Pacific: Korea; China; Japan. Introduced in the Eastern Pacific (San Francisco Bay area) about 1954. Now also found in Australia.

Habitat: Estuarine brackish waters.

Size: Maximum total length 51 mm (δ), 55 mm ($\mathcal{Q}$).

Interest to Fishery: Liu (1955:53) cited the species in his list of economically important prawns from N. China. Yoshida's listing of the species among the commercial shrimps of Korea is incorrect, Kubo (1942:48) showed that Yoshida's specimens were *P. gravieri*. In Tokyo the species is sold as food (A.C.J. Burgers, in Litt.). In San Francisco Bay the species was so abundant in 1957 that it turned up in commercial shrimp catches (Newman, 1963).

| *Palaemon maculatus* (Thallwitz, 1891) | PALAEM Palaem 8 |

Leander maculatus Thallwitz, 1891, Abh.Ber.Zool.-Anthropol.-Ethnogr.Mus.Dresd., 1890-91 (3):19, 49

FAO Names: Zaire prawn (En), Bouquet zaïre (Fr), Camarón zairense (Sp).

Literature: De Man, 1925:36, Fig. 8; Schmitt, 1926a:25, Fig. 65.

Distribution: Eastern Atlantic: West Africa from Senegal to Angola.

Habitat: Brackish water.

Size: Maximum total length 43 mm.

Interest to Fishery: Dartevelle (1950:33) stated that "ces Nageurs, for recherchés par les résidents et estivant [of the coast near the mouth of the Congo River], dont le nombre augmente, deviennent plus rare au fur et à mesure que la pêche s'en fait plus acharnée".

| *Palaemon northropi* (Rankin, 1898) | PALAEM Palaem 9 |

Leander northropi Rankin, 1898, Ann.N.Y.Acad.Sci., 12:539

Synonymy: *Palaemon brachylabis* M.J. Rathbun, 1900; *Palaemon (Palaeander) northropi* - Holthuis, 1950.

FAO Names: Caribbean bait prawn (En), Bouquet zélateur caraïbe (Fr), Camarón cebador (Sp).

Local Names: Potitinga (Pernambuco, Brazil).

Literature: Holthuis, 1952:192, Pl. 47.

Distribution: Western Atlantic: Bermuda and Florida to Uruguay.

Habitat: Shallow water. Bottom mud. Marine.

Size: Maximum total length 33 mm (δ), 38 mm ($\female$).

Interest to Fishery: In N.E. Brazil of secondary importance, used there as bait for fishing (P.A. Coelho & M. de Araujo Ramos, in Litt.).

| *Palaemon ortmanni* M.J. Rathbun, 1902 | PALAEM Palaem 10 |

Palaemon ortmanni M.J. Rathbun, 1902, Proc.U.S.Natl.Mus., 26:53

Synonymy: *Palaemon longipes* Ortmann, 1890 (not *P. l.* Olivier, 1811); *Leander longipes* - De Man, 1907.

FAO Names: Gladiator prawn (En), Bouquet gladiateur (Fr), Camarón gladiador (Sp).

Literature: Kubo, 1942:52, Figures (as *Leander longipes*).

Distribution: Indo-West Pacific: China and Japan.

Habitat: Littoral. Marine.

Size: Maximum total length 78.5 mm.

Interest to Fishery: Liu (1955:54) listed the present species among the economically important shrimps and prawns of N. China.

| *Palaemon pacificus* (Stimpson, 1860) | PALAEM Palaem 11 |

Leander pacificus Stimpson, 1860, <u>Proc.Acad.Nat.Sci.Phila.</u>, 1860:40

Synonymy: *Leander peringueyi* Stebbing, 1915; *Leander gilchristi* Stebbing, 1915; *Leander okiensis* Kamita, 1951.

FAO Names: Indian bait prawn (En), Bouquet zélateur indien (Fr), Camarón celador indio (Sp).

Literature: Kemp, 1925:307; Kubo, 1942:42, Figures; Holthuis, 1950:87, Fig. 19.

Distribution: Indo-West Pacific: Red Sea and S. Africa to Japan and Polynesia. Perhaps the S. African form must be considered a distinct species.

Habitat: Littoral. Marine.

Size: Maximum total length 53 mm.

Interest to Fishery: Kubo (1942:48) stated that this species is used as bait for fishing on the Pacific coast of Japan.

| *Palaemon pandaliformis* (Stimpson, 1871) | PALAEM Palaem 12 |

Leander pandaliformis Stimpson, 1871, <u>Ann.Lyc.Nat.Hist.</u>, New York, 10:130

Synonymy: *Leander potitinga* Müller, 1880; *Palaemon (Leander) potitinga* - Thallwitz, 1892; *Palaemonetes cubensis* Hay, 1903; *Leander cubensis* - Kemp, 1925.

FAO Names: Potitinga prawn (En), Bouquet potitinga (Fr), Camarón potitinga (Sp).

Local Names: Potitinga (Pernambuco, Brazil).

Literature: Holthuis, 1952:187, Pl. 46, Figs. g-1; Chace & Hobbs, 1969:111, Figs. 26,28,a.

Distribution: Western Atlantic: West Indies and east coast of American continent from Guatemala to S. Brazil.

Habitat: Fresh and brackish water. Muddy bottom.

Size: Maximum total length 38 mm ($\male$), 43 mm ($\female$).

Interest to Fishery: Secondary. Used as bait for fishing in N.E. Brazil (P.A. Coêlho & M. de Araújo Ramos, in Litt.).

| *Palaemon paucidens* De Haan, 1844 | PALAEM Palaem 13 |

Palaemon paucidens De Haan, 1844, <u>In</u> Von Siebold, Fauna Japonica, Crustacea (6/7):Pl. 45, Fig. 11

Synonymy: *Leander paucidens* - Stimpson, 1860.

FAO Names: Lake prawn (En), Bouquet de lac (Fr), Camarón de lago (Sp).

Local Names: Suji ebi (Japan).

Literature: Kubo, 1942:25, Figures; Kamita, 1961:83, Figures.

Distribution: Indo-West Pacific: S.E. Siberia; Korea; China; Saghalin; Japan; Ryukyu Islands.

Habitat: Fresh, brackish (and salt?) water.

Size: Maximum total length up to 66 mm.

Interest to Fishery: In Japan *Palaemon paucidens* is fished at the same time as *Macrobrachium nipponense*, and evidently not or not always separated when processed. I myself did buy a can of Japanese prawns exported to Seattle, U.S.A., which contained both species. According to Kemp (1918: 271) "The species forms one of the most important commercial products of Lake Biwa [Japan], being caught near Otsu in very large numbers in small basket traps". Kamita (1954:33) indicated that in Tottori Prefecture, Japan "fishermen catch them by trawling" and that they are eaten cooked or fried.

Palaemon serratus (Pennant, 1777)	PALAEM Palaem 1

Astacus serratus Pennant, 1777, British Zoology, (ed. 4)4:15

Synonymy: *Melicerta triliana* Risso, 1816; *Palaemon trilianus* - Risso, 1826; *Palaemon treillianus* H. Milne Edwards, 1837; *Palaemon punctulatus* Risso, 1844 (nomen nudum); *Cancer captivus* Nardo, 1847; *Leander latreillianus* (with vars. *intermedia* and *aberrans* and forms *gigantea, typica* and *transitans* and monstrosity *sculpta*) - Czerniavsky, 1884; *Leander serratus* - Sharp, 1893; *Leander treillianus* - Adensamer, 1898; *Palaemon rostratus* Gimenez, 1922; *Palaemon oratelli* Monod, 1931 (nomen nudum).

FAO Names: Common prawn (En), Bouquet (commun) (Fr), Camarón común (Sp).

Local Names: Gruntvannsreke (Norway), Sägegarnele (Germany), Common prawn (British Isles), Bouquet, Crevette rose (Paris markets, France), Salicoque (Normandy, France), Chevrette (Brittany, France), Santé (Gironde, France), Cambon (Languedoc, France), Ligubam (Nice, France), Gambaru russu (Monaco), Camarão (Portugal), Camarón (Spain, official name), Quisquilla (Spain), Gambero sega, Gambero delle rocce, Palemone, Gamberetto (Italy; Palombi & Santarelli, 1961:362, give a large number of local Italian names for this species), Gamblu (Malta), Kozica obična (Jugoslavia) Garidáki (Greece), Teke (Turkey), Qapzan (Israel), Gembri (Tunis).

Distribution: Eastern Atlantic: from Denmark to Rio de Oro, West Africa; Mediterranean; Black Sea.

Habitat: Shallow water (0 to 40 m). Marine.

Size: Maximum total length 110 mm.

Interest to Fishery: Cole (1956:202) stated that although the landings of the present species in Great Britain "are very small in comparison with those of shrimps [*Crangon crangon*], the very high prices realized demonstrate that the market is largely unsatisfied" and the prawns "vie with Pyefleet (Colchester) oysters for the title of the highest priced British marine product". "Substantial landings are made at various points between Bognor and Plymouth". In 1966 the English Channel coast yielded less than 10 t of this species, but at the French Atlantic coast the fishery was far more important, the catch being 700 t (Longhurst, 1970:265). Also in Spain (especially in Galicia) and Portugal the species is fished for and sold on the markets. Brian (1942:33) reported it from the markets of Genoa (both as food and bait) and also elsewhere in Italy the species is caught and greatly esteemed. Gruvel (1923:83,84) described the fishery of this species on the Atlantic coast of Morocco and its sale on the markets of Casablanca and Rabat. Gruvel (1926:64; 1926a:36) indicated the present species among the edible prawns of Algeria and Tunisia respectively. In England and France laboratory experiments have been carried out for aquaculture of this prawn (see Reeve, 1969:1 067-1 073; Forster & Wickins, 1972:7,8; Ling & Costello, 1976).

Palaemon serrifer (Stimpson, 1860)   PALAEM Palaem 14

Leander serrifer Stimpson, 1860, Proc.Acad.Nat.Sci.Phila., 1860:41

Synonymy: *Leander fagei* Yu, 1930; *Leander serrifer longidactylus* Yu, 1930.

FAO Names: Carpenter prawn (En), Bouquet charpentier (Fr), Camarón carpintero (Sp).

Literature: Kubo, 1942:33, Figures.

Distribution: Indo-West Pacific: Birma; Malay Archipelago; S. Siberia; China; Japan.

Habitat: Marine.

Size: Maximum total length 36 mm.

Interest to Fishery: Liu (1955:52) listed this species among the economically important prawns of N. China, Yoshida (1941:26) did the same for Korea. Balss (1914:57) reported upon material obtained at the fishmarket in Tokio. Yasuda (1957:196) indicated that in Japan the species is fished for bait.

Palaemon xiphias Risso, 1816   PALAEM Palaem 15

Palaemon xiphias Risso, 1816, Hist.Nat.Crust.Nice, 102

Synonymy: *Palemon trisetaceus* Risso, 1816; *Palemon crenulatus* Risso, 1827; *Leander xiphias* - Ortmann, 1890; *Palemon sogiontii* Monod, 1931 (nomen nudum).

FAO Names: Posidonia prawn (En), Bouquet posidonie (Fr), Camarón posidonia (Sp).

Literature: Pesta, 1918:121, Fig. 40.

Distribution: Eastern Atlantic: Mediterranean; Canary Islands.

Habitat: Shallow water. Marine.

Size: Maximum total length 65 mm.

Interest to Fishery: Listed by Longhurst (1970:267) as of economic importance in the Mediterranean. Heldt & Heldt (1954:12) ranged the species among the edible Crustacea of Tunisia.

Palaemonetes kadiakensis M.J. Rathbun, 1902   PALAEM Palaemo 1

Palaemonetes kadiakensis M.J. Rathbun, 1902, Proc.U.S.Natl.Mus., 24:903

FAO Names: Mississippi grass shrimp (En), Bouquet mississippi (Fr), Camarón del Mississippi (Sp).

Local Names: Grass shrimp (U.S.A.).

Literature: Holthuis, 1952:212, Pl. 51, Fig. k-n, Pl. 52, Fig. a,b.

Distribution: Western Atlantic: S. Canada and U.S.A. between the Appalachians and the Rocky Mountains; N.E. Mexico.

Habitat: Fresh water.

Size: Maximum total length 53 mm.

Interest to Fishery: Minor. The species is used as bait and as fish food. Forbes (1876:5) stated that it is taken in great numbers at Pekin, Illinois, U.S.A. R. Rathbum (1884:819), who did not distinguish between the present and the next species, listed them among the economic crustaceans of the U.S.A. Creaser (1932:334) suggested its value as fish food, especially in trout hatcheries.

Palaemonetes paludosus (Gibbes, 1850)	PALAEM Palaemo 2

Hippolyte paludosa Gibbes, 1850, <u>Proc.Am.Assoc.Adv.Sci.</u>, 3:197

Synonymy: *Hippolyte caroliniana* Gibbes, 1848 (nomen nudum); *Palaemonetes exilipes* Stimpson, 1871; *Palaemonopsis exilipes* - Stimpson, 1871; *Hippolysmata paludosa* - Howard, 1883; *Palaemon (Palaemonetes) exilipes* - Thallwitz, 1892; *Palaemon (Palaemonetes) paludosa* - Thallwitz, 1892.

FAO Names: Eastern grass shrimp (En), Bouquet oriental des herbiers (Fr), Camarón yerbero (Sp).

Local Names: Grass shrimp (U.S.A.).

Literature: Holthuis, 1952:207, Pl. 51, Figs. e-j.

Distribution: Western Atlantic: eastern part of U.S.A. east of the Appalachians, New Jersey to Florida.

Habitat: Fresh water.

Size: Maximum total length 46 mm.

Interest to Fishery: Minor; like the previous species the present is mostly used as bait and fish food. R. Rathbun (1884:819) who treated both this and the previous species under the name *Palaemonetes exilipes*, included this among the economic crustaceans of the U.S.A., although he was "not aware of its ever having been used as food". Worth (1908:853) reported that the species is used as bait in the hook and line fishery: several shrimps being pur on one hook. He also described how large quantities of this species have been shipped from North Carolina to other localities in the U.S.A. in order to improve the food situation for fishes in those areas.

Palaemonetes sinensis (Sollaud, 1911)	PALAEM Palaemo 3

Allocaris sinensis Sollaud, 1911, <u>Bull.Mus.Hist.Nat.Paris</u>, 17:50

Synonymy: *Palaemonetes chankensis* Buldovsky, 1933; *Palaemonetes venephicus* Birstein & Vinogradov, 1934.

FAO Names: Chinese grass shrimp (En), Bouquet chinois des herbiers (Fr), Camarón yerbero chino (Sp).

Literature: Holthuis, 1950:91, Figs. 20,21.

Distribution: Indo-West Pacific: S.E. Siberia; China.

Habitat: Fresh water.

Size: Maximum total length 46 mm.

Interest to fishery: Liu (1955:55) listed this species among the commercially important shrimps and prawns of N. China, while Ping (1931:183) mentioned from the region of Nanking a species of shrimp "of economic importance" which he named "*Palaemon sinensis* (Solland)" and with which evidently the present species and not *Palaemon sinensis* Heller (= *Macrobrachium nipponense*) is meant.

Palaemonetes tonkinensis (Sollaud, 1914) | PALAEM Palaemo 4

Coutierella tonkinensis Sollaud, 1914, <u>Bull.Soc.Zool.Fr.</u>, 39:318

FAO Names: Tonkin grass shrimp (En), Bouquet tonkinois (Fr), Camarón tonkinés (Sp).

Local Names: Con tôm giong (Tonkin, Viet Nam).

Distribution: Indo-West Pacific: Viet Nam.

Habitat: Fresh water.

Size: Maximum total length 33 mm.

Interest to Fishery: In the original description of this species Solland (1914:314) stated that the species belongs to the "formes les plus communément pêchées dans le delta du fleuve Rouge". It is used for the preparation of a native pasty dish "mam tôm".

Palaemonetes varians (Leach, 1814) | PALAEM Palaemo 5

Palaemon varians Leach, 1814, <u>In</u> Brewster, Edinburgh Encycl., 7:401

Synonymy: *? Astacus albescens* Pennant, 1812; *Palaemon variabilis* Bouchard-Chantereaux, 1829; *Leander varians* - Czerniavsky, 1884; *Palaemonetes varians microgenitor* Boas, 1889; *Palaemonetes varians occidentalis* Sollaud, 1923.

FAO Names: Atlantic ditch shrimp (En), Bouquet atlantique des canaux (Fr), Camarón de acequia del Atlántico (Sp).

Local Names: Steurkrab (Netherlands), Prawn (British Isles).

Literature: Sollaud, 1938:637.

Distribution: Eastern Atlantic: W. Baltic and North Sea to the Atlantic coast of Morocco; Mediterranean coast of N.W. Africa.

Habitat: Brackish water.

Size: Maximum total length 50 mm.

Interest to Fishery: Used as bait for line and hook fishing in the Netherlands. Leach (1816: Pl 43) indicated that the species "is very common on the Devonshire, Glamorgan and Norfolk coasts, where it is taken as an article of food". Leach queried the identity of this species with *Astacus squilla* sensu Pennant 1777 (= *Astacus albescens* Pennant, 1812), the "White Shrimp", of which Pennant (1777:19; 1812:25) stated that it "inhabits the coast of <u>Kent</u>; it is sold in <u>London</u> under the name of <u>the white shrimp</u>, as it assumes that color when boiled".

Remarks: White (1857:135) used the name "White Shrimp" for *Palaemon elegans* a species indicated by him as *Palaemon squilla*, but he added "Other species besides this are named "White Shrimp"". It will be difficult, if not impossible, therefore, to identify *Astacus albescens* Pennant, 1812; this name is older than any of the names (with the exception of *Astacus serratus* Pennant, 1777) that at present are used for British Palaemonidae, and thus forms a potential nomenclatural danger.

Palaemonetes vulgaris (Say, 1818) | PALAEM Palaemo 6

Palaemon vulgaris Say, 1818, <u>J.Acad.Nat.Sci.Phila.</u>, 2:248

Synonymy: *Palaemonopsis vulgaris* - Stimpson, 1871; *Palaemonetes carolinus* Stimpson, 1871; *Palaemonopsis carolinus* - Stimpson, 1871; *Palaemon (Leander) vulgaris* - Von Martens, 1872; *Palaemon (Palaemonetes) carolinus* - Thallwitz, 1892.

FAO Names: Marsh shrimp (En), Bouquet des marais (Fr), Camarón de fangal (Sp).

Local Names: Grass shrimp, Common grass shrimp, Common American prawn (U.S.A.).

Literature: Holthuis, 1952:231, Pl. 54, Figs. f-1.

Distribution: Western Atlantic: New Brunswick, Canada to Texas, U.S.A.

Habitat: Salt or brackish water.

Size: Maximum total length 30 mm (♂), 42 mm (♀).

Interest to Fishery: R. Rathbun (1884:818) listed the present species among the economic crustaceans of the U.S.A., but stated that it "doest not rank among our food invertebrates on account of its small size". Fowler (1912:327) reported it to be used as bait for fishing in New Jersey. U.S. Bureau of Commercial Fisheries (1958:8) listed both *Palaemonetes vulgaris* and *P. carolinus* as being caught for bait shrimp in New York and New Jersey. It is possible that with the latter name *P. pugio* Holthuis, 1949, the "Dagger shrimp" was meant.

SUPERFAMILY ALPHEOIDEA Rafinesque, 1815

Alpheoida Holthuis, 1955, Zool.Verh.Leiden, 26:81

This superfamily contains four families, all of which are represented in this list, but none of the species is of great commercial importance.

FAMILY ALPHEIDAE Rafinesque, 1815

Alphidia Rafinesque, 1815, Analyse de la Nature, 98

This family has a great number of genera and species, but only very few of these are of commercial importance and even then their value is quite minor.

Alpheus bisincisus De Haan, 1844   ALPH Alph 1

Alpheus bis-incisus De Haan, 1844, In Von Siebold, Fauna Japonica, Crustacea (6/7):Pl.45, Fig. 3

Synonymy: *Crangon bis-incisus* - Urita, 1921.

FAO Names: Flathead snapping shrimp (En), Cardon nez camus (Fr), Camarón chato (Sp).

Literature: Banner & Banner, 1966:125, Fig. 46.

Distribution: Indo-West Pacific: South and East Africa to Japan, Indonesia, and New Caledonia.

Habitat: Depth 1 to at least 70 m. Marine.

Size: Total length 21 to 32 mm; carapace length 10 mm.

Interest to Fishery: Minor. Tiwari (1963:304) mentioned a specimen purchased on the market of Nha-Trang, Viet Nam.

| *Alpheus brevicristatus* De Haan, 1844 | ALPH Alph 2 |

Alpheus brevicristatus De Haan, 1844, In Von Siebold, Fauna Japonica, Crustacea (6/7):Pl. 45, Fig. 1

Synonymy: *Alpheus kingsleyi* Miers, 1879; *Crangon brevicristatus* - Maki & Tsuchiya, 1923.

FAO Names: Teppo snapping shrimp (En), Cardon teppo (Fr), Camarón tepo (Sp).

Local Names: Teppo ebi (Japan).

Distribution: Indo-West Pacific: S.E. Siberia; China; Japan; Taiwan.

Habitat: Depth 8 to 10 m. Marine.

Size: Maximum total length 100 mm.

Interest to Fishery: Liu (1955:30) listed this species among the economic prawns and shrimps of North China. Harada (1968:82) reported that it is fished for by commercial fishermen in the Lake Naka-umi area, Honshu, Japan.

| *Alpheus digitalis* De Haan, 1844 | ALPH Alph 3 |

Alpheus digitalis De Haan, 1844, In Von Siebold, Fauna Japonica, Crustacea (6/7):Pl. 45, Fig. 4

Synonymy: *Alpheus distinguendus* De Man, 1909; *Crangon (Alpheus) distinguendus* - Gee, 1925.

FAO Names: Forceps snapping shrimp (En), Cardon tenaille (Fr), Camarón tenaza (Sp).

Literature: De Man, 1909:155, Pl. 7, Figs. 9-14 (as *A. distinguendus*).

Distribution: Indo-West Pacific: Japan; China; Mergui Archipelago; Australia.

Habitat: Depth 1 to 10 m. Marine.

Size: Maximum total length 74 mm.

Interest to Fishery: The species is listed by Liu (1955:29) among the shrimps and prawns of economic importance in N. China. Banner & Smalley (1969:43) indicated that in parts of Moreton Bay, Queensland, this species, together with *Alpheus stephensoni* Banner & Smalley, occurs "in the prawn trawls during summer nights .... Occasionally, a night's effort will catch over 100 lbs of large snapping shrimp, though usually they are thrown back with the trash".

| *Alpheus euphrosyne* De Man, 1897 | ALPH Alph 4 |

Alpheus euphrosyne De Man, 1897, Zool.Jahrb.(Syst.Geogr.Biol.Thiere), 9:745

Synonymy: *Crangon euphrosyne* - Suvatti, 1937.

FAO Names: Nymph snapping shrimp (En), Cardon nymphe (Fr), Camarón palomilla (Sp).

Literature: De Man, 1899:317, Pl. 4, Fig. 2; De Man, 1911a:413.

Distribution: Indo-West Pacific: Bangladesh; Thailand; Indonesia.

Habitat: Probably estuarine.

Size: Maximum total length 58 mm.

Interest to Fishery: Listed by Ahmad (1957:16) among the prawns that are fished for in Bangladesh.

Alpheus glaber (Olivi, 1792) | ALPH Alph 5 |

Cancer glaber Olivi, 1792, Zool.Adriat., 51

Synonymy: *Cryptophthalmus ruber* Rafinesque, 1814;   *Autonomaea olivii* Risso, 1816;   *Astacus (Autonomea) olivii* - Voigt, 1836,   *Alpheus ruber* - H. Milne Edwards, 1837;   *Phleusa cynea* Nardo, 1847;   *Crangon ruber* - Johnson, Everest & Young, 1947.

FAO Names: Red snapping shrimp (En), Cardon rouge (Fr), Camarón carneo (Sp).

Literature: Zariquiey Alvarez, 1968:147, Fig. 59b.

Distribution: Eastern Atlantic: Atlantic coast of Europe from Great Britain south; Mediterranean; Sea of Marmara.

Habitat: Depth 35 to 100 m.   Bottom mud.   Marine.

Size: Maximum total length 43 mm (♂).

Interest to Fishery: Paolucci (1909:248) when dealing with this species from the Adriatic Sea near Ancona, Italy, stated "Qualche volta ne viene raccolta poca quantità e venduta al mercato, ma non è molto buono a mangiarsi".   As stated by Zariquiey Alvarez (1968:148) on the northeastern coast of Spain the species is often caught by trawlers ("cogido frecuentemente por las barcas de arrastre") and so reaches the fish markets;   however, it generally is considered trash or sold as an admixture to other species.

Alpheus gracilipes Stimpson, 1860 | ALPH Alph 6 |

Alpheus gracilipes Stimpson, 1860, Proc.Acad.Nat.Sci.Phila., 1860:31

Synonymy: *Crangon gracilipes* - Edmondson, 1925.

FAO Names: Daisy snapping shrimp (En), Cardon marguerite (Fr), Camarón margarita (Sp).

Local Names: Ashiboso teppo ebi (Japan).

Literature: Miya, 1974:154, Pl. 30.

Distribution: Indo-West Pacific: East Africa and Jibuti to Japan, Hawaii and Polynesia.

Habitat: Depth intertidal to 3.3. m.   Coral reefs.   Marine.

Interest to Fishery: Minor.   Tiwari (1963:298) mentioned a specimen purchased at the market of Nha-trang, Viet Nam.

Alpheus heterochaelis Say, 1818 | ALPH Alph 7 |

Alpheus heterochaelis Say 1818, J.Acad.Nat.Sci.Phila., 2:243

Synonymy: *Halopsyche lutaria* De Saussure, 1857;   *Alpheus lutarius* - De Saussure, 1858;   *Crangon heterochaelis* Hay & Shore, 1918.

FAO Names: Bigclaw snapping shrimp (En), Cardon grandes pinces (Fr), Camarón tamarú (Sp).

Local Names: Big-clawed snapping shrimp (U.S.A.), Tamarú (Pernambuco, Brazil).

Literature: Williams, 1965:66, Fig. 54; Chace, 1972:67.

Distribution: Western Atlantic: Bermuda; North Carolina, U.S.A. to S. Brazil; West Indies. Not all records are trustworthy; according to Chace, 1972, the certain records of the species are in the area from North Carolina to Texas, U.S.A., Cuba, Curaçao and Surinam.

Habitat: Depth 0 to 30 m. Muddy estuarine areas.

Size: Maximum total length 40 mm (δ), 50 mm ($\female$).

Interest to Fishery: In N.E. Brazil the species is of secondary commercial importance, it is usually caught to be used as bait for fishing (P.A. Coelho & M. de Araújo Ramos, in Litt.).

Alpheus hoplocheles Coutière, 1897	ALPH Alph 8

Alpheus hoplocheles Coutière, 1897, Notes Leyden Mus., 19:197

Synonymy: *Crangon (Alpheus) hoplocheles* - Gee, 1925.

FAO Names: Armed snapping shrimp (En), Cardon épineux (Fr), Camarón armado (Sp).

Distribution: Indo-West Pacific: China, possibly also Japan and Indonesia.

Habitat: Marine.

Size: Total length 35 mm.

Interest to Fishery: Liu (1955:32) listed the species in his enumeration of economic shrimps and prawns of N. China.

Alpheus japonicus Miers, 1879	ALPH Alph 9

Alpheus japonicus Miers, 1879, Proc.Zool.Soc.Lond., 1879:53

Synonymy: *Alpheus longimanus* Bate, 1888; *Crangon japonica* Yu, 1935.

FAO Names: Japanese snapping shrimp (En), Cardon japonais (Fr), Camarón chasqueador (Sp).

Local Names: Tenagateppô ebi (Japan).

Distribution: Indo-West Pacific: S.E. Siberia; China; Japan.

Habitat: Depth 5 to 90 m. Marine.

Size: Maximum total length 46 mm.

Interest to Fishery: Listed by Liu (1955:31) among the economic prawns and shrimps of N. China.

Alpheus spongiarum Coutière, 1897	ALPH Alph 10

Alpheus spongiarum Coutière, 1897, Bull.Mus.Hist.Nat., Paris, 3:236

Synonymy: *Alpheus crinitus spongiarum* - Coutière, 1898; *Alpheus paraculeipes* Coutière, 1905.

FAO Names: Bristle snapping shrimp (En), Cardon brosse (Fr), Camarón cepillo (Sp).

Local Names: Kaimen teppo ebi (Japan).

Literature: Miya, 1974:148, Pl. 28.

Distribution: Indo-West Pacific: western Indian Ocean to Japan, Indonesia and Australia.

Habitat: Depth 0 to 113 m. Associated with sponges. Marine.

Size: Total length 8.6 to 20.6 mm; carapace length 3 to 7.5 mm.

Interest to Fishery: Tiwari (1963:293, under *Alpheus paraculeipes*) mentioned a specimen purchased at the market of Nha-trang, Viet Nam.

Alpheus stephensoni Banner & Smalley, 1969	ALPH Alph 11

Alpheus stephensoni Banner & Smalley, 1969, Proc.R.Soc.Queensl., 81(3):43

FAO Names: Queensland snapping shrimp (En), Cardon australien (Fr), Camarón australiano (Sp).

Distribution: Indo-West Pacific: Moreton Bay, Queensland, Australia.

Habitat: Depth 9 to 18 m. Bottom mud or sandy mud. Marine.

Size: Maximum total length 70 mm.

Interest to Fishery: The species, together with *A. digitalis* "consistently occurs in the prawn trawls during summer nights in parts of Moreton Bay. Occasionally, a night's effort will catch over 100 lbs of large snapping shrimp, though usually they are thrown back with the trash" (Banner & Smalley, 1969:43).

Alpheus sublucanus (Forskål, 1775)	ALPH Alph 12

Cancer sublucanus Forskål, 1775, Descriptiones Animalium, 94

Synonymy: *Cancer (Astacus) sublucanus* - Herbst, 1793; *Alpheus lottini* Guérin, 1829; *Alpheus ventrosus* H. Milne Edwards, 1837; *Alpheus laevis* Randall, 1840; *Alpheus rouxii* Guérin, 1857; *Alpheoides laevis* - Paulson, 1875; *Crangon laevis* - Urita, 1921; *Crangon ventrosus* - Edmondson, 1923; *Crangon latipes* Banner, 1953.

FAO Names: Coral snapping shrimp (En), Cardon coraille (Fr), Camarón de coral (Sp).

Literature: Banner & Banner, 1966:91, Fig. 31 (as *A. lottini*).

Distribution: Indo-West Pacific: Red Sea and East Africa to Japan, Australia and Polynesia. Eastern Pacific: Clipperton Island; Gulf of California; Bay of Panama; Galapagos Islands; Easter Island.

Habitat: Depth 1 to 36 m. Living in association with madrepore corals. Marine

Size: Maximum total length 42 mm.

Interest to Fishery: Tiwari (1963:286) reported material of this species as offered for sale at the market of Nha-trang, Viet Nam.

Remarks: Until recently *Cancer sublucanus* Forskål has been considered an unidentifiable species. The original description, being based on Forskål's field notes, is mainly concerned with colour; and in preserved specimens all colour disappears, so that Museum specialists were at a loss as how to interpret Forskål's (1775) description. During two stays with an Israel Expedition in the Red Sea (1962, 1965), special attention was given by me to the possibility of recognizing Forskål's crustacean species with the help of living material. Comparing living specimens of the present species with Forskål's description made it perfectly clear that he had this *Alpheus* before him. The striking colour pattern ("incarnatus, dorso nigro") showed this, while also the morphological characters mentioned by Forskål fit the species. As there was no uniformity in the use of a specific name for the present Alpheid (until about 1910 the name *Alpheus laevis* was mostly used, then, under the influence of H. Coutière, the name *Alpheus ventrosus* took over; although Stebbing, 1915, pointed out that the name *Alpheus lottini* has priority over *A. ventrosus*, it was only after 1950 that this name became accepted) it seems best to keep here strictly to priority.

FAMILY OGYRIDIDAE Hay & Shore, 1918

Ogyridae Hay & Shore, 1918, Bull.U.S.Bur.Fish., 35:388

The family contains only one genus, a single species of which has been reported to be of commercial importance.

Ogyrides orientalis (Stimpson, 1860)   OGY Ogy 1

Ogyris orientalis Stimpson, 1860, Proc.Acad.Nat.Sci.Phila., 1860:36

Synonymy: *Ogyris sibogae* De Man, 1911; *Ogyrides sibogae* - De Man, 1922.

FAO Names: Telescope shrimp (En), Crevuche télescope (Fr), Camarón telescopio (Sp).

Literature: Fujino & Miyake, 1970:255, Fig. 6.

Distribution: Indo-West Pacific: India; Indonesia; Philippines; China; Japan.

Habitat: Depth 9 to 535 m. Bottom sand. Marine.

Size: Maximum total length 18 mm; maximum carapace length up to 5.7 mm.

Interest to Fishery: The species is listed by Liu (1955:34) among the economic prawns and shrimps of N. China.

FAMILY HIPPOLYTIDAE Bate, 1888

Hippolytidae Bate, 1888, Rep.Voyage Challenger, (Zool.), 24:xii,xli,480,503,574,576

Although seven genera of this family are enumerated here as of commercial importance, this importance in all cases is of a minor nature, and hardly any hippolytid is fished on a large scale. The specimens usually are either too small or too scarce to be of economic interest.

Eualus leptognathus (Stimpson, 1860)   HIPPOL Eual 1

Hippolyte leptognatha Stimpson, 1860, Proc.Acad.Nat.Sci.Phila., 1860:34

Synonymy: *Spirontocaris leptognatha* - Balss, 1914; *Spirontocaris japonica* Yokoya, 1930; *Eualus japonica* - Derjugin & Kobjakova, 1935.

FAO Names: Yamato shrimp (En), Bouc yamato (Fr), Camarón yamato (Sp).

Local Names: Yamato mo ebi (Japan).

Literature: Hayashi & Miyake, 1968:128, Fig. 3.

Distribution: Indo-West Pacific: S.E. Siberia; China; Japan.

Habitat: Shallow water. Marine.

Size: Maximum total length about 25 mm.

Interest to Fishery: The species is listed by Liu (1955:41) among the economic shrimps and prawns of N. China.

Eualus macilentus (Kröyer, 1841)	HIPPOL Eual 2

Hippolyte macilenta Kröyer, 1841, Naturhist.Tidsskr., 3:574

Synonymy: *Spirontocaris macilenta* - M.J. Rathbun, 1904; *Spirontocarella macilenta* - Brashnikov, 1907.

FAO Names: Greenland shrimp (En), Bouc groenland (Fr), Camarón de Groenlandia (Sp).

Distribution: Northwestern Atlantic: West Greenland to Nova Scotia (Canada). Northern Pacific: Bering Sea to Okhotsk Sea.

Habitat: Depth 27 to 540 m. Marine.

Size: Total length 21 to 68 mm; maximum carapace length 16 mm.

Interest to Fishery: Potential. Couture (1971:31) stated that this species, notwithstanding its small size, in the province of Québec, Canada, is "an important potential resource".

Eualus sinensis (Yu, 1931)	HIPPOL Eual 3

Spirontocaris sinensis Yu, 1931, Bull.Mus.Hist.Nat., Paris, (2)3:514

FAO Names: Iso shrimp (En), Bouc iso (Fr), Camarón iso (Sp).

Local Names: Iso mo ebi (Japan).

Literature: Hayashi & Miyake, 1968:125, Fig. 2.

Distribution: Indo-West Pacific: China; Japan.

Habitat: Littoral zone. Marine.

Size: Maximum total length 12 mm ($\male$), 22 mm ($\female$).

Interest to Fishery: The species is listed by Liu (1955:40) among the economic shrimps and prawns of N. China.

| *Exhippolysmata ensirostris* (Kemp, 1914) | HIPPOL Exhip 2 |

Hippolysmata ensirostris Kemp, 1914, <u>Rec.Indian Mus.</u>, 10:118

FAO Names: Hunter shrimp (En), Bouc chasseur (Fr), Camarón cazador (Sp).

Distribution: Indo-West Pacific: West coast of India to the Malay Archipelago.

Habitat: Shallow water. Marine.

Size: Maximum total length 79 mm.

Interest to Fishery: Longhurst (1970:281) stated that along the N.W. coast of India the present species, together with *Nematopalaemon tenuipes* is the dominant caridean species in the trawl catches; the two species are caught in enormous numbers. In Kutch, India, the species is occasionally present in commercial prawn catches (Ramamurthy, 1967:1426). Kagwade (1967:1379) remarked that in the Bombay area it is less common in the offshore catches, and more common in the inshore waters. Kunju (1967: 1 382) stated that in the commercial prawn catches of the Maharashtra coast of India (west coast) "more than half the total catch is made up of small shrimps such as *Palaemon tenuipes, Hippolysmata ensirostris* and *Acetes indicus*". Jones (1967:1 337) mentioned it among the fishery resources of the Gangetic Delta and other parts of India.

| *Exhippolysmata hastatoides* (Balss, 1914) | HIPPOL Exhip 3 |

Mimocaris hastatoides Balss, 1914, <u>Zool.Anz.</u>, 44:596

Synonymy: *Hippolysmata hastatoides* - Holthuis, 1947.

FAO Names: Companion shrimp (En), Bouc compagnon(Fr), Camarón compañero (Sp).

Literature: Balss, 1925:289, text-figs. 68-74, Pl. 28; De Man, 1925:29, Fig. 5.

Distribution: Eastern Atlantic: West Africa from Sierra Leone to N. Angola.

Habitat: Depth 1 to 15 m. Bottom sand and mud. Estuarine.

Size: Maximum total length 73 mm.

Interest to Fishery: Longhurst (1970:278) indicated this species as of importance at least in Nigeria where *Nematopalaemon hastatus* and it were estimated to produce some hundreds of tons annually from beach seine catches alone.

| *Exhippolysmata oplophoroides* (Holthuis, 1948) | HIPPOL Exhip 1 |

Hippolysmata (Exhippolysmata) oplophoroides Holthuis, 1948, <u>Proc.K.Ned.Akad.Wet.</u>, 51:1 106

FAO Names: Cock shrimp (En), Crevette buhotte (Fr), Camarón gallo (Sp).

Local Names: Cock shrimp (Guyana), Kaka, Tranga bakka (Surinam), Camarão espinho (Brazil), Camarão vermelho (N.E. Brazil), Camarão ovado (S.E. Brazil).

Distribution: Western Atlantic: North Carolina, U.S.A. to Santa Catarina, Brazil.

Habitat: Depth 10 to 45 m. Bottom mud, or muddy sand. Marine and estuarine.

Size: Maximum total length 79 mm.

Interest to Fishery: With inshore fishing in the Guiana's quantities of *Nematopalaemon schmitti* and *Exhippolysmata oplophoroides* are taken. Until 1959 this was the only production of shrimp in (British) Guyana (Lindner, 1957:21; Longhurst, 1970:296). In Surinam also, the two species are taken together: *Nematopalaemon* always in far larger numbers than *Exhippolysmata*, the percentage of the latter is negligible (Holthuis, 1959:115). In N.E. Brazil the species is of considerable commercial importance; it is eaten directly or used in local dishes (P.A. Coelho & M. de Araújo Ramos, in Litt.); Fausto Filho (1968:27) on the other hand listed the species from the same area as being of insignificant commercial value. This species was observed in small numbers in the landings made at Santos and Santa Catarina State (S.E. Brazil). FAO (1964:9).

Remarks: It is interesting that all three species of *Exhippolysmata* cited here, although occurring in three different zoogeographical regions, as well as on three different continents, are always found as admixtures with catches of *Nematopalaemon*.

| *Heptacarpus brevirostris* (Dana, 1852) | HIPPOL Hept 1 |

Hippolyte brevirostris Dana, 1852, Proc.Acad.Nat.Sci.Phila., 6:24

Synonymy: *Spirontocaris brevirostris* - Walker, 1898.

FAO Names: Shortspine shrimp (En), Bouc tiépines (Fr), Camarón espinilla (Sp).

Local Names: Short spine shrimp (U.S.A,),

Literature: Schmitt, 1921:66, Fig. 44.

Distribution: Eastern Pacific: Aleutian Islands to California.

Habitat: Depth 0 to 45 m. Marine.

Size: Maximum total length 49 mm.

Interest to Fishery: R. Rathbun (1884:818) stated that "in San Francisco Bay it is taken with the *Crangons* for food"

| *Heptacarpus futilirostris* (Bate, 1888) | HIPPOL Hept 2 |

Nauticaris futilirostris Bate, 1888, Rep.Voyage Challenger, (Zool.), 24:606

Synonymy: This species has often been confused with *H. rectirostris* (Stimpson), but Miyake & Hayashi (1968:437) straightened the taxonomic position and the synonymy of the two species out in an admirable precise way.

FAO Names: Toy shrimp (En), Bouc caprice (Fr), Camarón capricho (Sp).

Local Names: Ashinaga mo ebi modoki (Japan).

Literature: Miyake & Hayashi, 1968:437, Figs. 3,4,6,7e,f; Hayashi & Miyake, 1968:139, Fig. 9.

Distribution: Indo-West Pacific: China; Japan.

Habitat: Depth 0 to 20 m. Marine.

Size: Maximum total length 35 mm ($\male$), 30 mm ($\female$).

Interest to Fishery: Liu (1955:36) listed this species (as *Heptacarpus rectirostris*) among the economic shrimps and prawns of N. China.

Heptacarpus geniculatus (Stimpson, 1860)   HIPPOL Hept 3

Hippolyte geniculata Stimpson, 1860, Proc.Acad.Nat.Sci.Phila., 1860:34

Synonymy: *Spirontocaris geniculata* - M.J. Rathbun, 1902; *Spirontocaris alcimede* De Man, 1906.

FAO Names: Flexed shrimp (En), Bouc courbe (Fr), Camarón corva (Sp).

Local Names: Koshimagari mo ebi, Kosimagari ebi, Kusakosi ebi (Japan).

Literature: Hayashi & Miyake, 1968:132, Fig. 5.

Distribution: Indo-West Pacific: China; Japan.

Habitat: Shallow water to 20 m deep. Marine.

Size: Maximum total length 51 mm.

Interest to Fishery: The species is listed by Liu (1955:38) among the economic shrimps and prawns of N. China.

Heptacarpus pandaloides (Stimpson, 1860)   HIPPOL Hept 4

Hippolyte pandaloides Stimpson, 1860, Proc.Acad.Nat.Sci.Phila., 1860:34

Synonymy: *Spirontocaris propugnatrix* De Man, 1906; *Spirontocaris pandaloides* - De Man, 1907; *Heptacarpus propugnatrix* - Miyake, 1961.

FAO Names: Tsuno shrimp (En), Bouc suno (Fr), Camarón suno (Sp).

Local Names: Tsuno mo ebi (Japan).

Literature: Hayashi & Miyake, 1968:136, Fig. 7.

Distribution: Indo-West Pacific: China; Japan.

Habitat: Shallow water, 0 to 30 m deep. Marine.

Size: Maximum total length 52 mm.

Interest to Fishery: This species is listed by Liu (1955:37) among the economic prawns and shrimps of N. China. Parisi (1919:74) mentioned specimens obtained at the market of Yokohama.

Latreutes acicularis Ortmann, 1890   HIPPOL Latr 1

Latreutes acicularis Ortmann, 1890, Zool.Jahrb.(Syst.Geogr.Biol.Thiere), 5:506

FAO Names: Hoso shrimp (En), Bouc oso (Fr), Camarón oso (Sp).

Local Names: Hoso mo ebi (Japan).

Literature: Hayashi & Miyake, 1968:144, Fig. 11.

Distribution: Indo-West Pacific: Japan.

Habitat: Shallow water. Marine.

Size: Maximum total length 18 mm (♂), 31 mm (♀).

Interest to Fishery: Yasuda (1957:196) mentioned that in Japan this species is used as bait for fishing.

| *Latreutes anoplonyx* Kemp, 1914 | HIPPOL Latr 2 |

Latreutes anoplonyx Kemp, 1914, <u>Rec.Indian Mus.</u>, 10:104

FAO Names: Medusa shrimp (En), Bouc méduse (Fr), Camarón medusa (Sp).

Local Names: Kurage mo ebi (Japan).

Literature: Hayashi & Miyake, 1968:149, Fig. 13.

Distribution: Indo-West Pacific: India; Burma; Indonesia; China; Japan.

Habitat: Depth 0 to 15 m. Often associated with medusae. Marine.

Size: Maximum total length 39 mm.

Interest to Fishery: Listed by Liu (1955:42) among the economic shrimps and prawns of N. China.

| *Latreutes laminirostris* Ortmann, 1890 | HIPPOL Latr 3 |

Latreutes laminirostris Ortmann, 1890, <u>Zool.Jahrb.(Syst.Geogr.Biol.Thiere)</u>,5:506

FAO Names: Platenose shrimp (En), Bouc nez lamelleux (Fr), Camarón laminilla (Sp).

Distribution: Indo-West Pacific: China; Japan.

Habitat: Depth 0 to 9 m. Marine.

Size: Maximum total length 53 mm.

Interest to Fishery: The species is mentioned by Liu (1955:45) among the economic shrimps and prawns of N. China.

| *Latreutes planirostris* (De Haan, 1844) | HIPPOL Latr 4 |

Hippolyte planirostris De Haan, 1844, <u>In</u> Von Siebold, Fauna Japonica, Crustacea, (6/7):Pl. 45, Fig. 7

Synonymy: *Lysmata planirostris* - De Haan, 1849; *Cyclorhynchus planirostris* - De Haan, 1849; *Rhynchocyclus planirostris* - Stimpson, 1860; *Latreutes dorsalis* Stimpson, 1860; *Platybema planirostris* - Bate, 1888.

FAO Names: Flatnose shrimp (En), Bouc nez émoussé (Fr), Camarón romo (Sp).

Local Names: Hiratsuno mo ebi (Japan).

Literature: Hayashi & Miyake, 1968:147, Fig. 12.

Distribution: Indo-West Pacific: Kuriles; Japan; China; N.W. Australia.

Habitat: Depth 5 to 110 m. Marine.

Size: Maximum total length 28 mm.

Interest to Fishery: Liu (1955:43) listed this species among the economic shrimps and prawns of N. China.

| *Lysmata californica* (Stimpson, 1866) | HIPPOL Lys 1 |

Hippolysmata californica Stimpson, 1866, Proc.Chicago Acad.Sci., 1:48

Synonymy: *Hippolyte lineata* Lockington, 1877.

FAO Names: Lined shrimp (En), Bouc rayé (Fr), Camarón listado (Sp).

Local Names: Red rock shrimp, Southern transparent shrimp, Striped tide-pool shrimp, Large transparent shrimp (California, U.S.A.).

Literature: Schmitt, 1921:49, Fig. 27; Limbaugh, Pedersen & Chace, 1961:249, Fig. 7.

Distribution: Eastern Pacific: California, U.S.A. to Guadeloupe Island, Mexico.

Habitat: Littoral (tide pools) to about 70 m depth. Marine.

Size: Maximum total length 70 mm.

Interest to Fishery: The species is used exclusively for bait (Turner & Sexsmith, 1964:40) "Nightly trapping along breakwaters and other rocky areas produces a good supply for bait dealers to sell alive and fresh each day".

| *Lysmata seticaudata* (Risso, 1816) | HIPPOL Lys 2 |

Melicerta seticaudata Risso, 1816, Hist.Nat.Crust.Nice, 110

Synonymy: *Aglaope striata* Rafinesque, 1814; *Palaemon cognetii* Risso, 1816; *Alpheus cougneti* - Risso, 1827; *Lysmata aberrans* Czerniavsky, 1884; *Miersia clavigera* Chun, 1888.

FAO Names: Monaco shrimp (En), Bouc monégasse (Fr), Camarón monagués (Sp).

Local Names: Crevette monégasque (France), Gambarǔ monegascu (Monaco), Gamberetto rosso (Italy), Gamblu tas-said (Malta), Creveta rosie (Romania).

Literature: Bacescu, 1967:143, Figs. 5,29,41,74-78.

Distribution: Eastern Atlantic: West coast of Europe from the Channel Islands south; Mediterranean; Black Sea.

Habitat: Depth 4 to 60 m. Marine.

Size: Maximum total length 26 mm (♂), 45 mm (♀).

Interest to Fishery: Brian (1941:41) mentioned that this species is sometimes sold in small quantities at the fish market in Genoa, Italy. Several authors (Stalio, 1877:801; Paolucci, 1909:44); Pesta, 1918:110) indicated that in the Adriatic the species is very good to eat, but because of its scarcity not commercially important (they "stellen aber keine spezielle Marktware vor, wohl ohne Zweifel wegen des vereinzelten Vorkommens", Pesta, 1918). Gruvel (1926a:36) cited the species for Tunisia, but "peu abondante".

<table><tr><td>*Lysmata vittata* (Stimpson, 1860)</td><td>HIPPOL Lys 3</td></tr></table>

Hippolysmata vittata Stimpson, 1860, <u>Proc.Acad.Nat.Sci.Phila.</u>, 1860:30

Synonymy: *Nauticaris unirecedens* Bate, 1888; *Hippolysmata vittata subtilis* Thallwitz, 1891.

FAO Names: Indian lined shrimp (En), Bouc rayé indien (Fr), Camarón rayado indio (Sp).

Local Names: Akashima mo ebi (Japan).

Literature: Hayashi & Miyake, 1968:156, Fig. 17.

Distribution: Indo-West Pacific: Red Sea and S.E. Africa to China, Japan and the Malay Archipelago.

Habitat: Depth 0 to 54 m. Marine.

Size: Maximum total length 43 mm.

Interest to Fishery: Liu (1955:45) included this species among the economic shrimps and prawns of N. China. Holthuis (1947:68) listed some specimens obtained at the fishmarket of Batavia (=Djakarta, Java, Indonesia). Kurian & Sebastian (1967:92) mentioned this species among commercially important prawns of India, but they stated that it was "found only in small numbers". Kunju (1967:1 385) reported it as occurring in the fishery off the Maharashtra coast of India.

<table><tr><td>*Spirontocaris lilljeborgii* (Danielssen, 1859)</td><td>HIPPOL Spir 1</td></tr></table>

Hippolyte lilljeborgii Danielssen, 1859 <u>Nyt Mag.Naturvidensk.</u>, 11:5

Synonymy: *Hippolyte securifrons* Norman, 1862; *Spirontocaris securifrons* - Norman, 1893.

FAO Names: Friendly spine shrimp (En), Bouc épineux (Fr), Camarón saborete espinudo (Sp).

Literature: Kemp, 1910:103, Pl. 14, Figs. 2-10.

Distribution: Northern Atlantic: Arctic Ocean south to British Isles and Massachusetts, U.S.A.

Habitat: Depth 20 to 1 200 m. Marine.

Size: Maximum total length 74 mm.

Interest to Fishery: Longhurst (1970:258) in dealing with the prawn resources of the Northwest Atlantic stated that stocks of this species, *S. spinus* and *Pandalus montagui* "are known to occur, but their potential is not known, and they are only exploited incidentally to the fishery for *Pandalus borealis*". In Norway the species also occurs commonly in the prawn trawls used for catching *Pandalus borealis*, but it (as well as other non-Pandalids) are considered trash "and the catch must be cleansed of this before it is sold" (Hjort & Ruud, 1938:108).

<table><tr><td>*Spirontocaris spinus* (Sowerby, 1805)</td><td>HIPPOL Spir 2</td></tr></table>

Cancer spinus Sowerby, 1805, British Miscellany, 47

Synonymy: *Astacus spinus* - Pennant, 1812; *Alpheus spinus* - Leach, 1814; *Hippolyte sowerbaei* Leach, 1817; *Hippolyte spinus* - White, 1847; *Sowerbyus spinus* - Hoek, 1887.

FAO Names: Parrot shrimp (En), Bouc perroquet (Fr), Camarón loro (Sp).

Literature: Kemp, 1910:103, Pl. 14, Fig. 1.

Distribution: North Atlantic: Arctic Ocean south to the North Sea and Massachusetts, U.S.A. ? North Pacific.

Habitat: Depth 16 to 400 m. Marine

Size: Maximum total length about 60 mm.

Interest to Fishery: Longhurst (1970:258) indicated that in the N.W. Atlantic the present species and *S. lilljeborgii* (see there) are only exploited incidentally to the fishery of *Pandalus borealis*.

FAMILY PROCESSIDAE Ortmann, 1896

Processidae Ortmann, 1896, Zool.Jahrb.(Syst.Geogr.Biol.Thiere), 9:415,424

Processa canaliculata Leach, 1815   PROC Proc 1

Processa canaliculata Leach, 1815, Malacostraca podophthalmata Britanniae, Pl. 41

Synonymy: *Nika couchii* Bell, 1847; *Nika edulis britanica* Czerniavsky, 1884; *Nika mediterranea* Parisi, 1915; *Processa prostatica* Zariquiey Cenarro, 1941; *Processa mediterranea* - Zariquiey Alvarez, 1955.

FAO Names: Processa shrimp (En), Guernade processe (Fr), Camarón procesa (Sp).

Literature: Nouvel & Holthuis, 1957:41, Figs. 205-220 (as *Processa mediterranea*); Al-Adhub & Williamson, 1975:694, Figs. 1c,d,2c,d,4.

Distribution: Eastern Atlantic: British Isles to the Mediterranean (as far east as Aegean Sea).

Habitat: Depth 70 to 600 m. Bottom mud. Marine.

Size: Maximum total length 67 mm (♂), 75 mm (♀).

Interest to Fishery: Brian (1941:42) reported *Processa canaliculata* from the fish market in Genoa, Italy, where it was sold "in quantità discreta". Judging by the size of Brian's specimens (68 to 75 mm) and the depth from which they were taken (120 to 130 m), they indeed belong to the present species. Zariquiey Alvarez (1968:159; under *P. mediterranea*) remarked that the species is "cogida en gran cantidad por las barcas de arrastre de Rosas, Blanes y Barcelona [all three localities on the Mediterranean N.E. coast of Spain], a profundidades de más de 200 metros; se vende en el mercado". As the specimens of this species are larger than those of *P. edulis*, they are more attractive commercially; on the other hand, the species lives far deeper and can be caught in quantity by deep trawling only.

Remarks: This species was treated by Nouvel & Holthuis, 1957, under the name *Processa mediterranea* (Parisi). However, Al-Adhub & Williamson, 1975, who examined the holotype of *Processa canaliculata* Leach, 1815, found that it belongs in the present species, so that the specific name *mediterranea* Parisi, 1915, falls as a junior synonym of *canaliculata* Leach, 1815. The species that Nouvel & Holthuis (1957) had indicated with the name *Processa canaliculata* Leach, 1815, was given the new name *Processa nouveli* by Al-Adhub & Williamson.

Processa edulis (Risso, 1816)	PROC Proc 2

Nika edulis Risso, 1816, <u>Hist.Nat.Crust.Nice</u>, 85

Synonymy: *Nika edulis typica* Czerniavsky, 1884.

FAO Names: Nika shrimp (En), Guernade nica (Fr), Camarón nica (Sp).

Local Names: Saletto (Adriatic Sea, Italy; vid. Pesta, 1918:137), Italienischer Granatkrebs (Germany), Green shrimp (England, see Patterson, 1905:332).

Literature: Nouvel & Holthuis, 1957:10, Figs. 1-27.

Distribution: Eastern Atlantic: British Isles to the Mediterranean. The typical subspecies is restricted to the Mediterranean, in the Atlantic there are two subspecies *P. e. arcassonensis* Nouvel & Holthuis, so far only known from S.W. France and *P. e. crassipes* Nouvel & Holthuis from the rest of the European Atlantic coast.

Habitat: Shallow water (often among <u>Zostera</u> and <u>Posidonia</u>). Marine.

Size: Maximum total length 30 mm (♂), 44 mm (♀).

Interest to Fishery: The specific name *edulis* already shows that the species is eaten. Risso (1816:86) in the original description stated on this account "c'est particulièrement cette espèce qui est employée comme comestible aux environs de Nice, et qu'on vend pendant toute l'année", and (on p. 85) "La chair ... offre, en tout temps un mets savoureux et agréable; et l'on s'en sert comme d'un excellent appât pour prendre les poissons". Pesta (1918:140), under the name *Processa canaliculata*, remarked for the Adriatic area that "Die Form wird auf den Fischmärkten (mit der "Minutaglia") als essbar verkauft". This is confirmed by Giordani Soika (1948:26), who reported that at the fishmarket of Venice *"Processa canaliculata"* was sold between November and January mixed with *Crangon crangon* and *Palaemon adspersus*. As both Pesta and Giordani Soika dealt with shallow water shrimps it is most likely that their material belongs to the present species rather than to the deep sea *Processa canaliculata*. Although *Processa edulis* is the most common Mediterranean shallow water *Processa*, it is possible that older records of it dealt partly (or entirely) with other Mediterranean shallow water forms like *P. acutirostris* Nouvel & Holthuis, *P. robusta* Nouvel & Holthuis, etc., as several of these species have only been distinguished rather recently (see under Remarks below).

Outside the Mediterranean the present species is hardly of commercial importance, although it is occasionally eaten in Great Britain, as shown by Bell's (1847:277) remark that the specimen of "Nika edulis" "from which my figure and the above description are given was accidentally found by myself in a dish of boiled prawns, on which I was about to breakfast, at Bognor, in the year 1842".

Remarks: Until 1936 most zoologists were of the opinion that the genus *Processa* was represented in Eastern Atlantic waters by a single species which was indicated with the name *Processa canaliculata* Leach, 1815, or *Processa* (or *Nika*) *edulis* (Risso, 1816). In 1936 Lebour showed that *P. edulis* and *P. canaliculata* are distinct species, and in 1957 Nouvel & Holthuis recognized no less than eight species of *Processa* in European waters, one represented by three subspecies. In 1975 Al-Adhub & Williamson showed that the species that Nouvel & Holthuis had indicated with the name *Processa mediterranea* (Parisi, 1915) should bear the name *Processa canaliculata* Leach, 1815, while the species to which the latter name was assigned by Nouvel & Holthuis needed a new name *P. nouveli* Al-Adhub & Williamson, 1975.

The great confusion that has existed in the species taxonomy and the nomenclature of *Processa* makes it difficult to correctly evaluate old records. This is especially true for the shallow water species.

SUPERFAMILY PANDALOIDEA Haworth, 1825

Pandaloida Alcock, 1901, Descr.Catal.Indian.Deep Sea Crust.Macr.Anom, 55

Of the three families in this superfamily only one is known to contain species of commercial interest.

FAMILY PANDALIDAE Haworth, 1825

Pandalidae Haworth, 1825, Philos.Mag.J., 65:184

The family Pandalidae is, from a commercial point of view, one of the most important families of prawns, second only to the Penaeidae. While the fishery for Penaeidae is mostly confined to the tropics and subtropics, that for Pandalidae is done in colder waters of both the northern and southern hemisphere. Several genera of Pandalidae are of commercial importance, *Pandalus* being the foremost among these.

| *Chlorotocus crassicornis* (Costa, 1871) | PANDL Chlo 1 |

Pandalus crassicornis Costa, 1871, Annu.Mus.Zool.Univ.Napoli, 6:89

Synonymy: *Chlorotocus gracilipes* A. Milne Edwards, 1882; *Palaemon chlorotocus* Filhol, 1886.

FAO Names: Green shrimp (En), Crevette verte (Fr), Camarón verde (Sp).

Literature: Crosnier & Forest, 1973:184, Figs. 58-60.

Distribution: Eastern Atlantic: from the Bay of Biscay to Congo; Mediterranean. Records from South and East Africa, India and China Sea need confirmation.

Habitat: Depth 75 to 600 m. Bottom mud and sandy mud. Marine.

Size: Maximum total length 78 mm.

Interest to Fishery: Brian (1941:40) noted that since in Italy in the Genoa area trawlfishing had started at depths between 150 and 400 m, the species is rather frequently caught and is relatively common at the fishmarket, although these prawns are not sold in great quantities. Zariquiey Alvarez (1946:67) indicated that the species is caught "con bastante frequencia" by trawlers along the entire Catalonian coast of Spain. Heldt & Heldt (1954:11) listed the species among the edible shrimps of Tunisia, but remarked that it is not sold separately on the market, always being mixed with *Parapenaeus*. Longhurst (1970:299) reported that off the coast of Natal, S. Africa *Chlorotocus crassicornis* is taken in "quantities, which are often not marketed". The systematic and nomenclatural status of the S.E. African *Chlorotocus* is not yet positively known and the form occurring there may be a distinct species.

| *Dichelopandalus bonnieri* Caullery, 1896 | PANDL Dich 1 |

Dichelopandalus bonnieri Caullery, 1896, Ann.Univ.Lyon, 26:379

Synonymy: *Pandalus bonnieri* - Calman, 1899.

FAO Names: Whip shrimp (En), Crevette fouet (Fr), Camarón latiguillo (Sp).

Literature: Calman, 1899:34, Pls. 1-4, Fig. 3.

Distribution: Eastern Atlantic: West coast of Europe from Norway to the Bay of Biscay.

Habitat: Depth 60 to 1 200 m. Marine.

Size: Maximum total length 120 mm.

Interest to Fishery: Cole (in Graham:1956:194) stated that in the Clyde below Millport (S.W. Scotland) there exist "considerable quantities of *Pandalus bonnieri* ... a prawn ..., obviously of commercial importance if it is present in sufficient quantities".   Longhurst (1970:265) confirmed this.

Heterocarpoides levicarina (Bate, 1888)	PANDL Het 1

Dorodotes levicarina Bate, 1888, Rep.Voyage Challenger, (Zool.), 24:680

Synonymy: *Heterocarpus (Heterocarpoides) levicarina* - De Man, 1917.

FAO Names: Dorodotes shrimp (En), Crevette dorodo (Fr), Camarón dorodó (Sp).

Literature: De Man, 1920:178, Pl. 15, Fig. 44.

Distribution: Indo-West Pacific: Red Sea to Japan and Indonesia.

Habitat: Depth 31 to 274 m.   Marine.

Size: Maximum total length 45 mm.

Interest to Fishery: Minor if at all.   Yasuda (1957:30) listed the species among those that are important in the shrimp fishery in the Inland Sea of Japan near Seto.

Heterocarpus dorsalis Bate, 1888	PANDL Heter 1

Heterocarpus dorsalis Bate, 1888, Rep.Voyage Challenger, (Zool.), 24:630

Synonymy: *Heterocarpus alphonsi* Bate, 1888.

FAO Names: Madagascar nylon shrimp (En), Crevette nylon malgache (Fr), Camarón nailón malgache (Sp).

Literature: De Man, 1920:171, Pl. 15, Fig. 43.

Distribution: Indo-West Pacific: East and South-east Africa to Japan, the Philippines and Indonesia.

Habitat: Depth 185 to 1 325 m.   Bottom mud or sandy mud.   Marine.

Size: Maximum total length 154 mm (δ), 165 mm ($\female$);   maximum carapace length (without rostrum) 34.5 mm (δ), 36.5 mm ($\female$).

Interest to Fishery: Crosnier & Jouannic (1973:13) considered this species "éventuellement commercialisable" on the continental slope of Madagascar.

Heterocarpus ensifer A. Milne Edwards, 1881	PANDL Heter 2

Heterocarpus ensifer A. Milne Edwards, 1881, Ann.Sci.Nat.Paris(Zool.), (6)11(4):8

Synonymy: *Pandalus carinatus* Smith, 1882; *Heterocarpus carinatus* - Agassiz, 1888; *Atlantocaris gigas* Ortmann, 1893; *Procletes atlanticus* Lenz & Strunck, 1914; *Procletes gigas* - Gurney & Lebour, 1941.

FAO Names: Armed nylon shrimp (En), Crevette nylon armée (Fr), Camarón nailón armado (Sp).

Literature: Crosnier & Forest, 1973:189, Fig. 61a.

Distribution: Western Atlantic: from North Carolina (U.S.A.) south to the Caribbean area. Eastern Atlantic: from off S. Spain to the Congo. Indo-West Pacific: near Madagascar, Reunion and Hawaii (several other Indo-West Pacific records of this species may pertain to different forms).

Habitat: Depth 146 to 885 m. Bottom mud. Marine.

Size: Maximum total length 124 mm; maximum carapace length 34.8 mm.

Interest to Fishery: Experiments carried out near Reunion indicated a potential commercial importance of this species, which was obtained at great depths (250 to 650 m) with fish traps (Guézé, 1976:279). The species then proved commercially less attractive, however, than *H. laevigatus* with which it was often captured together. Crosnier & Jouannic (1973:11) reported upon the potential commercial importance of the species near Madagascar, Reunion and Hawaii.

Heterocarpus gibbosus Bate, 1888	PANDL Heter 3

Heterocarpus gibbosus Bate, 1888, Rep.Voyage Challenger, (Zool.), 24:634

FAO Names: Humpback nylon shrimp (En), Crevette nylon bossue (Fr), Camarón nailón jorobado (Sp).

Literature: De Man, 1920:163, Pl. 14, Fig. 39.

Distribution: Indo-West Pacific: East Africa to the Philippines and Indonesia.

Habitat: Depth 265 to 1 280 m. Bottom mud. Marine.

Size: Maximum total length 140 mm; maximum carapace length (rostrum excluded) 40 mm.

Interest to Fishery: Potential. Off S.W. India the species, although trawled in small numbers only, seems to have commercial possibilities (Jones, 1969:747; Suseelan, 1976; Kurian & Sebastian, 1976:94).

Heterocarpus laevigatus Bate, 1888	PANDL Heter 4

Heterocarpus laevigatus Bate, 1888, Rep.Voyage Challenger, (Zool.), 24:636

FAO Names: Smooth nylon shrimp (En), Crevette nylon inerme (Fr), Camarón nailón liso (Sp).

Literature: Crosnier & Forest, 1973:195, Fig. 61c.

Distribution: Eastern Atlantic: Madeira to Cape Verde Islands. Indo-West Pacific: South Africa and the Arabian Sea to the Malay Archipelago and Hawaii.

Habitat: Depth 302 to 1 156 m. Bottom sand or sandy mud. Marine.

Size: Maximum total length 181 mm (♂), 180 mm (♀); maximum carapace length 44 mm (♂), 49 mm (♀).

Interest to Fishery: According to Crosnier & Jouannic (1973:13) the species is "éventuellement commercialisable" on the continental slope of Madagascar. Experiments carried out near Reunion indicated a potential commercial importance of this species there, if fished at great depths (550 to 800 m) with fish traps (Guézé, 1976:270,282). The species is found there together with *H. ensifer*, but at the depths of 550 to 800 m it forms 75% of the catch.

| *Heterocarpus reedi* Bahamonde, 1955 | PANDL Heter 5 |

Heterocarpus reedi Bahamonde, 1955, Invest.Zool.Chil., 2:105

FAO Names: Chilean nylon shrimp (En), Crevette nylon chilienne (Fr), Camarón nailón (Sp).

Local Names: Camarón nailon, Camarón de profundidad, Gamba (Chile).

Literature: Bahamonde & Henriquez, 1970:1 607-1 627, Figs. 1-7.

Distribution: Eastern Pacific: off Chile between 25°S and 39°S.

Habitat: Depth 155 to 424 m. Bottom clay, mud or sandy mud. Marine.

Size: Maximum carapace length (without rostrum) 34 mm (♂), 39 mm (♀).

Interest to Fishery: Considerable. This species is trawled, it formed 95% of the total shrimp catch of Chile (Hancock & Henriquez, 1968). The species is used fresh, dried, boiled and peeled. It is exported also. According to Longhurst (1970:303) it also is fished in Peru. The catch (in metric tons) taken annually in Chile amounted to 8 300 (in 1973), 7 550 (in 1974), 7 935 (in 1975), and 6 197 (in 1976).

| *Heterocarpus sibogae* De Man, 1917 | PANDL Heter 6 |

Heterocarpus sibogae De Man, 1917, Zool.Meded., Leiden, 3:283

FAO Names: Mino nylon shrimp (En), Crevette nylon mino (Fr), Camarón nailón mino (Sp).

Local Names: Mino ebi (Japan).

Literature: De Man, 1920:169, Pl. 14, Fig. 42.

Distribution· Indo-West Pacific: Maldives to Japan and Indonesia.

Habitat: Depth 230 to 560 m. Bottom mud. Marine.

Size: Maximum total length 140 mm.

Interest to Fishery: Yasuda (1957:30) listed this species among those that are important in the shrimp fishery in the Inland Sea of Japan near Seto.

| *Heterocarpus tricarinatus* Alcock & Anderson, 1894 | PANDL Heter 7 |

Heterocarpus tricarinatus Alcock & Anderson, 1894, J.Asiat.Soc.Bengal, 63(2):154

FAO Names: Scarred nylon shrimp (En), Crevette nylon balafrée (Fr), Camarón nailón chirlo (Sp).

Literature: De Man, 1920:161, Pls. 13,14, Fig. 38.

Distribution: Indo-West Pacific: S.E. Africa and Arabian Sea to Indonesia.

Habitat: Depth 500 to 2 000 m. Bottom mud. Marine.

Size: Total length 119 mm (♂), 58 to 94 mm (♀).

Interest to Fishery: Crosnier & Jouannic (1973:13) considered this species "éventuellement commercialisable" on the continental slope of Madagascar.

| *Heterocarpus vicarius* Faxon, 1893 | PANDL Heter 8 |

Heterocarpus vicarius Faxon, 1893, <u>Bull.Mus.Comp.Zool.Harv.Coll.</u>, 24:203

FAO Names: Northern nylon shrimp (En), Crevette nylon nordique (Fr), Camarón nailón norteño (Sp).

Local Names: Camello, Torobado, Small red shrimp (Costa Rica, Panama).

Literature: Faxon, 1895:148, Pl. 40, Fig. 1, Pl. 41, Fig. 2.

Distribution: Eastern Pacific: Mexico to Panama.

Habitat: Depth 73 to 550 m. Bottom mud. Marine.

Size: Total length 28 to 110 mm; carapace length (without rostrum) 7.5 to 29 mm.

Interest to Fishery: The species is commercially fished for in Costa Rica and Panama at depths of 180 to 270 m (I. Pérez-Farfante, in Litt.; see also Vidal & Rosetti, 1971, 1971a).

| *Heterocarpus woodmasoni* Alcock, 1901 | PANDL Heter 9 |

Heterocarpus woodmasoni Alcock, 1901, <u>Descr.Cat.Indian Deep Sea Crust.Macr.Anom.</u>, 108

FAO Names: Indian nylon shrimp (En), Crevette nylon indienne (Fr), Camarón nailón indio (Sp).

Literature: De Man, 1920:156, Pl. 13, Fig. 36.

Distribution: Indo-West Pacific: E. Africa to Indonesia.

Habitat: Depth 290 to 640 m. Bottom mud. Marine.

Size: Maximum total length 131 mm (♂), 149 mm (♀); maximum carapace length (rostrum excluded) 27 mm (♂), 32 mm (♀).

Interest to Fishery: Crosnier & Jouannic (1973:11) listed this species as "éventuellement commercialisable" on the continental slope of Madagascar. Like *H. gibbosus*, the present species was mentioned by Jones (1969:747), Suseelan (1976) and Kurian & Sebastian (1976:94) as of possible commercial importance in Indian waters.

| *Pandalopsis dispar* M.J. Rathbun, 1902 | PANDL Pand 1 |

Pandalopsis dispar M.J. Rathbun, 1902, <u>Proc.U.S.Natl.Mus.</u>, 24:902

Synonymy: *Pandalus dispar* - Taylor, 1912.

FAO Names: Sidestripe shrimp (En), Crevette à flancs rayés (Fr), Camarón de banda (Sp).

Local Names: Side-stripe shrimp (Canada; U.S.A.), Giant red shrimp (Canada).

Literature: M.J. Rathbun, 1904:54, Pl. 1, Fig. 2.

Distribution: Eastern Pacific: Alaska to Oregon, U.S.A.

Habitat: Depth 38 to 630 m (fished in 80 to 150 m). Bottom green mud. Marine.

Size: Maximum total length 200 mm; maximum carapace length 39 mm.

Interest to Fishery: In the area of British Columbia the importance of the species is minor compared to that of the *Pandalus* species. In the Bering Sea and Gulf of Alaska the species represents 5 to 15% of the shrimp catch (Longhurst, 1970:271); exploitation of larger areas may sharply increase its production. The species is sold as such, whole, peeled and cooked.

| *Pandalopsis japonica* Balss, 1914 | PANDL Pand 2 |

Pandalopsis dispar japonica Balss, 1914, Abh.Bayer.Akad.Wiss., (suppl.) 2(10):32

Synonymy: ?*Pandalopsis multidentata* Kobjakova, 1936.

FAO Names: Morotoge shrimp (En), Crevette morotoge (Fr), Camarón morotoje (Sp).

Local Names: Morotoge aka ebi (Japan).

Distribution: Indo-West Pacific: Sea of Okhotsk and Sea of Japan; Siberia; Korea; Japan.

Habitat: Depth 64 to 650 m. Marine.

Size: Maximum total length 150 mm.

Interest to Fishery: Yoshida (1941:25) listed the species as being of economic importance in Korea.

| *Pandalus borealis* Krøyer, 1838 | PANDL Pandal 1 |

Pandalus borealis Krøyer, 1838, Naturhist.Tidsskr., 2:254

Synonymy: *Dymas typus* Krøyer, 1861; *Pandalus borealis typica* Retovsky, 1946.

FAO Names: Northern shrimp (En), Crevette nordique (Fr), Camarón norteño (Sp).

Local Names: Dybvannsreke (Norway), Dybhavsreje, Store røde Dybhavsreje, Drammensreje, Norsk reje, Svelviksreje (Denmark), Nordhavsräka (Sweden), Pohjanmeren katkarapu (Finland), Севернь Шримс (U.S.S.R.), Noorse garnaal (Netherlands), Pink shrimp, Deepwater prawn (Great Britain, Canada, U.S.A.), Kampalampi (Iceland), Kingugssvaq, Râfa kingugpak (Greenland), Deep-sea prawn, Great northern prawn, Crevette nordique (Canada), Northern shrimp (U.S.A.), Hokkoku aka ebi, Hokkai ebi (Japan).

Literature: Sars, 1900:31, Pls. 9,10; Hjort & Ruud, 1938:1-144, Figs. 1-21.

Distribution: North Atlantic: Spitsbergen and Greenland south to the North Sea and to Massachusetts (U.S.A.). North Pacific: Bering Sea to S.E. Siberia, Japan and Oregon (U.S.A.). The taxonomic status of the North Pacific form, usually considered a subspecies *Pandalus borealis eous* Makarov, 1935, is not fully clear yet.

Habitat: Depth 20 to 1 380 m. Bottom clay and mud. Marine.

Size: Maximum total length 120 mm (δ), 165 mm ($\female$).

Interest to Fishery: Commercially this is one of the most important carideans of the North Atlantic; only *Crangon crangon* may be more important. Longhurst (1970:258) called it the principal product of the prawn fisheries of the northwestern Atlantic, being concentrated off Greenland, while in more recent years also more to the south fisheries for the species have started, e.g., in the Gulf of St. Lawrence, the Bay of Fundy and the Gulf of Maine (as far south as Gloucester, Mass.). There is an intensive fishery around Iceland and a most important one off the Norwegian coast. In the Kattegat and Skagerak it is fished for by Danish trawlers. In the northern and central North Sea Danish, Norwegian, British, German and Dutch trawlers fish for the species. Experiments for the aquaculture of this species have been undertaken in England.

In the Northern Pacific *Pandalus borealis eous* also is of economic importance. Longhurst (1970:270-272) mentioned that the species is important on the west coast of Kamchatka, while in the Bering Sea and Gulf of Alaska it forms 80 to 90% of the shrimp catch. Yoshida (1941:23) listed the species among the commercial shrimps of Korea. Off the west coast of Canada and Washington (U.S.A.) the species is trawled commercially and with *P. jordani* forms the most important species in the fishery. According to U.S. Bureau of Commercial Fisheries (1958:12) this shrimp is landed in Washington, Oregon and California, U.S.A.

Pandalus danae Stimpson, 1857	PANDL Pandal 2

Pandalus danae Stimpson, 1857, Proc.Boston Soc.Nat.Hist., 6:87

Synonymy: *Pandalus franciscorum* Kingsley, 1878

FAO Names: Dock shrimp (En), Crevette des quais (Fr), Camarón de muelle (Sp).

Local Names: Coon stripe shrimp, Coon-striped shrimp, Dock shrimp (Canada, U.S.A.), California prawn (U.S.A., see R. Rathbun, 1893:821).

Literature: Schmitt, 1921:44, textfig. 25, Pl. 13, Fig. 3.

Distribution: Eastern Pacific: Alaska, U.S.A. to California, U.S.A.

Habitat: Depth 18 to 200 m. Bottom sand, gravel. Marine.

Size: Maximum total length 88 mm ($\male$), 105 mm ($\female$); maximum carapace length 22 mm ($\male$), 29 mm ($\female$).

Interest to Fishery: Butler (1968:523) listed the commercial Pandalidae of British Columbia, Canada, "in order of decreasing importance" of the six species *P. danae* came last. R. Rathbun (1884:821) stated that the species was "commonly brought to the San Francisco market, and is caught in the open ocean" off San Francisco.

Pandalus goniurus Stimpson, 1860	PANDL Pandal 3

Pandalus goniurus Stimpson, 1860, Proc.Acad.Nat.Sci.Phila., 1860:36

Synonymy: *Pandalus dapifer* Murdoch, 1884.

FAO Names: Humpy shrimp (En), Crevette gibbeuse (Fr), Camarón jiboso (Sp).

Local Names: Humpy shrimp (U.S.A.), Benisuji ebi (Japan).

Literature: M.J. Rathbun, 1904:38, Pl. 1, Fig. 3.

Distribution: Northern Pacific: Bering Sea to Sea of Japan and Washington, U.S.A.

Habitat: Depth 5 to 450 m. Marine.

Size: Maximum total length 142 mm; maximum carapace length (exclusive of rostrum) 70 mm.

Interest to Fishery: This is the commonest Pandalid in the N.W. Pacific and in the Okhotsk Sea it seems to be present in commercially attractive quantities (Longhurst, 1970:276). In the Bering Sea the importance of the species is far less (being less than 5% of the total Pandalid stock), but it seems to be more important in the Anadyr Gulf (= Anadyrskiy Zaliv), N.E. Siberia (Longhurst, 1970:271). This species, together with *P. hypsinotus,* is taken in small quantities in Alaska, but it is far less important than either *P. borealis* or *Pandalopsis dispar* (cf. Harry, 1964:64).

| *Pandalus hypsinotus* Brandt, 1851 | PANDL Pandal 4 |

Pandalus hypsinotus Brandt, 1851, In Middendorff, Reise N. und O. Sibiriens, 2(1):125

Synonymy: *Pandalus gracilis* Stimpson, 1860.

FAO Names: Coonstripe shrimp (En), Crevette à front rayé (Fr), Camarón malacho (Sp).

Local Names: Humpback shrimp (Canada, U.S.A.), King shrimp (Canada), Coon-stripe shrimp (U.S.A.), Toyama ebi, Taraba ebi, Botan ebi (Japan).

Literature: M.J. Rathbun, 1904:46, Pl. 2, Fig. 5.

Distribution: Northern Pacific: Bering Sea to Washington, U.S.A., Korea and N. Japan.

Habitat: Depth 5 to 400 m. Marine.

Size: Maximum total length 209 mm (♂); maximum carapace length (without rostrum) 43 mm.

Interest to Fishery: This species dominates the prawn catch off Korea (Longhurst, 1970:270; Yoshida, 1941:22). In the Bering Sea it is of minor importance, forming with *P. goniurus* and *P. platyceros* less than 5% of the prawn catch. Off British Columbia *Pandalus hypsinotus* is commercially "of minor importance" (Butler, 1964:1 428).

| *Pandalus jordani* M.J. Rathbun, 1902 | PANDL Pandal 5 |

Pandalus jordani M.J. Rathbun, 1902, Proc.U.S.Natl.Mus., 24:900

FAO Names: Ocean shrimp (En), Crevette océanique (Fr), Camarón oceánico (Sp).

Local Names: Ocean shrimp (U.S.A.: official name in California), Smooth pink shrimp, Pink shrimp (Canada, U.S.A.), Ocean pink shrimp (U.S.A.).

Literature: Dahlstrom, 1970:1 377-1 416, Figs. 1-17.

Distribution: Eastern Pacific: Alaska to San Diego, California, U.S.A.

Habitat: Depth 36 to 457 m (fished in depths of 73 to 237 m). Bottom sand and mud, green mud. Marine.

Size: Maximum total length 161 mm; maximum carapace length 18 mm (♂), 30 mm (♀).

Interest to Fishery: Butler (1950:34) stated that the species in British Columbia had been "found in limited commercial quantities", about twenty years later it was of major commercial importance there, being trawled for food, used as such, whole or peeled and cooked. Off Washington and Oregon (U.S.A.) the species supports a trawl fishery (Longhurst, 1970:272). Off California also the fishery for this species is of major importance; most of the catch here is vacuum-packed, small amounts are sold fresh or cooked. In 1962 Washington produced 1.4 million lbs of this species, Oregon 2.0 million lbs and California 1.6 million lbs (Harry, 1964:66).

| *Pandalus kessleri* Czerniavsky, 1878 | PANDL Pandal 6 |

Pandalus kessleri Czerniavsky, 1878, Trav.Soc.Natural.St.Pétersbourg, 7:25

Synonymy: *Pandalus kessleri fluviatilis* Czerniavsky, 1878; *Pandalus latirostris* M.J. Rathbun, 1902.

FAO Names: Hokkai shrimp (En), Crevette hokkai (Fr), Camarón de Hokkai (Sp).

Local Names: Hokkai ebi (Japan), Травяной шримс (U.S.S.R.).

Literature: Urita & Nomura, 1938:235-252, Figs. 1-4.

Distribution: Western North Pacific: S.E. Siberia; Korea; Sachalin; N. Japan. Around 1959 the species has been introduced into the Black Sea.

Habitat: Depth 0.5 to 9 m; there are records from as deep as 300 m. Marine.

Size: Maximum total length 157 mm; maximum carapace length (rostrum excluded) 31 mm.

Interest to Fishery: Longhurst (1970:270) indicated that this species, together with *P. hypsinotus* is dominant in the catches in North Korean waters. Yoshida (1941:24) also listed it as of economic importance in Korea. Urita & Nomura (1938) state that it "may be looked on as a special product of Saghalien and Hokkaidô ... In Saghalien, it is the only commercial shrimp that is canned". More recently Tanikawa (1971:182) also commented on the importance of the species in Hokkaido and the Kurile Islands, in Hokkaido the annual production being about 100 tons. Kobjakova (1966:203) also indicated that the species is "of commercial value in the Sea of Japan, near South Sakhalin and at the southern Kuriles" (cf. also Ivanov, 1955:16-23).

| *Pandalus montagui* Leach, 1814 | PANDL Pandal 7 |

Pandalus montagui Leach, 1814, *In* Brewster, Edinburgh Encycl., 7:432

Synonymy: *Astacus maculatus* (Montagu MS) Leach, 1814; *Pandalus annulicornis* Leach, 1815; *Astacus (Pandalus) annulicornis* - Moore, 1839; *Pandalus levigatus* Stimpson, 1853; *Pandalus leptorhynchus* Kinahan, 1858; *?Boreocaris moebiusi* Ortmann, 1893.

FAO Names: Aesop shrimp (En), Crevette ésope (Fr), Camarón esópico (Sp).

Local Names: Blomsterreke, Spraglete reke (Norway), Rekekongen (Denmark), Felsengarnele, Rote Schwimmgarnele (Germany), Pink shrimp, Pink prawn, Aesop shrimp, Aesop prawn, Prawn, Sprawn, Shank, Fleetwood prawn (Great Britain), Striped pink prawn, Striped pink shrimp (Canada).

Literature: Simpson, Howell & Warren, 1970:1 225-1 249, Figs. 1-4.

Distribution: Northern Atlantic: Arctic Ocean south to Nova Scotia, Canada, the British Isles and the southern North Sea near Belgium.

Habitat: Depth 4 to 700 m (most common between 20 and 100 m). Bottom sand, mud, gravel and rock, usually a hard substratum. Marine.

Size: Maximum total length 160 mm.

Interest to Fishery: In the northeastern Atlantic region the species "is only fished commercially by Britain" (Longhurst, 1970:265). On the whole the importance is small. In the northwestern Atlantic the species with two species of *Spirontocaris* is "only exploited incidentally to the fishery for *Pandalus borealis*" (Longhurst, 1970:258). Couture (1971:42) reported that a fishery of secondary importance for this species existed in Denmark, the Faröe Islands, Iceland, Norway, Sweden, Holland, Belgium and England, and that it also has commercial possibilities on the east coast of Canada.

| *Pandalus nipponensis* Yokoya, 1933 | PANDL Pandal 8 |

Pandalus nipponensis Yokoya, 1933, J.Coll.Agric.Imp.Univ.Tokyo, 12:17

FAO Names: Botan shrimp (En), Crevette botan (Fr), Camarón botán (Sp).

Local Names: Botan ebi (Japan).

Distribution: Indo-West Pacific: Korea; Japan.

Habitat: Depth 76 to 583 m. Marine

Size: About 85 mm.

Interest to Fishery: Yoshida (1941:22, Pl. 13, Fig. 3) figured this species in his list of economically important Macrura of Korea, but, apart from including it in his key, did not treat it in the text. Yasuda (1957:30) listed the species as important in the shrimp fishery of the Inland Sea of Japan near Seto.

Pandalus platyceros Brandt, 1851	PANDL Pandal 9

Pandalus platyceros Brandt, 1851, In Middendorff, Reise N. und O. Sibiriens, 2(1):123

Synonymy: *Pandalus pubescentulus* Dana, 1852.

FAO Names: Spot shrimp (En), Crevette tache (Fr), Camarón manchado (Sp).

Local Names: Prawn, Spot shrimp (Canada, U.S.A.), Hokkai ebi (Japan).

Literature: Butler, 1970:1 289-1 315, Figs. 1-7.

Distribution: Northern Pacific: Bering Strait south to S. California, and to Japan and Korea.

Habitat: Depth 4 to 487 m. Bottom hard on fairly steep edge. Marine.

Size: Maximum total length 253 mm; maximum carapace length 61 mm.

Interest to Fishery: Along the Pacific American coast it is of commercial importance (of major importance in British Columbia). It is mainly caught with traps, but is also obtained incidentally in trawling for other species of Pandalidae. According to Longhurst (1970:271,272) in the Bering Sea and the Gulf of Alaska the catch of this species, together with that of *P. goniurus* and *P. hypsinotus* constitutes less than 5% of the total shrimp catch. Trap catching for *P. platyceros* in California was of negligible importance. In England aquaculture experiments with this species have been carried out, but without too encouraging results for commercial breeding (Forster & Wickins, 1972:9-10).

Parapandalus narval (Fabricius, 1787)	PANDL Parapnd 1

Astacus narval Fabricius, 1787, Mantissa Insectorum, 1:331

Synonymy: *Cancer narval* - Gmelin, 1789; *Palaemon narval* - Bosc, 1801; *Palaemon pristis* Risso, 1816; *Pandalus narval* - Desmarest, 1823; *Pontophilus pristis* - Risso, 1827; *Pandalus pristis* - Roux, 1831; *Palaemon tarentinum* Costa, 1844; *Pandalus tarentinus* - Hope, 1851; *Nisea formosa* (Risso MS) Monod, 1931. In older literature the name *Parapandalus narval* has often incorrectly been used for *Plesionika edwardsii*.

FAO Names: Narwal shrimp (En), Crevette narval (Fr), Camarón narval (Sp).

Literature: Zariquiey Alvarez, 1968:111; Crosnier & Forest, 1973:221, Fig. 69a.

Distribution: Eastern Atlantic: Western Mediterranean, including the Adriatic Sea; from Madeira and the Canary Islands south to Angola. Also reported from the Western Indian Ocean and the Red Sea.

Habitat: Depth 10 to 910 m. Bottom mud and muddy sand. Marine.

Size: Maximum total length 95 mm, without rostrum.

Interest to Fishery: According to Figueira (1960:4) "In Madeira there is a small commercial fishery for the species". Zariquiey Alvarez (1946:68), mentioned that it is caught by the "vacas" (= trawlers) off the Catalonian coast of Spain. It is found on the Spanish fishmarkets usually in small quantities with other prawns. Brian (1941:36) reported it from the fishmarket at Genoa, Italy, but it was there of little commercial importance. Dieuzeide (1931:132) remarked that he had never seen the species (which he dealt with under the name *Parapandalus pristis*) on the fishmarket of Algiers, while *Plesionika edwardsii* (mentioned as *Parapandalus narval*) was abundant there. Heldt & Heldt (1954:10) listed the species among the edible shrimps of Tunisia. Guézé (1976:275) in the course of fishery experiments with traps in 150 to 350 m off Reunion, found the species at times abundant and of possible, but restricted, economic interest.

Parapandalus spinipes (Bate, 1888)	PANDL Parapnd 2

Plesionika spinipes Bate, 1888, Rep.Voyage Challenger, (Zool.), 24:646

Synonymy: *Pandalus (Parapandalus) serratifrons* Borradaile, 1899; *Pandalus (Parapandalus) tenuipes* Borraidale, 1899; *Pandalus (Parapandalus) spinipes* - Alcock, 1901; *Plesionika spinipes grandis* Doflein, 1902.

FAO Names: Oriental narwal shrimp (En), Crevette narval orientale (Fr), Camarón narval oriental (Sp).

Literature: De Man, 1920:142, Pls. 12, 13, Fig. 33.

Distribution: Indo-West Pacific: Red Sea to Japan, Melanesia and the Kermadec Islands.

Habitat: Depth 50 to 805 m. Marine.

Size: Maximum total length 130 mm.

Interest to Fishery: So far evidently none, but Jones (1969:747), Suseelan (1976) and Kurian & Sebastian (1976:94) listed this species with a number of others as potentially interesting as a subject for commercial fishery in India, especially off Kerala.

Plesionika acanthonotus (S.I. Smith, 1882)	PANDL Plesion 3

Pandalus acanthonotus S.I. Smith, 1882, Bull.Mus.Comp.Zool.Harv.Coll., 10:61

Synonymy: *Pandalus parfaiti* A. Milne Edwards, 1883; *Pandalus geniculatus* A. Milne Edwards, 1883; *Nothocaris geniculatus* - Bate, 1888; *Plesionika parfaiti* - De Man, 1920; *Plesionika geniculata* - De Man, 1920.

FAO Names: Lesser striped shrimp (En), Crevette naine rayée (Fr), Camarón rayado menor (Sp).

Literature: Zariquiey Alvarez, 1968:102, Figs. 39c,43,44a,b; Crosnier & Forest, 1973:203, Figs. 64d,65a.

Distribution: Eastern Atlantic: Bay of Biscay to S.W. Africa; Western Mediterranean. Western Atlantic: South Carolina, U.S.A. to Brazil.

Habitat: Depth 190 to 1 350 m. Bottom mud. Marine.

Size: Maximum total length 84 mm.

Interest to Fishery: Minor. Zariquiey Alvarez (1946:66) indicated that the species is caught by trawlers off the Catalonian coast of Spain. The specimens form a minor portion of the catch and are usually either discarded or sold mixed with other shrimps. Massuti (1968:306) also reported the species from the Baleares as "con menor intéres comercial o nulo".

| *Plesionika alcocki* (Anderson, 1896) | PANDL Plesion 4 |

Pandalus alcocki Anderson, 1896, J.Asiat.Soc.Bengal, 65(2):92

FAO Names: Gondwana striped shrimp (En), Crevette gondwana (Fr), Camarón gondwana.

Literature: Alcock, 1901:97.

Distribution: Indo-West Pacific: Western Indian Ocean from East Africa and the Gulf of Aden to the Bay of Bengal.

Habitat: Depth 500 to 1 170 m. Marine.

Size: Maximum carapace length 20.5 mm ($\male$), 22 mm ($\female$).

Interest to Fishery: This species was considered by Crosnier & Jouannic (1973:13) "éventuellement commercialisable" on the continental slope of Madagascar.

| *Plesionika antigai* Zariquiey Alvarez, 1955 | PANDL Plesion 5 |

Plesionika antigai Zariquiey Alvarez, 1955, Publ.Inst.Biol.Apl., Barc., 19:111

FAO Names: Catalonian striped shrimp (En), Crevette catalane (Fr), Camarón catalán (Sp).

Literature: Zariquiey Alvarez, 1968:100, Fig. 37.

Distribution: Eastern Atlantic: Western Mediterranean; probably also West Africa.

Habitat: Depth 168 to 400 m. Marine.

Size: Maximum carapace length (without rostrum) 17.5 mm.

Interest to Fishery: Minor if at all. Caught by trawlers off the Catalonian coast of Spain and brought to the fishmarkets, where it is sold as an admixture with other prawns (Zariquiey Alvarez, 1955).

| *Plesionika edwardsii* (Brandt, 1851) | PANDL Plesion 2 |

Pandalus (Pontophilus) edwardsii Brandt, 1851, In Middendorff, Reise N. und O. Sibiriens, 2(1):121

Synonymy: *Pandalus guerinii* Risso, 1844 (nomen nudum).

FAO Names: Striped soldier shrimp (En), Crevette édouard (Fr), Camarón soldado rayado (Sp).

Local Names: Carabinero (Spain).,

Literature: Zariquiey Alvarez, 1968:109, Fig. 45; Crosnier & Forest, 1973:202, Figs. 63b,64b.

Distribution: Eastern Atlantic: Mediterranean; West Africa as far south as Sierra Leone. Western Atlantic: S. Carolina, U.S.A. to Gulf of Mexico.

Habitat: Depth 180 to 680 m. Bottom mud. Marine.

Size: Maximum total length 166 mm.

Interest to Fishery: Zariquiey Alvarez (1946:68) reported the species as being caught by trawlers off the Spanish Mediterranean coast. The shrimps are brought here to the markets and sold usually as an admixture with other shrimps. Massuti (1968:305,307) reported this species as one of the three species of shrimp that are of economic interest in the region of the Baleares, Spain, while also on the Atlantic coast of Spain it seems to be of some importance. Brian (1941:32) mentioned the species as being sold on the fishmarkets in Genoa, Italy, be it in limited numbers and often mixed in with *Parapenaeus longirostris*. In Algeria the same is true: "On le rencontre couramment sur les marchés algériens, mélangé à la Crevette rose pâle: *Parapenaeus longirostris* Lucas" (Dieuzeide, 1931: 128); this was later confirmed by the same author (Dieuzeide, 1952:38), who stated that in Algerian waters the present species is the only Pandalid which has "une importance économique". Heldt & Heldt (1954:11) reported the same for Tunis: "Il s'en trouve quelquefois au marché de Tunis, mélangé à la crevette rose *(Parapenaeus)*".

Plesionika ensis (A. Milne Edwards, 1881)	PANDL Plesion 6

Acanthephyra ensis A. Milne Edwards, 1881, Ann.Sci.Nat.Paris, (Zool.), (6)11(4):14

Synonymy: *Pandalus ensis* - A. Milne Edwards, 1883; *Plesionika uniproducta* Bate, 1888.

FAO Names: Striped gladiator shrimp (En), Crevette gladiateur rayée (Fr), Camarón gladiador rayado (Sp).

Literature: Holthuis, 1951:55, Fig. 10; Suseelan & Mohamed, 1969:88, Figs. 1-4.

Distribution: Circumtropic: Western Atlantic: Florida (U.S.A.); West Indies; Brazil. Eastern Atlantic: Morocco to Angola. Indo-West Pacific: Arabian Sea; Bay of Bengal; Fiji; Hawaiian Archipelago.

Habitat: Depth 100 to 1 250 m. Bottom mud. Marine.

Size: Maximum total length 128 mm.

Interest to Fishery: So far the species is not fished for, but Suseelan & Mohamed (1969), Suseelan (1976) and Kurian & Sebastian (1976:94) found it to be of potential commercial value off the west coast of India (Kerala).

Plesionika gigliolii (Senna, 1903)	PANDL Plesion 7

Pandalus gigliolii Senna, 1903, Boll.Soc.Entomol.Ital., 34:315

Synonymy: *Pandalus subtilirostris* Riggio, 1905; *Pandalus (Nothocaris) ocellus subtilirostris* - Riggio, 1905.

FAO Names: Italian deepsea shrimp (En), Crevette profonde italienne (Fr), Camarón italiano de fondo (Sp).

Literature: Zariquiey Alvarez, 1968:106, Fig. 44c.

Distribution: Eastern Atlantic: Western Mediterranean; West Africa south to Sierra Leone.

Habitat: Depth 118 to 800 m. Bottom mud. Marine.

Size: Maximum total length 62 mm.

Interest to Fishery: Practically nil. The species is rarely caught by trawlers off the Catalonian coast of Spain (Zariquiey Alvarez, 1946:66), and comes on the fishmarkets as an admixture with other prawns.

Plesionika heterocarpus (Costa, 1871)	PANDL Plesion 8

Pandalus heterocarpus Costa, 1871, <u>Annu.Mus.Zool.Univ.Napoli</u>, 6:89

Synonymy: *Pandalus sagittarius* A. Milne Edwards, 1883; *Pandalus longicarpus* A. Milne Edwards, 1883.

FAO Names: Arrow shrimp (En), Crevette flèche (Fr), Camarón flecha (Sp).

Literature: Crosnier & Forest, 1973:199, Figs. 63a,64a.

Distribution: Eastern Atlantic: Mediterranean; Atlantic coast from Portugal to Angola.

Habitat: Depth 35 to 850 m. Bottom mud. Marine.

Size: Maximum total length 88 mm (♂), 106 mm (♀).

Interest to Fishery: The species is taken by trawlers off the Catalonian coast of Spain (Zariquiey Alvarez, 1946:66; Zariquiey Alvarez, 1955:105,111), sometimes in large quantities. These specimens however are of minor commercial importance and are usually sold as admixtures with other species of shrimp. Brian (1941:34, Fig. 9) listed the species among the edible Crustacea of the Genoa (Italy) fishmarket where it usually is found in small numbers mixed with other shrimps. Heldt & Heldt (1954:11,12) enumerated the species among the edible Crustacea of Tunisian waters, and indicated that in certain places, although it is as abundant as *Parapenaeus*, it is considered trash and not sold separately on the market.

Plesionika martia (A. Milne Edwards, 1883)	PANDL Plesion 1

Pandalus martius A. Milne Edwards, 1883, Recueil   Figures Crustacés nouveaux ou peu connus, Pl. 21, Fig. 2

Synonymy: *Plesionika semilaevis* Bate, 1888; *Plesionika (Pandalus) sicherii* Riggio, 1900; *Plesionika cottei* Kotte, 1902.

FAO Names: Golden shrimp (En), Crevette dorée (Fr), Camarón de oro (Sp).

Local Names: Golden prawn (New Zealand).

Literature: Kemp, 1910:93, Pl. 12, Figs. 1-4; Chace, 1940:190, Fig. 57; Crosnier & Forest, 1973:212, Figs. 63d,64e,66.

Distribution: Circumtropic: Western Atlantic: Bermuda and South Carolina (U.S.A.) to Gulf of Mexico and Brazil. Eastern Atlantic: Ireland south to S. Africa; Mediterranean. Indo-West Pacific: Gulf of Aden and S.E. Africa to Japan, Hawaii, Australia and Kermadec Islands.

Habitat: Depth 180 to 2 100 m. Bottom mud. Marine.

Size: Maximum total length 169 mm.

Interest to Fishery: Along the Catalonian coast of Spain the species is occasionally caught by trawlers (Zariquiey Alvarez, 1946:66), and so reaches the fishmarkets, where it may be sold as an admixture with other prawns, but its value is negligible. Brian (1941:28,31) remarked that at the fishmarket of Genoa, Italy, this species is seen rather frequently, but in limited numbers, usually mixed in with *Aristeus* and *Aristaeomorpha*. Crosnier & de Bondy (1967:41) mentioned this species as of possible commercial importance off tropical West Africa. Longhurst (1970:278) stated that Spanish trawlers off Sierra Leone and Senegal fish this species together with a number of others. Longhurst (1970:299) indicated that *Plesionika martia* is landed in Natal (South Africa) in rather small quantities and often not marketed. Crosnier & Jouannic (1973:12) ranged this species among those "éventuellement commercialisables" on the continental slope of Madagascar. Jones (1969:747), Suseelan (1976) and Kurian & Sebastian (1976:95) listed a number of species, among which the present, that might become of economic value off the west coast of India. Longhurst (1970:285) mentioned the possibility of a commercial fishery for this species on the continental slope of N. Sumatra and N.W. Malaysia. In a list of species important in the shrimp fishery in the Inland Sea of Japan near Seto, the present species also occurs (Yasuda, 1957:30). In a pamphlet put out by the New Zealand Marine Department (Anon., 1964:5,9) a number of prawn species is listed as commercial (probably potentially commercial is meant) for New Zealand waters; among these is also *Plesionika martia*.

Plesionika williamsi Forest, 1963	PANDL Plesion 9

Plesionika williamsi Forest, 1963, Bull.Mus.Hist.Nat.Paris, (2)35:621

FAO Names: Guinea striped shrimp (En), Crevette rayée guinéenne (Fr), Camarón rayado de Guinea (Sp).

Literature: Crosnier & Forest, 1973:211, Fig. 65e.

Distribution: Eastern Atlantic: West Africa, Guinea and Ivory Coast.

Habitat: Depth 300 to 455 m. Bottom mud. Marine.

Size: Maximum total length 166 mm.

Interest to Fishery: Forest (1963:628) suggested, that the species might prove to be of commercial value, because of its abundance, size and quality of the meat.

SUPERFAMILY CRANGONOIDEA Hawarth, 1825

Crangonidea Bate, 1888, Rep.Voyage Challenger, (Zool.), 24:480-1

Of the two families in this superfamily only one contains species of commercial interest.

FAMILY CRANGONIDAE Haworth, 1825

Crangonidae Haworth, 1825, Philos.Mag.J., 65:184

Among the Crangonidae only a few species are of considerable commercial importance; such species are found in temperate and boreal waters.

Argis lar (Owen, 1839)	CRANG Arg 1

Crangon lar Owen, 1839, In Beechey, Voyage Blossom, (Zool.), 88

Synonymy: *Crangon (Nectocrangon) lar* - Brandt, 1851.

FAO Names: Kuro shrimp (En), Crevette kuro (Fr), Camarón kuro (Sp).

Local Names: Kuro zako-ebi (Japan).

Literature: M.J. Rathbun, 1904:137, Figs. 74,75.

Distribution: Northern Pacific: Alaska and Bering Sea to Korea and N. Japan. Atlantic records of this species pertain almost certainly to *A. dentata* (Rathbun).

Habitat: Depth 22 to 400 m. Marine.

Size: Maximum total length 109 mm.

Interest to Fishery: Yoshida (1941:29) listed this species among the economically important shrimps of Korea.

Crangon affinis De Haan, 1849	CRANG Crang 2

Crangon affinis De Haan, 1849, In Von Siebold, Fauna Japonica, Crustacea, (6):183

Synonymy: The taxonomic status of the N.W. Pacific *Crangon* is very unsettled. A thorough revision must decide whether the forms described as *Crangon propinquus* Stimpson, 1860; *Steiracrangon orientalis* var. *longicauda* forma *pacifica* Czerniavsky, 1884; *Crangon crangon affinis* Ortmann, 1895; *Crangon vulgaris shidlovskii* Ostroumoff, 1896; *Crangon hakodatei* M.J. Rathbun, 1902; *Crangon consobrinus* De Man, 1906; *Crangon cassiope* De Man, 1906; *Crangon septemspinosa amurensis* Brashnikov, 1907; *Crangon septemspinosa anivensis* Brashnikov, 1907, are identical with *Crangon affinis*, and even whether or not the latter species is distinct from *Crangon crangon* (L.). For the time being the authors are followed who consider *C. affinis* the only species of the *Crangon crangon* group in the N.W. Pacific.

FAO Names: Japanese sand shrimp (En), Crevette japonaise (Fr), Quisquilla japonesa (Sp).

Local Names: Zako ebi, Ebi zako (Japan).

Distribution: Northwestern Pacific: Siberia; Korea; China; Saghalin; Japan.

Habitat: Depth 0 to 219 m. Marine, sometimes in somewhat brackish water.

Size: Maximum total length 68 mm ($\female$); maximum carapace length 17 mm.

Interest to Fishery: Liu (1955:58,59,60) listed *Crangon crangon*, *C. cassiope* and *C. affinis* among the shrimps of economic importance in N. China. Harada (1963:82) indicated that the species is fished for by commercial fishermen in the region of Lake Naka-umi on the west coast of Honshu, Japan. Also in the Inland Sea of Japan near Seto *Crangon affinis* is of some importance in the shrimp fishery (Yasuda, 1956:9; 1957:30).

Crangon alaskensis Lockington, 1877	CRANG Crang 3

Crangon alaskensis Lockington, 1877, Proc.Calif.Acad.Sci., 7:34

Synonymy: *Crago alaskensis* - Shelford, 1935.

FAO Names: Alaska shrimp (En), Crevette alaska (Fr), Quisquilla de Alaska (Sp).

Local Names: Alaska shrimp, Gray shrimp (U.S.A.).

Literature: M.J. Rathbun, 1904:114, Figs. 52,53.

Distribution: Northeastern Pacific: Bering Sea to Washington, U.S.A.

Habitat: Depth 6 to 72 m. Marine.

Size: Maximum total length 77 mm.

Interest to Fishery: According to Flora & Fairbanks (1966:172) this species is "sometimes netted commercially for food " presumably in the Puget Sound area.

Crangon communis Rathbun, 1899   **CRANG Crang 4**

Crangon communis M.J. Rathbun, 1899, Fur Seals & Fur Seal Islands, 3:556

Synonymy: _Sclerocrangon communis_ - Brashnikov, 1907; _Crago communis_ - Schmitt, 1921; _Crangon (Neocrangon) communis_ - Zarenkov, 1965.

FAO Names: Gray shrimp (En), Crevette cendrée (Fr), Quisquilla gris (Sp).

Local Names: Gray shrimp (U.S.A.).

Literature: M.J. Rathbun, 1904:123, Fig. 64; Schmitt, 1921:95, Fig. 63.

Distribution: Northeastern Pacific: Bering Sea to S. California, U.S.A.

Habitat: Depth 32 to 555 m. Marine.

Size: Maximum total length 73 mm.

Interest to Fishery: Flora & Fairbanks (1966:173) cited this species among the shrimp from Puget Sound area that are of commercial value, be it that it is less important than _C. franciscorum_. Also Ricketts, Calvin & Hedgpeth (1968:286) mentioned "commercially netted _Crago communis_ in Puget Sound".

Crangon crangon (Linnaeus, 1758)   **CRANG Crang 1**

Cancer crangon Linnaeus, 1758, Syst.Nat., (ed. 10) 1:632

Synonymy: _Astacus crangon_ - Müller, 1776; _Crangon vulgaris_ Fabricius, 1798; _Crago vulgaris_ - Lamarck, 1801; _Crangon rubropunctatus_ Risso, 1816; _Crangon maculosa_ Rathke, 1837; _Crangon maculatus_ Marcusen, 1867; _Crangon maculosa typica_ Czerniavsky, 1884; _Crangon maculosa brevirostris_ Czerniavsky, 1884; _Crangon maculosa suchumica_ Czerniavsky, 1884; _Steiracrangon orientalis_ Czerniavsky, 1884 (with var. _longicauda_ forma _intermedia_ and var. _brevicauda_); _Crangon crangon typicus_ Doflein, 1900; _Crangon crangon mediterranea_ Brashnikov, 1907.

FAO Names: Common shrimp (En), Crevette grise (Fr), Quisquilla (Sp).

Local Names: Sandreke, Hestereke (Norway), Hestereje, Sandhest (Denmark), Räkhäst, Sandräka (Sweden), Hieta katkarapu (Finland), Nordseegarnele, Nordseekrabbe, Krabbe, Granat, Kraut, Porre, Sanduhl (Germany), Garnaal, Noordzeegarnaal, Garnaat, Garn (Netherlands, Belgium), Shrimp, Common shrimp, Brown shrimp (Great Britain), Crevette grise (France, Belgium), Sauticot (Normandy, France), Bouc (Brittany, France), Cabra, Camarão mouro, Camarão branco (Portugal), Quisquilla (Spain; official name), Gambaro gris (Provence, France), Gambero della sabbia, Gamberetto grigio (Italy; Palombi & Santarelli, 1961:368, indicate many local Italian names for the species), Pieskorovna kozica (Yugoslavia), Cali karidesi (Turkey), Creveta de nisip, Garida de nisip (Romania), Garĩda (Israel), Bargouth bharr (Tunisia), Обь кнтовеннь й Шримс,   Гранат (U.S.S.R.).

Literature: Tiews, 1970:1 167-1 224, Figs. 1-20.

Distribution: Eastern Atlantic: Baltic, Atlantic coast of Europe from the White Sea to Portugal; Mediterranean; Black Sea; Atlantic coast of Morocco.

Habitat: Shallow coastal waters (0 to 20 m) although there are records of up to 130 m depth. Bottom sand or muddy sand. Marine or slightly brackish.

Size: Maximum total length 89 mm.

Interest to Fishery: The commercial fishery for *Crangon crangon* is carried out along the entire North Sea coasts of Germany, the Netherlands and Belgium, on the east, southeast and northwest coasts of England, and the Atlantic coasts of France especially near the estuaries. In Portugal it is caught with special nets, the so called "mugigangas" (Nobre, 1936, 176). In Morocco it is also fished and sold. Gruvel (1923:84) remarked: "On la rencontre en petit nombre, surtout sur le marché de Casablanca et aussi sur celui de Mogador ... Sa consommation est très réduite" (compared to *Parapenaeus* and *Palaemon longirostris*). Summarizing we can say that in the northeastern Atlantic *Crangon crangon* is caught in far greater quantities than any other crustacean; it is especially important on the North Sea coasts of Germany, the Netherlands, and Belgium, and seems to diminish in economic value farther away from this center.

As far as the Mediterranean is concerned, in Algeria *Crangon crangon* forms the main part of the catches from the shrimping grounds near Nemours and Oran (Ivanov, 1967:56). Although Heldt & Heldt (1954) do not mention the species, Gruvel (1926a:36) and Kouki (1970?:95) treated it among the edible Crustacea of Tunis. Brian (1941:46) stated that the species is sold at the fishmarket of Genoa, Italy, where this shrimp is fished in great quantities. Giordani Soika (1948:27) also indicated that *Crangon crangon* in the Venice area is of considerable commercial importance, being greatly esteemed as food.

Invanov's (1967:1) statement that the species is fished in Iceland must have been based on incorrect information: Stephenson (1939) did not even list the species among the Decapoda of Iceland.

Crangon franciscorum Stimpson, 1856	CRANG Crang 5

Crangon franciscorum Stimpson, 1856, Proc.Calif.Acad.Sci., 1:97

Synonymy: *Crago franciscorum* - Scofield, 1919.

FAO Names: California shrimp (En), Crevette californienne (Fr), Quisquilla californiana (Sp).

Local Names: California shrimp, Bay shrimp, Gray shrimp (U.S.A.)

Literature: M.J. Rathbun, 1904:120, Fig. 61; Schmitt, 1921:92, Fig. 62.

Distribution: Eastern Pacific: Alaska to South California, U.S.A.

Habitat: Depth 5 to 50 m. Bottom sand, mud. Marine.

Size: Maximum total length 80 mm.

Interest to Fishery: R. Rathbun (1884:818) indicated that this "is the Shrimp par excellence of the San Francisco market, where large quantities are sold during nearly every month of the year". "Up to 1954, Bay shrimp [= *C. franciscorum* (mainly), with *C. nigricauda* and *C. nigromaculata*] account for about 75 percent of the total California catch of shrimp" after that time the *Pandalus* catch exceeded the *Crangon* catch (U.S. Bureau of Commercial Fisheries 1958:8). According to McGinitie & McGinitie (1949: 275) "the main fisheries [for this species] are in Puget Sound and San Francisco Bay". Also Flora & Fairbanks (1966:173) indicated this species, together with *C. nigricauda* and *C. communis* as "of commercial value with *C. franciscorum* most important", presumably in the Puget Sound area.

Crangon nigricauda Stimpson, 1856	CRANG Crang 6

Crangon nigricauda Stimpson, 1856, Proc.Calif.Acad.Sci., 1:89

Synonymy: *Crago nigricauda* - Hilton, 1918; *Crangon (Neocrangon) nigricauda* - Zarenkov, 1965.

FAO Names: Blacktailed shrimp (En), Crevette queue noire (Fr), Quisquilla rabo negro (Sp).

Local Names: Black-tailed shrimp (U.S.A.).

Literature: M.J. Rathbun, 1904:112, Fig. 50; Schmitt, 1921:84, Fig. 56.

Distribution: Eastern Pacific: British Columbia, Canada to Baja California, Mexico.

Habitat: Depth 5 to 50 m. Bottom sand and mud. Marine.

Size: Maximum total length 68 mm.

Interest to Fishery: The species is sold with *Crangon franciscorum*, e.g. at the San Francisco market, but is much less important than that species (U.S. Bureau of Commercial Fisheries, 1958:8), the same seems to be true for the Puget Sound area (Flora & Fairbanks, 1966:173). Ricketts, Calvin & Hedgpeth (1968:286) called this "one of the common market shrimps in California". According to Bonnot (1932:14) in the California shrimp catches the present species is the second in importance, the first being *C. franciscorum*, the third *C. nigromaculata*; sometimes the order of importance between *C. nigricauda* and *C. nigromaculata* is revised.

Crangon nigromaculata Lockington, 1877	CRANG Crang 7

Crangon nigromaculata Lockington, 1877, Proc.Calif.Acad.Sci., 7:34

Synonymy: *Crago nigromaculatus* - Hilton, 1916; *Crangon (Neocrangon) nigromaculata* - Zarenkov, 1965.

FAO Names: Bay shrimp (En), Crevette baie (Fr), Quisquilla de caleta (Sp).

Local Names: Bay shrimp, Gray shrimp (U.S.A.).

Literature: M.J. Rathbun, 1904:114, Fig. 52; Schmitt, 1921:86, Fig. 57.

Distribution: Eastern Pacific: Northern California, U.S.A. to Baja California, Mexico.

Habitat: Depth 5 to 60 m. Bottom muddy sand or mud. Marine.

Size: Maximum total length 69 mm.

Interest to Fishery: This is one of the three commercial shrimps of the San Francisco Bay area: *Crangon franciscorum* being by far the most important, *C. nigricauda* is usually the next important and *C. nigromaculata* the third. According to Bonnot (1932:14) in some seasons *C. nigromaculata* is more numerous than *C. nigricauda*.

Crangon septemspinosa Say, 1818	CRANG Crang 8

Crangon septemspinosa Say, 1818, J.Acad.Nat.Sci.Phila., 1:246

Synonymy: *Crago septemspinosus* - M.J. Rathbun, 1905. This species has often been identified with *Crangon crangon* (L.) and its status, like that of *Crangon affinis*, is far from clear. Here *Crangon septemspinosa* is treated as the representative of the *Crangon crangon* group on the American Atlantic coast. A thorough revision of the genus will show the relation between the various forms and also make certain whether or not *C. septemspinosa* does occur in both sides of the northern Pacific as some authors think.

FAO Names: Sand shrimp (En), Crevette sable (Fr), Quisquilla arenera (Sp).

Local Names: Sand shrimp, Common shrimp, Bail shrimp, Gray shrimp (U.S.A.), Песчань и Шримс (U.S.S.R.).

Literature: Williams, 1965:89, Fig. 72.

Distribution: Northwestern Atlantic: Baffin Bay to east coast of Florida, U.S.A.

Habitat: Depth 0 to 90 m, rarely to 440 m. Bottom sand. Marine and estuarine.

Size: Maximum total length 50 mm (♂), 70 mm (♀).

Interest to Fishery: According to De Kay (1844:26) in New York it is "being used exclusively for bait". Also Gould (1841:331) stated that in Massachusetts "it is nowhere sufficiently abundant to make it an object to collect it for food". R. Rathbun (1884:817) however, mentioned that "In the neighbourhood of New York and about New Bedford, Mass., it is taken as food. Northward from there it is, so far as we know, only utilized to a slight extent, and for bait only ... from all the information we have been able to obtain, no notice is taken of it south of New York". The U.S. Bureau of Commercial Fisheries (1958:8) indicated that "in New York and New Jersey, where the fishery is almost entirely for bait shrimp, sand shrimp *Crangon vulgaris* and grass shrimp *Palaemonetes vulgaris* and *Palaemonetes carolinus* constitute the entire catch".

| *Pontocaris lacazei* (Gourret, 1887) | CRANG Pont 1 |

Crangon lacazei Gourret, 1887, C.R.Hebd.Séances Acad.Sci., Paris, 105:1 033

Synonymy: *Aegeon brendani* Kemp, 1906; *Aegeon lacazei* - Kemp, 1910.

FAO Names: Hardshell shrimp (En), Crevette crâne (Fr), Camarón de casco (Sp).

Literature: Kemp, 1910:156, Pl. 22, Figs. 1-5.

Distribution: Eastern Atlantic: from S.W. Ireland to S. Africa; Western Mediterranean. Indo-West Pacific: also reported from E. Africa and New Zealand.

Habitat: Depth 50 to 684 m. Marine.

Size: Maximum total length 49 mm.

Interest to Fishery: Probably nil. Zariquiey Alvarez (1946:90) indicated that the species is caught "con grandísima frecuencia" by the commercial trawlers off the Catalonian coast of Spain. Specimens do reach the fishmarkets, but usually as trash or as admixtures with other shrimps.

| *Pontocaris pennata* Bate, 1888 | CRANG Pont 2 |

Pontocaris pennata Bate, 1888, Rep.Voyage Challenger, (Zool.), 24:499

Synonymy: ?*Aegeon affine* Alcock, 1901; *Aegeon pennata* - Balss, 1914; *Aegeon obsoletum* - Balss, 1914.

FAO Names: Feather shrimp (En), Crevette emplumée (Fr), Camarón de pluma (Sp).

Literature: De Man, 1920:294, Pl. 24, Fig. 70.

Distribution: Indo-West Pacific: Red Sea to Japan and the Malay Archipelago.

Habitat: Depth 20 to 900 m. Bottom sandy mud. Marine.

Size: Maximum total length 43 mm.

Interest to Fishery: So far minor. Only Yasuda (1957:30) mentioned it as important in the shrimp fishery of the Inland Sea of Japan near Seto.

| *Pontophilus spinosus* (Leach, 1815) | CRANG Pontop 1 |

Crangon spinosus Leach, 1815, <u>Trans.Linn.Soc.Lond.</u>, 4:346

Synonymy: *Pontophilus spinosus* - Leach, 1817; *Astacus (Crangon) spinosus* - Moore, 1839; *Cheraphilus spinosus* - Kinahan, 1860.

FAO Names: Spiny shrimp (En), Crevette épine (Fr), Camarón espinudo (Sp).

Local Names: Spiny shrimp (Great Britain; White, 1857).

Literature: Kemp, 1910:160, Pl. 21, Fig. 8.

Distribution: Eastern Atlantic: Iceland and N. Norway south to the Mediterranean.

Habitat: Depth 20 to 1 550 m. Marine.

Size: Maximum total length 52 mm.

Interest to Fishery: Little if at all. Zariquiey Alvarez (1946:91) indicated that it is caught by commercial trawlers off the Catalonian coast of Spain. The species is not sold as such, but may be mixed in with other shrimps. Brian (1941:44, Fig. 11) found a few specimens of this species on the fishmarket of Genoa, Italy, mixed in with *Aristeus* and *Aristaeomorpha*.

| *Sclerocrangon salebrosa* (Owen, 1839) | CRANG Sclero 1 |

Crangon salebrosus Owen, 1839, <u>In</u> Beechey, Voyage Blossom, (Zool.), 88

FAO Names: Bering shrimp (En), Crevette bering (Fr), Camarón de Bering (Sp).

Local Names: Шримс - Медвежонок (U.S.S.R.), Kijin ebi (Japan).

Literature: Brashnikov, 1907:91, Pl. 2, Fig. 4; Urita, 1942:34, Fig. 10; Ivanov, 1955:32, Figs. 9,10.

Distribution: Northwestern Pacific: Bering Sea, Okhotsk Sea and northern Japan Sea as far south as Peter the Great Bay.

Habitat: Depth 10 to 250 m. Marine.

Size: Maximum total length 200 mm, seldom to 300 mm.

Interest to Fishery: The species is considered by Ivanov (1955:32-34) and Kobjakova (1955:151) to be potentially of commercial value along the east coast of Siberia. It is interesting to note that the related *Sclerocrangon boreas* in Greenland is considered unfit for consumption because of the dryness of the meat (Jensen, 1928:77).

3. LIST OF SPECIES BY MAJOR MARINE FISHING AREAS

DISTRIBUTION

MAJOR MARINE FISHING AREAS FOR STATISTICAL PURPOSES

SPECIES	PAGE	FRESH WATERS	18	21	27	31	34	37	41	47	48	51	57	58	61	67	71	77	81	87	88
FAMILY SOLENOCERIDAE																					
Hadropenaeus lucasii En: Trident shrimp Fr: Salicoque trident Sp: Camarón tridente	1											●	●		●		●	●			
Haliporoides diomedeae En: Chilean knife shrimp Fr: Salicoque couteau Sp: Camarón cuchilla	2																	●		●	
Haliporoides sibogae En: Jack-knife shrimp Fr: Salicoque canif Sp: Camarón cortapluma	2												●		●		●		●		
Haliporoides triarthrus En: Knife shrimp Fr: Salicoque navaja Sp: Camarón navaja	3									●		●									
Hymenopenaeus aequalis En: Veiled shrimp Fr: Salicoque voilée Sp: Camarón de velete	3											●	●		●		●				
Pleoticus muelleri En: Argentine red shrimp Fr: Salicoque rouge d'Argentine Sp: Camarón langostín argentino	3								●												

DISTRIBUTION

MAJOR MARINE FISHING AREAS FOR STATISTICAL PURPOSES

SPECIES	PAGE	FRESH WATERS	18	21	27	31	34	37	41	47	48	51	57	58	61	67	71	77	81	87	88
Plecticus robustus En: Royal red shrimp Fr: Salicoque royale rouge Sp: Camarón rojo real	4			●		●															
Solenocera africana En: African mud shrimp Fr: Solenocère d'Afrique Sp: Camarón fanguero africano	4						●			●											
Solenocera agassizii En: Kolibri shrimp Fr: Salicoque colibri Sp: Camarón chupaflor	5																	●		●	
Solenocera choprai En: Ridgeback shrimp Fr: Salicoque balafrée Sp: Camarón costurón	5											●	●		●		●				
Solenocera crassicornis En: Coastal mud shrimp Fr: Salicoque des vases côtières Sp: Camarón fanguero de orilla	5											●	●		●		●				
Solenocera florea En: Flower shrimp Fr: Salicoque fleur Sp: Camarón picaflor	6																	●		●	

– 157 –

DISTRIBUTION

SPECIES	PAGE	FRESH WATERS	18	21	27	31	34	37	41	47	48	51	57	58	61	67	71	77	81	87	88
Solenocera geijskesi En: Guiana mud shrimp Fr: Salicoque guyanaise Sp: Camarón guayanés	6					●			●												
Solenocera heatii En: Deep-sea mud shrimp Fr: Salicoque des vases profondes Sp: Camarón fanguero de altura	6											●	●								
Solenocera koelbeli En: Chinese mud shrimp Fr: Salicoque chinoise de vase Sp: Camarón fanguero chino	7														●		●				
Solenocera membranacea En: Atlantic mud shrimp Fr: Salicoque des vases (de l'Atlantique) Sp: Gamba de fango del Atlántico	7				●		●	●													
Solenocera pectinata En: Comb shrimp Fr: Salicoque peigne Sp: Camarón peine	8											●	●		●	●	●				
FAMILY ARISTEIDAE *Aristaeomorpha foliacea* En: Giant red shrimp Fr: Gambon rouge Sp: Gamba española	8			●	●	●	●	●				●	●		●		●		●		

MAJOR MARINE FISHING AREAS FOR STATISTICAL PURPOSES

DISTRIBUTION

MAJOR MARINE FISHING AREAS FOR STATISTICAL PURPOSES

SPECIES	PAGE	FRESH WATERS	18	21	27	31	34	37	41	47	48	51	57	58	61	67	71	77	81	87	88
Aristaeomorpha woodmasoni En: Indian red shrimp Fr: Gambon indien Sp: Gamba roja india	9											●	●								
Aristeus alcocki En: Arabian red shrimp Fr: Gambon d'Arabie Sp: Gamba roja arábiga	9											●	●								
Aristeus antennatus En: Blue and red shrimp Fr: Crevette rouge Sp: Gamba rosada	10				●		●	●													
Aristeus semidentatus En: Smooth red shrimp Fr: Gambon lisse Sp: Gamba roja lisa	10											●	●				●	●	●		
Aristeus varidens En: Striped red shrimp Fr: Gambon rayé Sp: Gamba listada	10						●			●											
Aristeus virilis En: Stout red shrimp Fr: Gambon gaillard Sp: Gambón colorado	11											●	●		●		●				

DISTRIBUTION

SPECIES	PAGE	FRESH WATERS	MAJOR MARINE FISHING AREAS FOR STATISTICAL PURPOSES

SPECIES	PAGE	FRESH WATERS	18	21	27	31	34	37	41	47	48	51	57	58	61	67	71	77	81	87	88
Plesiopenaeus edwardsianus En: Scarlet shrimp Fr: Gambon écarlat Sp: Gamba carabinero	11			●	●	●	●			●		●	●				●				
FAMILY PENAEIDAE *Artemesia longinaris* En: Argentine stiletto shrimp Fr: Crevette stylet d'Argentine Sp: Camarón estilete argentino	12								●												
Atypopenaeus formosus En: Orange shrimp Fr: Crevette orange Sp: Camarón naranja	12																●				
Atypopenaeus stenodactylus En: Periscope shrimp Fr: Crevette périscope Sp: Camarón periscopio	13											●	●		●		●				
Macropetasma africana En: Swimming shrimp Fr: Crevette nageuse Sp: Camarón nadador	13									●		●									
Metapenaeopsis acclivis En: Tora velvet shrimp Fr: Crevette chamois tora Sp: Camarón gamuza tora	13														●						

DISTRIBUTION

MAJOR MARINE FISHING AREAS FOR STATISTICAL PURPOSES

SPECIES	PAGE	FRESH WATERS	18	21	27	31	34	37	41	47	48	51	57	58	61	67	71	77	81	87	88
Metapenaeopsis andamanensis En: Rice velvet shrimp Fr: Crevette chamois des rizières Sp: Camarón gamuza de arrozal	14											●	●		●		●				
Metapenaeopsis barbata En: Whiskered velvet shrimp Fr: Crevette chamois barbulée Sp: Camarón gamuza barbudo	14											●	●		●		●				
Metapenaeopsis borradailei En: Reef shrimp Fr: Crevette des récifs Sp: Camarón de arrecife	15											●	●				●				
Metapenaeopsis crassissima En: Stout velvet shrimp Fr: Crevette chamois gaill Sp: Camarón gamuza toro	15												●								
Metapenaeopsis dalei En: Kishi velvet shrimp Fr: Crevette chamois kishi Sp: Camarón gamuza kishi	15														●						
Metapenaeopsis goodei En: Caribbean velvet shrimp Fr: Crevette chamois caraïbe Sp: Camarón gamuza del Caribe	16					●			●												

DISTRIBUTION

SPECIES	PAGE	FRESH WATERS	MAJOR MARINE FISHING AREAS FOR STATISTICAL PURPOSES																		
			18	21	27	31	34	37	41	47	48	51	57	58	61	67	71	77	81	87	88
Metapenaeopsis hilarula En: Minstrel shrimp Fr: Crevette chamois ménestrel Sp: Camarón gamuza bardo	16											●	●				●				
Metapenaeopsis lamellata En: Humpback shrimp Fr: Crevette bossue Sp: Camarón jorobado	16												●		●		●				
Metapenaeopsis lata En: Broad velvet shrimp Fr: Crevette chamois trappue Sp: Camarón gamuza espaldudo	17														●						
Metapenaeopsis mogiensis En: Mogi velvet shrimp Fr: Crevette chamois mogi Sp: Camarón gamuza mogi	17											●	●		●		●				
Metapenaeopsis novaeguineae En: Northern velvet shrimp Fr: Crevette chamois nordique Sp: Camarón gamuza norteño	17												●				●				
Metapenaeopsis palmensis En: Southern velvet shrimp Fr: Crevette chamois méridionale Sp: Camarón gamuza sureño	18												●				●		●		

DISTRIBUTION

MAJOR MARINE FISHING AREAS FOR STATISTICAL PURPOSES

SPECIES	PAGE	FRESH WATERS	18	21	27	31	34	37	41	47	48	51	57	58	61	67	71	77	81	87	88
Metapenaeopsis philippii En: Philip velvet shrimp Fr: Crevette chamois philippe Sp: Camarón gamuza Felipe	18											●	●				●				
Metapenaeopsis rosea En: Pink velvet shrimp Fr: Crevette chamois rosée Sp: Camarón gamuza rosado	19																●				
Metapenaeopsis stridulans En: Fiddler shrimp Fr: Crevette violoneux Sp: Camarón violinista	19											●	●				●				
Metapenaeopsis toloensis En: Tolo velvet shrimp Fr: Crevette chamois tolo Sp: Camarón gamuza tolo	19											●	●				●				
Metapenaeus affinis En: Jinga shrimp Fr: Crevette jinga Sp: Camarón jinga	20											●	●		●		●				
Metapenaeus alcocki En: Fire shrimp Fr: Crevette étincelle Sp: Camarón foguete	20											●									

DISTRIBUTION

MAJOR MARINE FISHING AREAS FOR STATISTICAL PURPOSES

SPECIES	PAGE	FRESH WATERS	18	21	27	31	34	37	41	47	48	51	57	58	61	67	71	77	81	87	88
Metapenaeus bennettae En: Greentail shrimp Fr: Crevette queue verte Sp: Camarón rabo verde	20																●		●		
Metapenaeus brevicornis En: Yellow shrimp Fr: Crevette jaune Sp: Camarón amarillo	21											●	●				●				
Metapenaeus conjunctus En: Wood shrimp Fr: Crevette bois Sp: Camarón leña	21																●				
Metapenaeus dalli En: Western school shrimp Fr: Crevette dali Sp: Camarón dali	22												●				●				
Metapenaeus demani En: Demon shrimp Fr: Crevette diable Sp: Camarón diablo	22																●				
Metapenaeus dobsoni En: Kadal shrimp Fr: Crevette kadal Sp: Camarón kadal	22											●	●				●				

DISTRIBUTION

MAJOR MARINE FISHING AREAS FOR STATISTICAL PURPOSES

SPECIES	PAGE	FRESH WATERS	18	21	27	31	34	37	41	47	48	51	57	58	61	67	71	77	81	87	88
Metapenaeus eboracensis En: York shrimp Fr: Crevette york Sp: Camarón york	23																●				
Metapenaeus elegans En: Fine shrimp Fr: Crevette élégante Sp: Camarón fino	23											●	●				●				
Metapenaeus endeavouri En: Endeavour shrimp Fr: Crevette devo Sp: Camarón devo	23												●				●		●		
Metapenaeus ensis En: Greasyback shrimp Fr: Crevette glissante Sp: Camarón resbaloso	24											●	●		●		●		●		
Metapenaeus insolitus En: Emerald shrimp Fr: Crevette éméraude Sp: Camarón esmeralda	24																●				
Metapenaeus intermedius En: Middle shrimp Fr: Crevette ceinture Sp: Camarón cintura	25														●		●				

DISTRIBUTION

SPECIES	PAGE	FRESH WATERS	MAJOR MARINE FISHING AREAS FOR STATISTICAL PURPOSES																		
			18	21	27	31	34	37	41	47	48	51	57	58	61	67	71	77	81	87	88
Metapenaeus joyneri En: Shiba shrimp Fr: Crevette siba Sp: Camarón siba	25														●						
Metapenaeus kutchensis En: Ginger shrimp Fr: Crevette gingembre Sp: Camarón jengibre	25											●									
Metapenaeus lysianassa En: Bird shrimp Fr: Crevette oiseau Sp: Camarón parancero	26											●	●				●				
Metapenaeus macleayi En: Eastern school shrimp Fr: Crevette de maclay Sp: Camarón maclayo	26																●		●		
Metapenaeus monoceros En: Speckled shrimp Fr: Crevette mouchetée Sp: Camarón moteado	26							●				●	●								
Metapenaeus moyebi En: Moyebi shrimp Fr: Crevette moyebi Sp: Camarón moyebi	27											●	●		●		●				

DISTRIBUTION

SPECIES	PAGE	FRESH WATERS	18	21	27	31	34	37	41	47	48	51	57	58	61	67	71	77	81	37	38
Metapenaeus papuensis En: Papua shrimp Fr: Crevette papou Sp: Camarón papuense	28																●				
Metapenaeus stebbingi En: Peregrine shrimp Fr: Crevette faucon Sp: Camarón peregrino	28							●				●									
Metapenaeus tenuipes En: Stork shrimp Fr: Crevette cigogne Sp: Camarón cigueña	29																●				
Parapenaeopsis acclivirostris En: Hawknose shrimp Fr: Crevette aquiline Sp: Camarón aguileño	29									●		●	●								
Parapenaeopsis arafurica En: Arafura shrimp Fr: Crevette arafura Sp: Camarón arafura	29																●				
Parapenaeopsis atlantica En: Guinea shrimp Fr: Crevette guinéenne Sp: Camarón guineo	30						●			●											

MAJOR MARINE FISHING AREAS FOR STATISTICAL PURPOSES

DISTRIBUTION

SPECIES	PAGE	FRESH WATERS	18	21	27	31	34	37	41	47	48	51	57	58	61	67	71	77	81	87	88
Parapenaeopsis cornuta En: Coral shrimp Fr: Crevette corail Sp: Camarón coral	30											●	●		●		●				
Parapenaeopsis coromandelica En: Coromandel shrimp Fr: Crevette coromandel Sp: Camarón coromandel	30											●	●				●				
Parapenaeopsis hardwickii En: Spear shrimp Fr: Crevette javelot Sp: Camarón lanzón	31											●	●		●		●				
Parapenaeopsis hungerfordi En: Dog shrimp Fr: Crevette chien Sp: Camarón perro	31														●		●				
Parapenaeopsis maxillipedo En: Torpedo shrimp Fr: Crevette torpille Sp: Camarón torpedo	31											●	●				●				
Parapenaeopsis nana En: Dwarf shrimp Fr: Crevette naine Sp: Camarón enano	32											●	●								

MAJOR MARINE FISHING AREAS FOR STATISTICAL PURPOSES

DISTRIBUTION

MAJOR MARINE FISHING AREAS FOR STATISTICAL PURPOSES

SPECIES	PAGE	FRESH WATERS	18	21	27	31	34	37	41	47	48	51	57	58	61	67	71	77	81	87	38
Parapenaeopsis probata En: Parole shrimp Fr: Crevette parole Sp: Camarón parolo	32																●				
Parapenaeopsis sculptilis En: Rainbow shrimp Fr: Crevette arc-en-ciel Sp: Camarón arco iris	32											●	●		●		●				
Parapenaeopsis stylifera En: Kiddi shrimp Fr: Crevette kidi Sp: Camarón kidi	33											●	●								
Parapenaeopsis tenella En: Smoothshell shrimp Fr: Crevette glabre Sp: Camarón liso	33											●	●		●		●				
Parapenaeopsis uncta En: Uncta shrimp Fr: Crevette uncta Sp: Camarón unta	34											●	●								
Parapenaeopsis venusta En: Adonis shrimp Fr: Crevette adonis Sp: Camarón adonis	34																●				

DISTRIBUTION

MAJOR MARINE FISHING AREAS FOR STATISTICAL PURPOSES

SPECIES	PAGE	FRESH WATERS	18	21	27	31	34	37	41	47	43	51	57	58	61	67	71	77	81	87	38
Parapenaeus australiensis En: Australian rose shrimp Fr: Crevette rose australienne Sp: Camarón rosado australiano	34																●		●		
Parapenaeus fissurus En: Neptune rose shrimp Fr: Crevette neptune Sp: Camarón rosado neptuno	35											●	●		●		●				
Parapenaeus investigatoris En: Explorer rose shrimp Fr: Crevette rose chercheuse Sp: Camarón explorador	35									●		●	●		●		●				
Parapenaeus lanceolatus En: Lancer rose shrimp Fr: Crevette rose lancier Sp: Camarón rosado lanzón	35														●						
Parapenaeus longipes En: Flamingo shrimp Fr: Crevette flamand Sp: Camarón flamenco	36											●	●		●		●				
Parapenaeus longirostris En: Deep-water rose shrimp Fr: Crevette rose du large Sp: Camarón de altura	36			●	●	●	●	●		●											

DISTRIBUTION

SPECIES	PAGE	FRESH WATERS	MAJOR MARINE FISHING AREAS FOR STATISTICAL PURPOSES																	
			18	21	27	31	34	37	41	47	48	51	57	58	61	67	71	77	81	87	88
Parapenaeus sextuberculatus En: Domino shrimp Fr: Crevette domino Sp: Camarón dominó	37											●	●		●		●				
Penaeopsis rectacuta En: Needle shrimp Fr: Crevette aiguille Sp: Camarón aguja	37											●	●		●		●				
Penaeopsis serrata En: Megalops shrimp Fr: Crevette megalops Sp: Camarón megalops	37					●	●														
Penaeus (Farfantepenaeus) aztecus En: Northern brown shrimp Fr: Crevette royale grise Sp: Camarón café norteño.	38			●		●															
Penaeus (Farfantepenaeus) brasiliensis En: Redspotted shrimp Fr: Crevette royale rose Sp: Camarón rosado con manchas	38			●		●		●													
Penaeus (Farfantepenaeus) brevirostris En: Crystal shrimp Fr: Crevette cristal Sp: Camarón cristal	39																	●		●	

DISTRIBUTION

MAJOR MARINE FISHING AREAS FOR STATISTICAL PURPOSES

SPECIES	PAGE	FRESH WATERS	18	21	27	31	34	37	41	47	48	51	57	58	61	67	71	77	81	87	88
Penaeus (Farfantepenaeus) californiensis En: Yellowleg shrimp Fr: Crevette pattes jaunes Sp: Camarón patiamarillo	39																	●		●	
Penaeus (Farfantepenaeus) duorarum En: Northern pink shrimp Fr: Crevette rodché du nord Sp: Camarón rosado norteño	39			●		●															
Penaeus (Farfantepenaeus) notialis En: Southern pink shrimp Fr: Crevette rodché du sud Sp: Camarón rosado sureño	40					●	●		●	●											
Penaeus (Farfantepenaeus) paulensis En: Sao Paulo shrimp Fr: Crevette de São Paulo Sp: Camarón de São Paulo	41								●												
Penaeus (Farfantepenaeus) subtilis En: Southern brown shrimp Fr: Crevette café Sp: Camarón café sureño	41					●			●												
Penaeus (Fenneropenaeus) chinensis En: Fleshy prawn Fr: Crevette charnue Sp: Camarón carnoso	41														●						

DISTRIBUTION

MAJOR MARINE FISHING AREAS FOR STATISTICAL PURPOSES

SPECIES	PAGE	FRESH WATERS	18	21	27	31	34	37	41	47	48	51	57	58	61	67	71	77	81	87	88
Penaeus (Fenneropenaeus) indicus En: Indian white prawn Fr: Crevette royale blanche (des Indes) Sp: Camarón blanco de la India	42									●		●	●		●		●				
Penaeus (Fenneropenaeus) merguiensis En: Banana prawn Fr: Crevette banana Sp: Camarón banana	43											●	●		●		●				
Penaeus (Fenneropenaeus) penicillatus En: Redtail prawn Fr: Crevette queue rouge Sp: Camarón rabo colorado	43											●	●		●		●				
Penaeus (Litopenaeus) occidentalis En: Western white shrimp Fr: Crevette royale blanche (du Pacifique) Sp: Camarón blanco del Pacifico	44																	●		●	
Penaeus (Litopenaeus) schmitti En: Southern white shrimp Fr: Crevette ligubam du sud Sp: Camarón blanco sureño	44						●		●												
Penaeus (Litopenaeus) setiferus En: Northern white shrimp Fr: Crevette ligubam du nord Sp: Camarón blanco norteño	45			●		●															

DISTRIBUTION

MAJOR MARINE FISHING AREAS FOR STATISTICAL PURPOSES

SPECIES	PAGE	FRESH WATERS	18	21	27	31	34	37	41	47	48	51	57	58	61	67	71	77	81	87	88
Penaeus (Litopenaeus) stylirostris En: Blue shrimp Fr: Crevette bleue Sp: Camarón azul	45																	●		●	
Penaeus (Litopenaeus) vannamei En: Whiteleg shrimp Fr: Crevette pattes blanches Sp: Camarón patiblanco	46																	●		●	
Penaeus (Marsupenaeus) japonicus En: Kuruma prawn Fr: Crevette kuruma Sp: Camarón kuruma	46							●				●	●		●		●				
Penaeus (Melicertus) canaliculatus En: Witch prawn Fr: Crevette sorcière Sp: Camarón brujo	47									●		●	●		●		●				
Penaeus (Melicertus) kerathurus En: Caramote prawn Fr: Caramote Sp: Camarón langostino espanol	47				●		●	●		●											
Penaeus (Melicertus) latisulcatus En: Western king prawn Fr: Crevette royale occidentale Sp: Camarón real	48											●	●		●		●				

DISTRIBUTION

SPECIES	PAGE	FRESH WATERS	MAJOR MARINE FISHING AREAS FOR STATISTICAL PURPOSES																		
			18	21	27	31	34	37	41	47	48	51	57	58	61	67	71	77	81	87	88
Penaeus (Melicertus) longistylus En: Redspot king prawn Fr: Crevette royale à taches rouges Sp: Camarón real manchado	43																●		●		
Penaeus (Melicertus) marginatus En: Aloha prawn Fr: Crevette aloha Sp: Camarón aloha	49									●		●	●		●		●	●	●		
Penaeus (Melicertus) plebejus En: Eastern king prawn Fr: Crevette royale orientale Sp: Camarón real oriental	49												●				●		●		
Penaeus (Penaeus) esculentus En: Brown tiger prawn Fr: Crevette tigrée brune Sp: Camarón tigre marrón	49												●				●		●		
Penaeus (Penaeus) monodon En: Giant tiger prawn Fr: Crevette géante tigrée Sp: Camarón tigre gigante	50									●		●	●		●		●				
Penaeus (Penaeus) semisulcatus En: Green tiger prawn Fr: Crevette tigrée verte Sp: Camarón tigre verde	51							●				●	●		●		●				

DISTRIBUTION

MAJOR MARINE FISHING AREAS FOR STATISTICAL PURPOSES

SPECIES	PAGE	FRESH WATERS	18	21	27	31	34	37	41	47	48	51	57	58	61	67	71	77	81	87	88
Protrachypene precipua En: Titi shrimp Fr: Crevette titi Sp: Camarón tití	51																	●		●	
Trachypenaeus anchoralis En: Hardback shrimp Fr: Crevette os Sp: Camarón huesudo	52												●				●		●		
Trachypenaeus byrdi En: Carabali shrimp Fr: Crevette carabali Sp: Camarón carabalí	52																	●		●	
Trachypenaeus constrictus En: Roughneck shrimp Fr: Crevette gambri Sp: Camarón fijador	52			●		●			●												
Trachypenaeus curvirostris En: Southern rough shrimp Fr: Crevette gambri archée Sp: Camarón fijador arquero	53							●				●	●		●		●				
Trachypenaeus faoe En: Indio shrimp Fr: Crevette gambri indienne Sp: Camarón fijador indio	54																	●		●	

DISTRIBUTION

MAJOR MARINE FISHING AREAS FOR STATISTICAL PURPOSES

SPECIES	PAGE	FRESH WATERS	18	21	27	31	34	37	41	47	48	51	57	58	61	67	71	77	81	87	88
Trachypenaeus fulvus En: Brown rough shrimp Fr: Crevette gambri brune Sp: Camarón fijador marrón	54												●				●				
Trachypenaeus fuscina En: Pinto shrimp Fr: Crevette pinto Sp: Camarón pinto	55																	●		●	
Trachypenaeus gonospinifer En: Northern rough shrimp Fr: Crevette gambri nordique Sp: Camarón fijador norteno	55												●				●				
Trachypenaeus granulosus En: Coarse shrimp Fr: Crevette gambri grenue Sp: Camarón fijador de granos	55										●	●		●		●				
Trachypenaeus pacificus En: Zebra shrimp Fr: Crevette zèbre Sp: Camarón cebra	56																	●		●	
Trachypenaeus sedili En: Malayan rough shrimp Fr: Crevette gambri malaise Sp: Camarón fijador malayo	56										●	●				●				

DISTRIBUTION

MAJOR MARINE FISHING AREAS FOR STATISTICAL PURPOSES

SPECIES	PAGE	FRESH WATERS	18	21	27	31	34	37	41	47	48	51	57	58	61	67	71	77	81	87	88
Trachypenaeus similis En: Yellow roughneck shrimp Fr: Crevette gambri jaune Sp: Camarón fijador amarillo	57					●			●												
Xiphopenaeus kroyeri En: Atlantic seabob Fr: Crevette seabob (de l'Atlantique) Sp: Camarón siete barbas	57			●		●			●												
Xiphopenaeus riveti En: Pacific seabob Fr: Crevette seabob (du Pacifique) Sp: Camarón botalón	58																	●		●	
FAMILY SICYONIIDAE: *Sicyonia brevirostris* En: Rock shrimp Fr: Boucot ovetgernade Sp: Camarón de piedra	58			●		●												●			
Sicyonia carinata En: Mediterranean rock shrimp Fr: Boucot méditerranéen Sp: Camarón de piedra mediterráneo	59				●		●	●													
Sicyonia cristata En: Ridgeback rock shrimp Fr: Boucot balafré Sp: Camarón de piedra costurón	60														●						

DISTRIBUTION

MAJOR MARINE FISHING AREAS FOR STATISTICAL PURPOSES

SPECIES	PAGE	FRESH WATERS	18	21	27	31	34	37	41	47	48	51	57	58	61	67	71	77	81	87	88
Sicyonia dorsalis En: Lesser rock shrimp Fr: Boucot nain Sp: Camaroncito de piedra	60			●		●			●												
Sicyonia galeata En: Tufted rock shrimp Fr: Sicyonie huppée Sp: Camarón penachudo	60						●			●											
Sicyonia ingentis En: Pacific rock shrimp Fr: Boucot du Pacifique Sp: Camarón de piedra del Pacífico	61																	●			
Sicyonia lancifera En: Knight rock shrimp Fr: Boucot chevalier Sp: Camarón de piedra lanzón	61											●	●		●		●				
Sicyonia stimpsoni En: Eyespot rock shrimp Fr: Boucot ocellé Sp: Camarón ocelado	61			●		●															
Sicyonia typica En: Kinglet rock shrimp Fr: Boucot roitelet Sp: Camarón reyecito	62			●		●			●												

DISTRIBUTION

SPECIES	PAGE	FRESH WATERS	18	21	27	31	34	37	41	47	48	51	57	58	61	67	71	77	81	87	88
FAMILY SERGESTIDAE																					
Acetes americanus En: Aviu shrimp Fr: Chevrette aviu Sp: Camarón aviú	63			●		●			●												
Acetes australis En: Australian paste shrimp Fr: Chevrette australienne Sp: Camarón de pasta australiano	63																●		●		
Acetes chinensis En: Northern mauxia shrimp Fr: Chevrette mauxia nordique Sp: Camaroncillo mauxia norteño	63														●						
Acetes erythraeus En: Tsivakihini paste shrimp Fr: Chevrette tsivakihini Sp: Camaroncillo tsivakihini	64											●	●	●	●		●				
Acetes indicus En: Jawla paste shrimp Fr: Chevrette jawla Sp: Camaroncillo javlá	64											●	●				●				
Acetes intermedius En: Taiwan mauxia shrimp Fr: Chevrette mauxia de Formose Sp: Camaroncillo mauxia de Formosa	65														●		●				

MAJOR MARINE FISHING AREAS FOR STATISTICAL PURPOSES

DISTRIBUTION

SPECIES	PAGE	FRESH WATERS	MAJOR MARINE FISHING AREAS FOR STATISTICAL PURPOSES																		
			18	21	27	31	34	37	41	47	48	51	57	58	61	67	71	77	81	87	88
Acetes japonicus En: Akiami paste shrimp Fr: Chevrette akiami Sp: Camaroncillo akiami	65											●	●		●		●				
Acetes serrulatus En: Southern mauxia shrimp Fr: Chevrette mauxia méridionale Sp: Camaroncillo mauxia sureño	66														●		●				
Acetes sibogae En: Alamang shrimp Fr: Chevrette alamang Sp: Camaroncillo alamang	66											●	●				●				
Acetes vulgaris En: Jembret shrimp Fr: Chevrette jembre Sp: Camaroncillo jembre	66														●		●				
Sergestes lucens En: Sakura shrimp Fr: Chevrette sakura Sp: Camarón sakura	67														●						
FAMILY NEMATOCARCINIDAE *Nematocarcinus africanus* En: African spider shrimp Fr: Chevrette araignée d'Afrique Sp: Camarón araña africano	68					●				●											

DISTRIBUTION

SPECIES	PAGE	FRESH WATERS	MAJOR MARINE FISHING AREAS FOR STATISTICAL PURPOSES																		
			18	21	27	31	34	37	41	47	48	51	57	58	61	67	71	77	81	87	88
FAMILY ATYIDAE																						
Atya gabonensis En: Gabon shrimp Fr: Saltarelle gabonaise Sp: Camarón gabonés	69	●																				
Atya innocous En: Basket shrimp Fr: Saltarelle panier Sp: Camarón cestillo	69	●																				
Atya pilipes En: Koros shrimp Fr: Saltarelle koros Sp: Camarón koros	69	●										●	●				●	●			
Atya scabra En: Camacuto shrimp Fr: Saltarelle camacuto Sp: Camarón camacuto	70	●																				
Atya spinipes En: Soldier brush shrimp Fr: Saltarelle soldat Sp: Camarón soldado	71	●																				
Atya sulcatipes En: Ekusa shrimp Fr: Saltarelle ekusa Sp: Camarón ecusa	71	●																				

DISTRIBUTION

MAJOR MARINE FISHING AREAS FOR STATISTICAL PURPOSES

SPECIES	PAGE	FRESH WATERS	18	21	27	31	34	37	41	47	48	51	57	58	61	67	71	77	81	87	88
Caridina africana En: African caridina Fr: Saltarelle africaine Sp: Caridina africana	72	●																			
Caridina denticulata En: Sawtooth caridina Fr: Saltarelle scie Sp: Caridina sierra	72	●																			
Caridina edulis En: Malagasy caridina Fr: Saltarelle malgache Sp: Caridina malgacha	73	●																			
Caridina gracilirostris En: Needlenose caridina Fr: Saltarelle aiguille Sp: Caridina aguja	73	●										●	●				●				
Caridina laevis En: Smooth caridina Fr: Saltarelle glabre Sp: Caridina lisa	73	●																			
Caridina nilotica (species complex) En: Common caridina Fr: Saltarelle commune Sp: Caridina común	74	●										●	●		●		●	●			

DISTRIBUTION

MAJOR MARINE FISHING AREAS FOR STATISTICAL PURPOSES

SPECIES	PAGE	FRESH WATERS	18	21	27	31	34	37	41	47	48	51	57	58	61	67	71	77	81	87	88
Caridina propinqua En: Bengal caridina Fr: Saltarelle bengalaise Sp: Caridina bengalí	75	●											●				●				
Caridina tonkinensis En: Tonkin caridina Fr: Saltarelle tonkinoise Sp: Caridina tonkinesa	75	●																			
Caridina weberi En: Pugnose caridina Fr: Saltarelle nez-camus Sp: Caridina ñata	75	●																			
Paratya compressa En: Nuka shrimp Fr: Saltarelle nuca Sp: Camarón nuca	76	●																			
FAMILY PASIPHAEIDAE *Glyphus marsupialis* En: Kangaroo shrimp Fr: Sivade kangourou Sp: Camarón canguro	77						●			●											
Leptochela gracilis En: Lesser glass shrimp Fr: Sivade cristal Sp: Camaroncito cristal	77														●		●				

DISTRIBUTION

SPECIES	PAGE	FRESH WATERS	\multicolumn{19}{c}{MAJOR MARINE FISHING AREAS FOR STATISTICAL PURPOSES}

SPECIES	PAGE	FRESH WATERS	18	21	27	31	34	37	41	47	48	51	57	58	61	67	71	77	81	87	88
Pasiphaea japonica En: Japanese glass shrimp Fr: Sivade japonais Sp: Camarón cristal japonés	77														●						
Pasiphaea multidentata En: Pink glass shrimp Fr: Sivade rose Sp: Camarón cristal rosado	78			●	●			●													
Pasiphaea sivado En: White glass shrimp Fr: Sivade blanc Sp: Camarón cristal blanco	78				●			●				●									
FAMILY RHYNCHOCINETIDAE *Rhynchocinetes typus* En: Rabbitnose shrimp Fr: Sauté des plages Sp: Camarón de playa	79																			●	
Lipkius holthuisi En: Wellington shrimp Fr: Sauté Wellington Sp: Camarón Wellington	80																		●		
FAMILY CAMPYLONOTIDAE *Campylonotus rathbunae* En: Sabre prawn Fr: Raguié sabre Sp: Camarón sable	80												●						●		

DISTRIBUTION

MAJOR MARINE FISHING AREAS FOR STATISTICAL PURPOSES

SPECIES	PAGE	FRESH WATERS	18	21	27	31	34	37	41	47	48	51	57	58	61	67	71	77	81	87	88
FAMILY PALAEMONIDAE																					
Cryphiops caementarius En: Changallo shrimp Fr: Bouquet changallo Sp: Camarón changallo	81	●																		●	
Exopalaemon annandalei En: Cipango prawn Fr: Bouquet cipango Sp: Camarón cipango	82	●																			
Exopalaemon carinicauda En: Ridgetail prawn Fr: Bouquet quille Sp: Camarón quilla	82														●						
Exopalaemon mani En: Mamtom prawn Fr: Bouquet mamtom Sp: Camarón mamtom	82	●																			
Exopalaemon modestus En: Siberian prawn Fr: Bouquet sibérien Sp: Camarón siberiano	83	●																			
Exopalaemon orientis En: Oriental prawn Fr: Bouquet oriental Sp: Camarón oriental	83	●													●						

DISTRIBUTION

MAJOR MARINE FISHING AREAS FOR STATISTICAL PURPOSES

SPECIES	PAGE	FRESH WATERS	18	21	27	31	34	37	41	47	48	51	57	58	61	67	71	77	81	87	88
Ecopalaemon styliferus En: Roshna prawn Fr: Bouquet rosna Sp: Camarón rosna	84	●										●	●				●				
Leptocarpus fluminicola En: Ganges delta prawn Fr: Bouquet du bas Gange Sp: Camarón estuarino del Ganges	84	●											●								
Leptocarpus potamiscus En: Bombay prawn Fr: Bouquet bombay Sp: Camarón de Bombay	84	●										●	●				●				
Macrobrachium acanthurus En: Cinnamon river prawn Fr: Bouquet cannelle Sp: Camarón canela	85					●			●												
Macrobrachium aemulum En: Noumea river prawn Fr: Bouquet nouméa Sp: Camarón de Numea	86	●																			
Macrobrachium amazonicum En: Amazon river prawn Fr: Bouquet amazone Sp: Camarón amazónico	86	●																			

DISTRIBUTION

SPECIES	PAGE	FRESH WATERS	MAJOR MARINE FISHING AREAS FOR STATISTICAL PURPOSES																		
			18	21	27	31	34	37	41	47	48	51	57	58	61	67	71	77	81	87	88
Macrobrachium americanum En: Cauque river prawn Fr: Bouquet cauque Sp: Camarón cauque	87	●																●		●	
Macrobrachium australe En: Koua river prawn Fr: Bouquet koua Sp: Camarón kúa	87	●										●	●				●	●			
Macrobrachium birmanicum En: Burma river prawn Fr: Bouquet birman Sp: Camarón birmano	88	●											●								
Macrobrachium caledonicum En: New Caledonia river prawn Fr: Bouquet néocalédonien Sp: Camarón de Nueva Caledonia	88	●																			
Macrobrachium carcinus En: Painted river prawn Fr: Bouquet pintade Sp: Camarón pintado	88	●				●			●												
Macrobrachium choprai En: Ganges river prawn Fr: Bouquet du haut Gange Sp: Camarón del río Ganges	89	●																			

DISTRIBUTION

SPECIES	PAGE	FRESH WATERS	18	21	27	31	34	37	41	47	48	51	57	58	61	67	71	77	81	87	88
										MAJOR MARINE FISHING AREAS FOR STATISTICAL PURPOSES											
Macrobrachium dayanum En: Kaira river prawn Fr: Bouquet kaira Sp: Camarón kaira	89	●																			
Macrobrachium dux En: Congo river prawn Fr: Bouquet congolais Sp: Camarón congoleño	90	●																			
Macrobrachium equidens En: Rough river prawn Fr: Bouquet chagrin Sp: Camarón lija	90	●										●	●		●		●				
Macrobrachium esculentum En: Sweet river prawn Fr: Bouquet saveur Sp: Camarón saborete	91	●																			
Macrobrachium formosense En: Crane river prawn Fr: Bouquet grue Sp: Camarón grulla	91	●																			
Macrobrachium geron En: Greybeard river prawn Fr: Bouquet barbegris Sp: Camarón barbagris	91	●																			

DISTRIBUTION

SPECIES	PAGE	FRESH WATERS	18	21	27	31	34	37	41	47	48	51	57	58	61	67	71	77	81	87	88
Macrobrachium grandimanus En: Hawaii river prawn Fr: Bouquet hawaïen Sp: Camarón hauaiano	92	●													●			●			
Macrobrachium heterochirus En: Cascade river prawn Fr: Bouquet cascade Sp: Camarón de cascada	92	●																			
Macrobrachium idae En: Orana river prawn Fr: Bouquet orana Sp: Camarón orana	92	●										●	●				●				
Macrobrachium idella En: Slender river prawn Fr: Bouquet hâve Sp: Camarón cenceño	93	●																			
Macrobrachium intermedium En: Striped river prawn Fr: Bouquet rayé Sp: Camarón rayado	93	●											●						●		
Macrobrachium jaroense En: Jaro river prawn Fr: Bouquet jaro Sp: Camarón jaro	94	●																			

MAJOR MARINE FISHING AREAS FOR STATISTICAL PURPOSES

DISTRIBUTION

SPECIES	PAGE	FRESH WATERS	MAJOR MARINE FISHING AREAS FOR STATISTICAL PURPOSES																		
			18	21	27	31	34	37	41	47	48	51	57	58	61	67	71	77	81	87	88
Macrobrachium javanicum En: Java river prawn Fr: Bouquet javanais Sp: Camarón javanés	94	●																			
Macrobrachium jelskii En: Agar river prawn Fr: Bouquet agar Sp: Camarón agareño	95	●				●			●												
Macrobrachium lamarrei En: Kuncho river prawn Fr: Bouquet kuncho Sp: Camarón kuncho	95	●										●	●								
Macrobrachium lanceifrons En: Philippine river prawn Fr: Bouquet philippin Sp: Camarón filipino	95	●																			
Macrobrachium lanchesteri En: Riceland prawn Fr: Bouquet rizière Sp: Camarón de arrozal	96	●										●	●				●				
Macrobrachium lar En: Monkey river shrimp Fr: Bouquet singe Sp: Camarón mono	96	●										●	●		●		●	●			

DISTRIBUTION

SPECIES	PAGE	FRESH WATERS	18	21	27	31	34	37	41	47	48	51	57	58	61	67	71	77	81	87	88
Macrobrachium latidactylus En: Scissor river prawn Fr: Bouquet cisseaux Sp: Camarón tijera	97	●															●				
Macrobrachium latimanus En: Mountain river prawn Fr: Bouquet montagne Sp: Camarón montés	97	●										●	●		●		●	●			
Macrobrachium lepidactyloides En: Malayan scale prawn Fr: Bouquet malais Sp: Camarón escamoso malayo	93	●																			
Macrobrachium lepidactylus En: Madagascar scale prawn Fr: Bouquet malgache Sp: Camarón escamoso malgache	98	●																			
Macrobrachium macrobrachion En: Brackish river prawn Fr: Bouquet saumâtre Sp: Camarón salobreño	98	●					●			●											
Macrobrachium malcolmsonii En: Monsoon river prawn Fr: Bouquet mousson Sp: Camarón monzón	99	●										●	●								

MAJOR MARINE FISHING AREAS FOR STATISTICAL PURPOSES

- 192 -

DISTRIBUTION

SPECIES	PAGE	FRESH WATERS	__MAJOR MARINE FISHING AREAS FOR STATISTICAL PURPOSES																		
			18	21	27	31	34	37	41	47	48	51	57	58	61	67	71	77	81	87	88
Macrobrachium mammillodactylus En: Knobtooth prawn Fr: Bouquet meule Sp: Camarón granuloso	99	●																			
Macrobrachium mirabile En: Shortleg river prawn Fr: Bouquet tipattes Sp: Camarón patojo	100	●											●				●				
Macrobrachium nipponense En: Oriental river prawn Fr: Bouquet nippon Sp: Camarón nipón	100	●													●						
Macrobrachium ohione En: Ohio river prawn Fr: Bouquet ohio Sp: Camarón de Ohio	101	●		●		●															
Macrobrachium olfersii En: Buchura river prawn Fr: Bouquet buchura Sp: Camarón buchura	101	●																			
Macrobrachium patsa En: Patsa river prawn Fr: Bouquet patsa Sp: Camarón patsa	102	●																			

DISTRIBUTION

SPECIES	PAGE	FRESH WATERS	MAJOR MARINE FISHING AREAS FOR STATISTICAL PURPOSES																			
			18	21	27	31	34	37	41	47	48	51	57	58	61	67	71	77	81	87	88
Macrobrachium pilimanus En: Muff prawn Fr: Bouquet manchon Sp: Camarón manguito	102	●																			
Macrobrachium raridens En: Volta river prawn Fr: Bouquet volta Sp: Camarón del Volta	102	●																			
Macrobrachium rosenbergii En: Giant river prawn Fr: Bouquet géant Sp: Camarón gigante	103	●										●	●		●		●				
Macrobrachium rude En: Hairy river prawn Fr: Bouquet velu Sp: Camarón de cerda	104	●										●	●								
Macrobrachium scabriculum En: Goda river prawn Fr: Bouquet goda Sp: Camarón goda	104	●										●	●				●				
Macrobrachium sintangense En: Sunda river prawn Fr: Bouquet krakatoa Sp: Camarón krakatoa	105	●																			

DISTRIBUTION

SPECIES	PAGE	FRESH WATERS	18	21	27	31	34	37	41	47	48	51	57	58	61	67	71	77	81	87	88
Macrobrachium tenellum En: Longarm river prawn Fr: Bouquet brasolargue Sp: Camarón brazolargo	105	•																•		•	
Macrobrachium trompii En: Forest river prawn Fr: Bouquet forestier Sp: Camarón guardabosque	106	•																			
Macrobrachium villosimanus En: Dimua river prawn Fr: Bouquet dimua Sp: Camarón dimúa	106	•																			
Macrobrachium vollenhovenii En: African river prawn Fr: Bouquet africain Sp: Camarón africano	106	•					•			•											
Nematopalaemon hastatus En: Estuarine prawn Fr: Bouquet étier Sp: Camarón estuarino	107						•			•											
Nematopalaemon schmitti En: Whitebelly prawn Fr: Bouquet covac Sp: Camarón cuac	107					•			•												
Nematopalaemon tenuipes En: Spider prawn Fr: Bouquet araignée Sp: Camarón araña	108											•	•				•				

MAJOR MARINE FISHING AREAS FOR STATISTICAL PURPOSES

DISTRIBUTION

SPECIES	PAGE	FRESH WATERS	18	21	27	31	34	37	41	47	48	51	57	61	67	71	77	81	87	88
								MAJOR MARINE FISHING AREAS FOR STATISTICAL PURPOSES											
Palaemon adspersus En: Baltic prawn Fr: Bouquet balte Sp: Camarón báltico	108				●			●												
Palaemon concinnus En: Mangrove prawn Fr: Bouquet mangrove Sp: Camarón del manglar	109	●										●	●	●		●	●			
Palaemon elegans En: Rockpool prawn Fr: Bouquet flaque Sp: Camarón de poza	110				●		●	●		●										
Palaemon gravieri En: Chinese ditch prawn Fr: Bouquet chinois des canaux Sp: Camarón chino de acequia	110													●						
Palaemon longirostris En: Delta prawn Fr: Bouquet delta Sp: Camarón delta	111	●			●			●												
Palaemon macrodactylus En: Migrant prawn Fr: Bouquet migrateur Sp: Camarón emigrante	111												●	●		●	●	●		

DISTRIBUTION

MAJOR MARINE FISHING AREAS FOR STATISTICAL PURPOSES

SPECIES	PAGE	FRESH WATERS	18	21	27	31	34	37	41	47	48	51	57	58	61	67	71	77	81	87	88
Palaemon maculatus En: Zaire prawn Fr: Bouquet zaïre Sp: Camarón zairense	112						●			●											
Palaemon northropi En: Caribbean bait prawn Fr: Bouquet zélateur caraïbe Sp: Camarón cebador	112					●			●												
Palaemon ortmanni En: Gladiator prawn Fr: Bouquet gladiateur Sp: Camarón gladiador	112														●						
Palaemon pacificus En: Indian bait prawn Fr: Bouquet zélateur indien Sp: Camarón celador indio	113									●		●	●		●		●	●			
Palaemon pandaliformis En: Potitinga prawn Fr: Bouquet potitinga Sp: Camarón potitinga	113	●				●			●												
Palaemon paucidens En: Lake prawn Fr: Bouquet de lac Sp: Camarón de lago	113	●													●						

DISTRIBUTION

SPECIES	PAGE	FRESH WATERS	18	21	27	31	34	37	41	47	48	51	57	58	61	67	71	77	81	87	88
Palaemon serratus En: Common prawn Fr: Bouquet (commun) Sp: Camarón común	114				●		●	●													
Palaemon serrifer En: Carpenter prawn Fr: Bouquet charpentier Sp: Camarón carpintero	115												●		●		●				
Palaemon xiphias En: Posidonia prawn Fr: Bouquet posidonie Sp: Camarón posidonia	115						●	●													
Palaemonetes kadiakensis En: Mississippi grass shrimp Fr: Bouquet mississippi Sp: Camarón del Mississippi	115	●																			
Palaemonetes paludosus En: Eastern grass shrimp Fr: Bouquet oriental des herbiers Sp: Camarón yerbero	116	●																			
Palaemonetes sinensis En: Chinese grass shrimp Fr: Bouquet chinois des herbiers Sp: Camarón yerbero chino	116	●																			

MAJOR MARINE FISHING AREAS FOR STATISTICAL PURPOSES

DISTRIBUTION

MAJOR MARINE FISHING AREAS FOR STATISTICAL PURPOSES

SPECIES	PAGE	FRESH WATERS	18	21	27	31	34	37	41	47	48	51	57	58	61	67	71	77	81	87	88
Palaemonetes tonkinensis En: Tonkin grass shrimp Fr: Bouquet tonkinois Sp: Camarón tonkinés	117	●																			
Palaemonetes varians En: Atlantic ditch shrimp Fr: Bouquet atlantique des canaux Sp: Camarón de acequia del Atlántico	117				●		●	●													
Palaemonetes vulgaris En: Marsh shrimp Fr: Bouquet des marais Sp: Camarón de fangal	117			●		●															
FAMILY ALPHEIDAE																					
Alpheus bisincisus En: Flathead snapping shrimp Fr: Cardon nez camus Sp: Camarón chato	118									●		●	●		●		●				
Alpheus brevicristatus En: Teppo snapping shrimp Fr: Cardon teppo Sp: Camarón tepo	119														●						
Alpheus digitalis En: Forceps snapping shrimp Fr: Cardon tenaille Sp: Camarón tenaza	119												●		●		●				

DISTRIBUTION

SPECIES	PAGE	FRESH WATERS	MAJOR MARINE FISHING AREAS FOR STATISTICAL PURPOSES																		
			18	21	27	31	34	37	41	47	48	51	57	58	61	67	71	77	81	87	88
Alpheus euphrosyne En: Nimph snapping shrimp Fr: Cardon nymphe Sp: Camarón palomilla	119												●				●				
Alpheus glaber En: Red snapping shrimp Fr: Cardon rouge Sp: Camarón carneo	120				●			●													
Alpheus gracilipes En: Daisy snapping shrimp Fr: Cardon marguerite Sp: Camarón margarita	120											●	●		●		●	●			
Alpheus heterochaelis En: Bigclaw snapping shrimp Fr: Cardon grandes pinces Sp: Camarón tamarú	120					●			●												
Alpheus hoplocheles En: Armed snapping shrimp Fr: Cardon épineux Sp: Camarón armado	121														●		●				
Alpheus japonicus En: Japanese snapping shrimp Fr: Cardon japonais Sp: Camarón chasqueador	121														●						

DISTRIBUTION

MAJOR MARINE FISHING AREAS FOR STATISTICAL PURPOSES

SPECIES	PAGE	FRESH WATERS	18	21	27	31	34	37	41	47	48	51	57	58	61	67	71	77	81	87	88
Alpheus spongiarum En: Bristle snapping shrimp Fr: Cardon brosse Sp: Camarón cepillo	121											●	●		●		●				
Alpheus stephensoni En: Queensland snapping shrimp Fr: Cardon australien Sp: Camarón australiano	122																●				
Alpheus sublucanus En: Coral snapping shrimp Fr: Cardon coraille Sp: Camarón de coral	122											●	●		●		●	●	●		
FAMILY OGYRIDIDAE *Ogyrides orientalis* En: Telescope shrimp Fr: Crevuche télescope Sp: Camarón telescopio	123											●	●		●		●				
FAMILY HIPPOLYTIDAE *Eualus leptognathus* En: Yamato shrimp Fr: Bouc yamato Sp: Camarón yamato	123														●						
Eualus macilentus En: Greenland shrimp Fr: Bouc groenland Sp: Camarón de Groenlandia	124			●											●	●					

DISTRIBUTION

SPECIES	PAGE	FRESH WATERS	MAJOR MARINE FISHING AREAS FOR STATISTICAL PURPOSES																		
			18	21	27	31	34	37	41	47	48	51	57	58	61	67	71	77	81	87	88
Eualus sinensis En: Iso shrimp Fr: Bouc iso Sp: Camarón iso	124														●						
Exhippolysmata ensirostris En: Hunter shrimp Fr: Bouc chasseur Sp: Camarón cazador	125											●	●				●				
Exhippolysmata hastatoides En: Companion shrimp Fr: Bouc compagnon Sp: Camarón compañero	125						●			●											
Exhippolysmata oplophoroides En: Cock shrimp Fr: Crevette buhotte Sp: Camarón gallo	125					●			●												
Heptacarpus brevirostris En: Shortspine shrimp Fr: Bouc tiépines Sp: Camarón espinilla	126															●		●			
Heptacarpus futilirostris En: Toy shrimp Fr: Bouc caprice Sp: Camarón capricho	126														●						

DISTRIBUTION

SPECIES	PAGE	FRESH WATERS	\multicolumn{19}{c}{MAJOR MARINE FISHING AREAS FOR STATISTICAL PURPOSES}																	
			18	21	27	31	34	37	41	47	48	51	57	58	61	67	71	77	81	87	88
Heptacarpus geniculatus En: Flexed shrimp Fr: Bouc courbe Sp: Camarón corva	127														●						
Heptacarpus pandaloides En: Tsuno shrimp Fr: Bouc suno Sp: Camarón suno	127														●						
Latreutes acicularis En: Hoso shrimp Fr: Bouc oso Sp: Camarón oso	127														●						
Latreutes anoplonyx En: Medusa shrimp Fr: Bouc méduse Sp: Camarón medusa	128											●	●		●		●				
Latreutes laminirostris En: Platenose shrimp Fr: Bouc nez lamelleux Sp: Camarón laminilla	128														●						
Latreutes planirostris En: Flatnose shrimp Fr: Bouc nez émoussé Sp: Camarón romo	129												●		●		●				

DISTRIBUTION

MAJOR MARINE FISHING AREAS FOR STATISTICAL PURPOSES

SPECIES	PAGE	FRESH WATERS	18	21	27	31	34	37	41	47	48	51	57	58	61	67	71	77	81	87	88
Lysmata californica En: Lined shrimp Fr: Bouc rayé Sp: Camarón listado	129																	●			
Lysmata seticaudata En: Monaco shrimp Fr: Bouc monégasse Sp: Camarón monagués	129				●			●													
Lysmata vittata En: Indian lined shrimp Fr: Bouc rayé indien Sp: Camarón rayado indio	130											●	●	●	●		●				
Spirontocaris lilljeborgii En: Friendly spine shrimp Fr: Bouc épineux Sp: Camarón saborete espinudo	130			●	●																
Spirontocaris spinus En: Parrot shrimp Fr: Bouc perroquet Sp: Camarón loro	130			●	●											●					
FAMILY PROCESSIDAE *Processa canaliculata* En: Processa shrimp Fr: Guernade processe Sp: Camarón procesa	131				●			●													

DISTRIBUTION

MAJOR MARINE FISHING AREAS FOR STATISTICAL PURPOSES

SPECIES	PAGE	FRESH WATERS	18	21	27	31	34	37	41	47	48	51	57	58	61	67	71	77	81	87	88
Processa edulis En: Nika shrimp Fr: Guernade nica Sp: Camarón nica	132				●			●													
FAMILY PANDALIDAE *Chlorotocus crassicornis* En: Green shrimp Fr: Crevette verte Sp: Camarón verde	133				●		●	●													
Dichelopandalus bonnieri En: Whip shrimp Fr: Crevette fouet Sp: Camarón latiguillo	133				●																
Heterocarpoides levicarina En: Dorodotes shrimp Fr: Crevette dorodo Sp: Camarón dorodó	134											●	●		●		●				
Heterocarpus dorsalis En: Madagascar nylon shrimp Fr: Crevette nylon malgache Sp: Camarón nailón malgache	134									●		●	●		●		●				
Heterocarpus ensifer En: Armed nylon shrimp Fr: Crevette nylon armée Sp: Camarón nailón armado	134				●	●	●					●						●			

- 205 -

DISTRIBUTION

MAJOR MARINE FISHING AREAS FOR STATISTICAL PURPOSES

SPECIES	PAGE	FRESH WATERS	18	21	27	31	34	37	41	47	48	51	57	58	61	67	71	77	81	87	88
Heterocarpus gibbosus En: Humpback nylon shrimp Fr: Crevette nylon bossue Sp: Camarón nailón jorobado	135											●	●				●				
Heterocarpus laevigatus En: Smooth nylon shrimp Fr: Crevette nylon inerme Sp: Camarón nailón liso	135						●			●		●	●				●	●			
Heterocarpus reedi En: Chilean nylon shrimp Fr: Crevette nylon chilienne Sp: Camarón nailón	136																			●	
Heterocarpus sibogae En: Mino nylon shrimp Fr: Crevette nylon mino Sp: Camarón nailón mino	136											●	●		●		●				
Heterocarpus tricarinatus En: Scarred nylon shrimp Fr: Crevette nylon balafrée Sp: Camarón nailón chirlo	136									●		●	●				●				
Heterocarpus vicarius En: Northern nylon shrimp Fr: Crevette nylon nordique Sp: Camarón nailón norteno	137																	●			

- 206 -

DISTRIBUTION

MAJOR MARINE FISHING AREAS FOR STATISTICAL PURPOSES

SPECIES	PAGE	FRESH WATERS	18	21	27	31	34	37	41	47	48	51	57	58	61	67	71	77	81	87	88
Heterocarpus woodmasoni En: Indian nylon shrimp Fr: Crevette nylon indienne Sp: Camarón nailón indio	137											●	●				●				
Pandalopsis dispar En: Sidestripe shrimp Fr: Crevette à flancs rayés Sp: Camarón de banda	137															●					
Pandalopsis japonica En: Morotoge shrimp Fr: Crevette morotoge Sp: Camarón morotoje	138														●						
Pandalus borealis En: Northern shrimp Fr: Crevette nordique Sp: Camarón norteño	138			●	●										●	●					
Pandalus danae En: Dock shrimp Fr: Crevette des quais Sp: Camarón de muelle	139															●		●			
Pandalus goniurus En: Humpy shrimp Fr: Crevette gibbeuse Sp: Camarón joboso	139														●	●					

DISTRIBUTION

MAJOR MARINE FISHING AREAS FOR STATISTICAL PURPOSES

SPECIES	PAGE	FRESH WATERS	18	21	27	31	34	37	41	47	48	51	57	58	61	67	71	77	81	87	88
Pandalus hypsinotus En: Coonstripe shrimp Fr: Crevette à front rayé Sp: Camarón malacho	140														●	●					
Pandalus jordani En: Ocean shrimp Fr: Crevette océanique Sp: Camarón oceánico	140															●		●			
Pandalus kessleri En: Hokkai shrimp Fr: Crevette hokkai Sp: Camarón de Hokkai	140														●						
Pandalus montagui En: Aesop shrimp Fr: Crevette ésope Sp: Camarón esópico	141			●	●																
Pandalus nipponensis En: Botan shrimp Fr: Crevette botan Sp: Camarón botán	141														●						
Pandalus platyceros En: Spot shrimp Fr: Crevette tache Sp: Camarón manchado	142														●	●		●			

DISTRIBUTION

MAJOR MARINE FISHING AREAS FOR STATISTICAL PURPOSES

SPECIES	PAGE	FRESH WATERS	18	21	27	31	34	37	41	47	48	51	57	58	61	67	71	77	81	87	88
Parapandalus narval En: Narwal shrimp Fr: Crevette narval Sp: Camarón narval	142						●	●		●											
Parapandalus spinipes En: Oriental narwal shrimp Fr: Crevette narval oriental Sp: Camarón narval oriental	143											●	●		●		●		●		
Plesionika acanthonotus En: Lesser striped shrimp Fr: Crevette naine rayée Sp: Camarón rayado menor	143				●	●	●	●	●	●											
Plesionika alcocki En: Gondwana striped shrimp Fr: Crevette gondwana Sp: Camarón gondwana	144											●	●								
Plesionika antigai En: Catalonian striped shrimp Fr: Crevette catalane Sp: Camarón catalán	144					●	●														
Plesionika edwardsii En: Striped soldier shrimp Fr: Crevette édouard Sp: Camarón soldado rayado	144					●	●	●													

DISTRIBUTION

MAJOR MARINE FISHING AREAS FOR STATISTICAL PURPOSES

SPECIES	PAGE	FRESH WATERS	18	21	27	31	34	37	41	47	48	51	57	58	61	67	71	77	81	87	88
Plesionika ensis En: Striped gladiator shrimp Fr: Crevette gladiateur rayée Sp: Camarón gladiador rayado	145					●	●		●	●		●	●				●	●			
Plesionika gigliolii En: Italian deepsea shrimp Fr: Crevette profonde italienne Sp: Camarón italiano de fondo	145						●	●													
Plesionika heterocarpus En: Arrow shrimp Fr: Crevette flèche Sp: Camarón flecha	146				●		●	●													
Plesionika martia En: Golden shrimp Fr: Crevette dorée Sp: Camarón de oro	146				●	●	●	●	●	●		●	●		●		●	●	●		
Plesionika williamsi En: Guinea striped shrimp Fr: Crevette rayée guinéenne Sp: Camarón rayado de Guinea	147						●														
FAMILY CRANGONIDAE *Argis lar* En: Kuro shrimp Fr: Crevette kuro Sp: Camarón kuro	147															●	●					

DISTRIBUTION

SPECIES	PAGE	FRESH WATERS	MAJOR MARINE FISHING AREAS FOR STATISTICAL PURPOSES																		
			18	21	27	31	34	37	41	47	43	51	57	58	61	67	71	77	81	87	88
Crangon affinis En: Japanese sand shrimp Fr: Crevette japonaise Sp: Quisquilla japonesa	148														●						
Crangon alaskensis En: Alaska shrimp Fr: Crevette alaska Sp: Quisquilla de Alaska	148															●					
Crangon communis En: Gray shrimp Fr: Crevette cendrée Sp: Quisquilla gris	149															●		●			
Crangon crangon En: Common shrimp Fr: Crevette grise Sp: Quisquilla	149				●		●	●													
Crangon franciscorum En: California shrimp Fr: Crevette californienne Sp: Quisquilla californiana	150															●		●			
Crangon nigricauda En: Blacktailed shrimp Fr: Crevette queue noire Sp: Quisquilla rabo negro	150															●		●			

DISTRIBUTION

MAJOR MARINE FISHING AREAS FOR STATISTICAL PURPOSES

SPECIES	PAGE	FRESH WATERS	18	21	27	31	34	37	41	47	48	51	57	58	61	67	71	77	81	87	88
Crangon nigromaculata En: Bay shrimp Fr: Crevette baie Sp: Quisquilla de caleta	151																	●			
Crangon septemspinosa En: Sand shrimp Fr: Crevette sable Sp: Quisquilla arenera	151			●		●															
Pontocaris lacazei En: Hardshell shrimp Fr: Crevette crâne Sp: Camarón de casco	152				●		●	●		●											
Pontocaris pennata En: Feather shrimp Fr: Crevette emplumée Sp: Camarón de pluma	152											●	●		●		●				
Pontophilus spinosus En: Spiny shrimp Fr: Crevette épine Sp: Camarón espinudo	153				●			●													
Sclerocrangon salebrosa En: Bering shrimp Fr: Crevette bering Sp: Camarón de Bering	153														●						

4. REFERENCES

Anon.,   Prawn surveys. Kai Moana, Food of the Waters, 2:1-9 (New Zealand Marine Department).
1964

Adamson, A.M., Non-marine invertebrate fauna of the Marquesas (exclusive of insects). Occas.Pap.
1935   Bernice P. Bishop Mus., 11(10):1-39

Ahmad, N., Prawn and prawn fishery of East Pakistan. Dacca East Pakistan Government Press, 31 p.
1957

Al-Adhub, A.H.Y. and D.I. Williamson, Some European Processidae (Crustacea, Decapoda, Caridea).
1975   J.Nat.Hist.Lond., 9:693-703

Alcock, A.W., A descriptive catalogue of the Indian deep-sea Crustacea Decapoda Macrura and Anomala
1901   in the Indian Museum, being a revised account of the deep-sea species collected by the
Royal Indian Marine Survey ship Investigator. Calcutta, 1-286

Anderson, W.W. and M.J. Lindner, A provisional key to the shrimps of the family Penaeidae with
1945   especial reference to American forms. Trans.Am.Fish.Soc., 37:284-319

Bacescu, M., Decapoda. Fauna Republ.Soc.Romania, 4(9):351 p.
1967

Bahamonde, N. and G. Henriquez, Sinopsis de datos biologicos sobre el camarón Nailon Heterocarpus
1970   reedi Bahamonde, 1955. FAO Fish.Rep., (57) Vol. 4:1607-27

Bahamonde, N. and M.T. López, Notas sobre el camarón de mar (Rhynchocinetes typus Milne Edwards,
1967   1837) (Crustacea, Decapoda, Rhynchocinetidae). Bol.Mus.Nac.Hist.Nat.Santiago de Chile,
29(8):121-7

Bailey, R.G. and M. Crichton,   Freshwater prawns of the genus Macrobrachium (Crustacea: Palaemo-
1971   nidae) in East Africa, with a key for their identification and notes on their
exploitation. J.E.Afr.Nat.Hist.Soc.Natl.Mus., Kenya, 28:1-8

Balss, H., Ostasiatische Decapoden. 2. Die Natantia und Reptantia. Abh.Bayer.Akad.Wiss.Math.-
1914   Naturwiss.Kl., (Suppl.)2(10):1-101

_____, Diagnosen neuer Macruren der Valdiviaexpedition. Zool.Anz., 44:592-9
1914

_____, Macrura der Deutschen Tiefsee-Expedition. 2. Natantia. Teil A. Wiss.Ergebn.Dtsch.
1925   Tiefsee-Exped.Valdivia, 20:217-315

Banner, A.H. and D.M. Banner, The alpheid shrimp of Thailand. Monogr.Siam Soc., (3):168 p.
1966

Banner, D.M. and C.R. Smalley, Two species of alpheid shrimp, one new, common in the prawn trawls
1969   of Moreton Bay, Queensland, Australia. Contributions to the knowledge of the alpheid
shrimp of the Pacific Ocean. Part 13. Proc.R.Soc.Queensl., 81(3):43-50

Bardach, J.E., J.H. Ryther and W.O. McLarney, Aquaculture: the farming and husbandry of fresh-
1972   water and marine organisms. New York, Wiley Interscience, 868 p.

Barnard, K.H., Descriptive catalogue of South African decapod Crustacea. Ann.S.Afr.Mus., 38:837 p.
1950

Bassindale, R., On the marine fauna of Ghana. Proc.Zool.Soc.Lond., 137:481-510
1961

Bate, C.S.,   Report on the Crustacea Macrura collected by H.M.S. Challenger during the years 1873-76.
    1888   Rep.Voy.Challenger (Zool.), (24):942 p.

Bates, D.H.,   Royal red shrimp. Sea Front., 3:9-13
    1957

Bell, T.,   A history of the British stalk-eyed Crustacea. London, J. van Voorst, 386 p.
    1844-53

Ben-Tuvia, A.,   Report on the fisheries investigations of the Israel South Red Sea Expedition, 1962.
    1968   Israel South Red Sea Expedition, 1962, Reports, 33. Bull.Sea Fish.Res.St.Haifa, (52):
            21-55

Blanco, G.J.,   The Atyidae of the Philippine Islands. Philipp.J.Sci., 56:29-37
    1935

_____,   A new species of Palaemon from northern Luzon. Philipp.J.Sci., 67:201-6
    1939

Bonnot, P.,   The California shrimp industry. Fish Bull.Calif.Dep.Fish Game, (38):22 p.
    1932

Boschi, E.E.,   Los camarones comerciales de la familia Penaeidae de la costa Atlántica de América del
    1963   Sur. Clave para el reconocimiento de las especies y datos bioecológicos. Bol.Inst.Biol.
            Mar.Mar del Plata, (3):39 p.

_____,   Estudio biológico pesquero del camaron *Artemesia longinaris* Bate de Mar del Plata.
    1969   Bol.Inst.Biol.Mar.Mar del Plata, (18):47 p.

Bouvier, E.L.,   Observations nouvelles sur les crevettes de la famille des Atyidés. Bull.Sci.Fr.Belg.,
    1905   39:57

_____,   Crustacés décapodes nouveaux recueillis à Païta (Pérou) par M. le Dr. Rivet. Bull.Mus.
    1907   Natl.Hist.Nat., Paris, 134:113-6

_____,   Recherches sur la morphologie, les variations, la distribution géographique des
    1925   crevettes de la famille des Atyidés. Encycl.Entomol.(A), 4:370 p.

Brashnikov, V.,   Matériaux pour servir à la connaissance de la faune des mers russes de l'est
    1907   rassemblés par le shooner "Storoz" en 1899-1902. Mem.Acad.Sci.St.Petersb., (Ser. 20)
            8:1-185

Brian, A.,   I crostacei eduli del mercato di Genova (Decapoda Natantia), 51 p. (Genova, Laboratorio
    1941   di Biologia Marina del Mare Ligure)

_____,   I crostacei eduli del mercato di Genova (Decapoda Natantia). Boll.Pesca Piscic.
    1942   Idrobiol., 18 (2-3):25-60

Bruin, de, G.H.P.,   Penaeid prawns of Ceylon (Crustacea Decapoda, Penaeidae). Zool.Meded.Leiden,
    1965   41:73-104

Brusher, H.A.,   The magnitude, distribution and availability of prawn (Penaeidae) resources in
    1976   coastal and estuarine waters of Kenya, 1970. J.Mar.Biol.Assoc.India, 16:335-48

Burkenroad, M.D.,   Littoral Penaeidae chiefly from the Bingham oceanographic collection. With a
    1934   revision of Penaeopsis and descriptions of two new genera and eleven new American
            species. Bull.Bingham Oceanogr.Collect., 4(7):109 p.

_____,   Penaeidae from the region of Lower California and Clarion Island, with descriptions
    1938   of four new species. The Templeton Crocker expedition, 13. Zoologica, N.Y., 23:55-91

_____,   Penaeidae. Decapoda Macrura. 1. Mission Robert Ph. Dollfus en Egypte, 25. Résult.
    1959   Sci.Mission Dollfus Egypte, 3:67-92, 285

Butler, T.H.,   The commercial shrimps of British Colombia.   Prog.Rep.Pac.Coast Stn.Fish.Res.Board Can.,
1950   (83):30-4

_____, Growth, reproduction, and distribution of pandalid shrimps in British Columbia.
1964   J.Fish.Res.Boad Can., 21(6):1403-52

_____, The shrimp fishery of British Columbia. FAO Fish.Rep., (57) Vol. 2:521-6
1968

_____, Synopsis of biological data on the prawn *Pandalus platyceros* Brandt, 1815. FAO Fish.
1970   Rep., (57) Vol. 4:1289:315

Calman, W.T., On the British Pandalidae. Ann.Mag.Nat.Hist., 7(3):27-39
1899

Carillo, V.F., Morfología de *Macrobrachium acanthurus* (Wiegmann) en el estado de Veracruz, México.
1968   FAO Fish.Rep., (57) Vol. 2:415-25

Chace, F.A., The bathypelagic Caridean Crustacea. Plankton of the Bermuda Oceanographic Expeditions
1940   9. Zoologica, N.Y., 25:117-209

_____, The shrimps of the Smithsonian-Bredin Caribbean Expeditions with a summary of the West
1972   Indian shallow-water species (Crustacea: Decapoda: Natantia). Smithsonian Contrib.
Zool., (98):179 p.

_____, Shrimps of the Pasiphaeid genus *Leptochela* with descriptions of three new species
1976   (Crustacea: Decapoda: Caridea). Smithsonian Contrib.Zool., (222):51 p.

Chace, F.A. and H.H. Hobbs, Jr., The freshwater and terrestrial decapod crustaceans of the West
1969   Indies with special reference to Dominica. Bull.U.S.Natl.Mus., (292):258 p.

Champion, H.F.B., New records of penaeid prawns from the east coast of southern Africa with notes on
1973   *Penaeus marginatus* Randall and a new species of *Metapenaeopsis*. Crustaceana, 25:181-203

Chen, T.P., Aquaculture practices in Taiwan. Farnham, Survey, Fishing News (Books) Ltd., 162 p.
1976

Cheung, T.S., A key to the identification of Hong Kong penaeid prawns with comments on points of
1960   systematic interest. Hong Kong Univ.Fish.J., 3:61-9

Chopra, B., Some food prawns and crabs of India and their fisheries. J.Bombay Nat.Hist.Soc., 41:
1939   221-34

_____, Prawn fisheries of India. Proc.Indian Sci.Congr., 30(2) (6):1-21
1943

Chopra B. and K.K. Tiwari, Decapoda Crustacea of the Patna State, Orissa. Rec.Indian Mus., 45:213-24
1949

Chuang, S.H., On Malayan shores, 225 p. Singapore, Muwu Shosa
1961

Cobb, S.P., A new species of Sicyonia (Decapoda, Penaeidae) from the western Atlantic with notes on
1971   *S. stimpsoni* Bouvier. Crustaceana, 20:104-12

Cobo, M. and H. Loesch, Estudio estadistico de la pesca del camarón en el Ecuador y de algunas
1966   caracteristicas biologicas de las especies explotadas. Bol.Cient.Tec.Inst.Nac.Pesca
Ecuador, 1(6):25 p.

Coelho, P.A. and M. de A. Ramos, Contribución al conocimiento de los camarones comerciales en el
1968   norte y nordeste del Brasil. Doc.Tec.CARPAS, 4(10):1-4

Cole, H.A.,   Benthos and the shellfish of commerce. In Sea fisheries, their investigation in the
   1956   United Kingdom, edited by M. Graham, London, Edward Arnold, pp. 139-206

Cook, H.L. and M.J. Lindner,   Synopsis of biological data on the brown shrimp *Penaeus aztecus aztecus*
   1970   Ives, 1891. FAO Fish.Rep., (57) Vol. 4:1471-97

Costello, T.J. and D.M. Allen,   Synopsis of biological data on the pink shrimp *Penaeus duorarum*
   1970   *duorarum* Burkenroad, 1939. FAO Fish.Rep., (57) Vol. 4:1499-1537

Coutière, H.,   Les Palaemonidae des eaux douces de Madagascar. Ann.Sci.Nat.Paris (Zool.), 8(12):
   1901   249-342

Couture, R.,   Shrimp fishing in the province of Quebec. Can.Fish.Rep., (17):31-44
   1971

Cowles, R.P.,   Palaemons of the Philippine Islands. Philipp.J.Sci., 9:319-403
   1914

Creaser, E.P.,   The decapod crustaceans of Wisconsin. Trans.Wis.Acad.Sci.Arts Lett., 27:321-38
   1932

Croker, R.S.,   The shrimp industry of Central America, the Caribbean Sea, and northern South America.
   1967   Foreign Fish.Leafl.U.S.Fish Wildl.Serv., (74):124 p.

Crosnier, A.,   Les crevettes Penaeids du plateau continental malgache. Etat de nos connaissances sur
   1965   leur biologie et leur pêche en septembre 1964. Cah.ORSTOM (Océanogr.), 3(3) (Suppl.):
       1-158

Crosnier, A. and E. de Bondy,   Les crevettes commercialisables de la côte ouest de l'Afrique inter-
   1967   tropicale. Etat de nos connaissances sur leur biologie et leur pêche en juillet 1967.
       Init.Doc.Tech.ORSTOM, (7):60 p.

Crosnier, A. and J. Forest,   Note préliminaire sur les Pénéides recueillis par l'"Ombango", au large
   1969   du plateau continental, du Gabon à l'Angola (Crustacea Decapoda Natantia). Bull.Mus.Natl.
       Hist.Nat.Paris, 2(4):544-54

_____,   Les crevettes profondes de l'Atlantique oriental tropical. Faune Trop., (19):409 p.
   1973

Crosnier, A. and C. Jouannic,   Note d'information sur les prospections de la pente continentale
   1973   malgache effectuées par le N.O. Vauban. Bathymétrie - Sédimentologie - Pêche au chalut.
       Doc.Sci.Cent.Nosy-Bé ORSTOM, (42):18 p.

Crosnier, A. and J.J. Tanter,   La pêche des crevettiers espagnols au large du Congo et de l'Angola.
   1968   Pêche Marit., (1805):3-4

Dahlstrom, W.A.,   Synopsis of biological data on the ocean shrimp *Pandalus jordani* Rathbun, 1902.
   1970   FAO Fish.Rep., (57) Vol. 4:1377-416

Dall, W.   A revision of the Australian species of Penaeinae (Crustacea Decapoda: Penaeidae).
   1957   Aust.J.Mar.Freshwat.Res., 8:136-230

Dartevelle, E.,   La côte et l'estuaire du Congo. Mém.Inst.R.Colon.Belge, (Sci.Nat.Méd.8°), 19 (2):
   1950   1-58

_____,   Les crustacés des environs de Léopoldville. Zooléo (Nouv.Ser.), 6:23-9
   1950

Davant, P.,   Clave para la identificación de los camarones marinos y de río. A key to the identifica-
   1963   tion of marine and fresh water shrimps of economical importance in the eastern part of
       Venezuela. Cuad.Oceanogr.Inst.Oceanogr.Univ.Oriente Venez., (1):113 p.

Day, J.H.,   A guide to marine life on South African shores. Cape Town Balkema, 300 p.
   1969

De Kay, J.E.,   Crustacea. Zoology of New-York, or the New-York fauna; comprising detailed descrip-
    1844   tions of all the animals hitherto observed within the State of New York, with brief notices
            of those occasionally found near its borders, and accompanied by appropriate illustrations.
            New York, vol.6(2):70 p.

Delmendo, M.N. and H.R. Rabanal,   Cultivation of "Sugpo" (jumbo tiger shrimp), *Penaeus monodon*
    1956   Fabricius, in the Philippines. Proc.IPFC, 6:424-31

Dieuzeide, R.,   Sur la répartition de deux *Pandalus* des côtes Algériennes. Bull.Trav.Stn.Aquicult.
    1931   Castiglione, 1930(1):125-36

_____,   Les "crevettes" des côtes d'Algérie. Proc.GFCM, 1:38-49
    1952

Djajadiredja, R. and M. Sachlan,   Shrimp and prawn fisheries in Indonesia with special reference to the
    1956   Kroya District. Proc.IPFC, 6:366-77

Domantay, J.S.,   Prawn fisheries of the Philippines. Proc.IPFC, 6:362-6
    1956

Durand, J.,   Notes sur le plateau continental guyanais. Les éléments principaux de la faune et leurs
    1961   relations avec le fond. Cah.ORSTOM, 3:1-93

Eales, N.B.,   The littoral fauna of Great Britain: a handbook for collectors. Cambridge, Cambridge
    1950   University Press, 305 p.

Edmondson, C.H.,   Reef and shore fauna of Hawaii. Spec.Publ.Bernice P. Bishop Mus., (22):381 p.
    1946

Enomoto, Y.,   Oceanographic survey and biological study of shrimps in waters adjacent to the eastern
    1971   coasts of the state of Kuwait. Bull.Tokai Reg.Fish Res.Lab., (66):74 p.

Ewald, J.J.,   The Venezuelan shrimp industry. FAO Fish.Rep., (57) Vol. 3:765-74
    1969

FAO,   Report to the governments of Brazil, Uruguay and Argentina on investigation and assessment of
    1964   shrimp resources. Based on the work of M.N. Mistakidis, FAO/EPTA Marine (Shrimp) Fisheries
            Biologist. Rep.FAO/EPTA, (1934):44 p.

Fausto Filho, J.,   Crustáceos Decápodos de valor comercial ou utilizados como alimento no nordeste
    1968   brasileiro. Bol.Soc.Cearenze.Agron., (9):27-8

Faxon, W.,   The stalk-eyed Crustacea. Reports on an exploration off the west coasts of Mexico,
    1895   Central and South America, and off the Galapagos Islands, in charge of Alexander Agassiz,
            by the U.S. Fish Commission steamer "ALBATROSS" during 1891, Lieut.commander Z.L.Tanner,
            U.S.N., commanding. Mem.Mus.Comp.Zool.Harv., 18:292 p.

Figueira, A.J.G.   On a small collection of decapod crustaceans from the Azores. Bocagiana, 6:1-13
    1960

Fischer, P.,   Crustacés podophthalmaires et Cirrhipèdes du Département de la Gironde et des côtes du
    1872   sud-ouest de la France. Act.Soc.Linn. Bordeaux, 28:405-38

Flora, C.J. and E. Fairbanks,   The sound and the sea: a guide to northwestern neritic invertebrate
    1966   zoology. Bellingham, Wash., Pioneer, 455 p.

Forbes, S.A.,   List of Illinois Crustacea, with descriptions of new species. Bull.Ill.Mus.Nat.Hist.,
    1876   1876(1):3-25

Forest, J.,   Sur une crevette recueillie au cours de la campagne de chalutage dans le Golfe de Guinée
    1963   (*Plesionika williamsi* sp.nov.). Bull.Mus.Natl.Hist.Nat., Paris, (2)35:620-9

Forskål, P.,   Descriptiones animalium, avium, amphibiorum, piscium, insectorum, vermium. Havniae,
    1775   Carsten Niebuhr, 164 p.

Forster, J.R.M. and J.F. Wickins, Prawn culture in the United Kingdom; its status and potential.
1972   Lab.Leafl.Dir.Fish.Res.G.B.(New Ser.), (27):32 p.

Fowler, H.W., The Crustacea of New Jersey. Ann.Rep.N.J.State Mus., 1911:29-650
1912

Fujino, T. and S. Miyake, Caridean and stenopodidean shrimps from the east China and the Yellow seas
1970   (Crustacea, Decapoda, Natantia). J.Fac.Agric.Kyushu Univ., 16:237-312

George, M.J., On a collection of penaeid prawns from the offshore waters of the south-west coast of
1966   India. Symp.Ser.Mar.Biol.Assoc.India, (2)Pt.1:337-46

_____, Synopsis of biological data on the penaeid prawn *Metapenaeus affinis* (H. Milne Edwards,
1970   1837). FAO Fish.Rep., (57) Vol. 4:1359-75

_____, Synopsis of biological data on the penaeid prawn *Metapenaeus dobsoni* (Miers, 1878).
1970   FAO Fish.Rep., (57) Vol. 4:1335-57

_____, Synopsis of biological data on the penaeid prawn *Metapenaus monoceros* (Fabricius, 1798).
1970   FAO Fish.Rep., (57) Vol. 4:1539-57

_____, Synopsis of biological data on the penaeid prawn *Metapenaeus brevicornis* (H. Milne
1970   Edwards, 1837). FAO Fish.Rep., (57) Vol. 4:1559-73

Giordani Soika, A., I decapodi della Laguna di Venezia. Arch.Oceanogr.Limnol., 5:1-40
1948

Gordon, I., On new or imperfectly known species of Crustacea Macrura. J.Linn.Soc.Lond.(Zool.), 39:
1935   307-51

_____, On the macruran genus *Rhynchocinetes*, with description of a new species. Proc.Zool.Soc.
1936   Lond., 1936:75-88

_____, A thermophilous shrimp from Tunisia. Nature, Lond., 182:1186
1958

Gorgy, S., Les pêcheries et le milieu marin dans le secteur méditerranéen de la République Arabe
1966   Unie. Rev.Trav.Inst.Pêches Marit., Nantes, 30:25,92

_____, Conbribution à l'étude du milieu marin et de la pêche en Mer Rouge (secteur de la
1966a   République Arabe Unie). Rev.Trav.Inst.Pêches Marit., Nantes, 30:93-112

Gould, A.A., Report on the Invertebrata of Massachusetts, comprising the Mollusca, Crustacea,
1841   Annelida and Radiata. Cambridge, Folsom, Wells and Thurston, 373 p.

Grant, E.M., Guide to fishes. Brisbane Government Printer, 280 p.
1965

Gruvel, A., Les pêcheries des côtes du Sénégal et des rivières du sud. Paris, Societé Edit.
1908   Geographique Maritime et Coloniale, 245 p.

_____, Les crustacés comestibles de la côte occidentale d'Afrique. Mission Gruvel sur la
1912   côte occidentale d'Afrique (1909-1910). Ann.Inst.Océanogr.Monaco, 5(1):18 p.

_____, L'industrie des pêches sur la côte occidentale d'Afrique (du Cap Blanc au Cap de Bonne
1913   Espérance). Paris, Larose, 193 p.

_____, L'industrie des pêches au Maroc, son état actuel, son avenir. Mém.Soc.Sci.Nat.Phys.
1923   Maroc, 3(2):1-236

_____, Les pêches maritimes en Algérie. Paris, Société d'Editions Géographiques, Maritimes et
1926   Coloniales, 170 p.

Gruvel, A., L'industrie des pêches sur les côtes tunisiennes. Bull.Stn.Océanogr.Salammbô, 4:1-135
1926a

Guerrero, L.A. and R.D. Guerrero, Culture of freshwater shrimps in fertilized ponds. Paper presented
1976   at the FAO Technical Conference on Aquaculture, Kyoto, Japan, 26 May-2 June, 1976. Rome,
FAO, FIR:AQ/Conf/76/E16:3 p.

Guézé, P., La pêche aux crevettes de profondeur à la Réunion (suite). Trav.Doc.ORSTOM, (47):269-83
1976

Gundlach, J., Crustáceos. Apuntes para la fauna Puerto-Riqueña. 6. An.Soc.Esp.Hist.Nat., 16:115-34
1887

Gurney, R., Appendix I to the report on the Crustacea Decapoda (Natantia and Anomura). Zoological
1927   results of the Cambridge expedition to the Suez Canal, 1924. Trans.Zool.Soc.Lond.,
22:228-9

Hale, H.M., The Crustacea of South Australia. 1. Adelaide, South Australian Museum, 201 p.
1927

Hall, D.N.F., Further taxonomic notes on the Malayan species. The Malayan Penaeidae (Crustacea,
1961   Decapoda). Part 2. Bull.Raffles Mus., (26):76-119

_____, Observations on the taxonomy and biology of some Indo-West Pacific Penaeidae (Crustacea,
1962   Decapoda). Fish.Publ.Colon.Off.Lond., (17):229 p.

Hancock, D.A. and G. Henriquez, Stock assessment in the shrimp (Heterocarpus reedi) fishery of Chile.
1968   FAO Fish.Rep., (57) Vol. 2:443-65

Harada, E., Seasonal changes in distribution and abundance of some decapod crustaceans. Ecology and
1968   biological production of Lake Naka-umi and adjacent regions. Spec.Publ.Seto Mar.Biol.
Lab., (ser.2)2(5):75-103

Harrison, G.G.T., G.L. Kesteven and C.G. Setter, Gulf of Carpentaria prawn survey committee progress
1965   report to 30th June, 1964. Fish.Notes Dep.Harb.Mar.Queensl., 2(1):1-22

Harry, G.Y., The shrimp fishery of Alaska. Proc.Gulf Carib.Fish.Inst., 16:64-71
1964

Hart, C.W., The freshwater shrimps (Atyidae and Palaemonidae) of Jamaica, W.I. with a discussion of
1961   their relation to the ancient geography of the western Caribbean area. Proc.Acad.Nat.Sci.
Philad., 113:61-80

Hartmann, G., Zur Biologie der peruanischen Garneele Cryphiops caementarius (Molina). (Palaemonidae;
1957   Decapoda). Kiel.Meeresforsch., 13:117- 24

Hayashi, K.I. and S. Miyake, Hippolytid fauna of the sea around the Amakusa Marine Biological
1968   Laboratory. Studies on the hippolytid shrimps from Japan. 5. Ohmu, 1:121-63

Hedgpeth, J.W., River shrimps, interesting crustaceans about which little has been written. Prog.
1947   Fish-Cult., 1947:181-4

Heldt, H. and J.H. Heldt, Les crustacés comestibles des mers tunisiennes et leur pêche. Ann.Stn.,
1954   Océanogr.Salammbô, 9:1-16

Heldt, J.H., La reproduction chez les Crustacés Décapodes de la famille des Pénéides. Ann.Inst.
1938   Océanogr.Monaco, 18:31-206

Henderson, J.R. and G. Matthai, On certain species of Palaemon from South India. Rec.Indian Mus.,
1910   5:277-305

Hernández, J.E., Contribución al conocimiento del Camarón de Río Cryphiops caementarius (Molina),
1967   Decapoda Paleomonidae. Symp.Ser.Mar.Biol.Assoc.India, (2)Pt 2:676-84

Hickson, S.J., On a new species of the genus *Atya (A. wyckii)* from Celebes. Ann.Mag.Nat.Hist.,
1888   (ser.6)vol.2:357-62

_____, A naturalist in north Celebes: a narrative of travels in Minahassa, the Sangir and
1889   Talaut Islands, with notices of the fauna, flora and ethnology of the districts visited
        London, John Murray, 392 p.

Hildebrand, H.H., A study of the fauna of the brown shrimp (*Penaeus aztecus* Ives) grounds in the
1954   western Gulf of Mexico. Publ.Inst.Mar.Sci.Texas, 3(2):231-336

Hjort, J. and J.T. Ruud, Deep-sea prawn fisheries and their problems. Hvalråd.Skr., (17):1-144
1938

Holthuis, L.B., The Hippolytidae and Rhynchocinetidae collected by the Siboga and Snellius Expedi-
1947   tions with remarks on other species. The Decapoda of the Siboga Expedition. Part 9.
        Siboga Exped.Mon., 39a(8):1-100

_____, Subfamily Palaemoninae. The Palaemonidae collected by the Siboga and Snellius Expedi-
1950   tions with remarks on other species. 1. The Decapoda of the Siboga Expedition. Part 10.
        Siboga Exped.Mon., 39a(9):1-268

_____, Decapoda (K IX) A. Natantia, Macrura Reptantia, Anomura en Stomatopoda (K X).
1950   Fauna Ned., 15:1-166

_____, The Caridean Crustacea of tropical West Africa. Atlantide Rep., 2:7-187.
1951

_____, The subfamily Palaemoninae. A general revision of the Palaemonidae (Crustacea Decapoda
1952   Natantia) of the Americas. 2. Occas.Pap.Allan Hancock Found., 12:396 p.

_____, On some indo-west pacific Palaemoninae (Crustacea Decapoda Caridea). Zool.Meded.Leiden,
1952a   31:201-11

_____, Crustacés Décapodes Macrures. Résult.Sci.Expéd.Océanogr.Belge Atl.Sud, 3(2):1-88
1952b

_____, The Crustacea Decapoda Macrura of Chile. Reports of the Lund University Chile Expedi-
1952c   tion 1948-49. 5. Acta Univ.Lund.(2), 47(10):1-110

_____, On a collection of Decapod Crustacea from the Republic of El Salvador (Central America).
1954   Zool.Verh., Leiden, 23:43 p.

_____, The Crustacea Decapoda of Suriname (Dutch Guiana). Zool.Verh., Leiden, 44:296 p.
1959

_____, The Atyidae of Madagascar. Mém.Mus.Natl.Hist.Nat.Paris (A Zool.), 33(1):1-48
1965

_____, The freshwater shrimps of the island of Annobon, West Africa. The R/V Pillsbury Deep-
1966   Sea Biological Expedition to the Gulf of Guinea 1964-65. 2. Stud.Trop.Oceanogr., 4(1):
        224-39

Holthuis, L.B. and E. Gottlieb, An annotated list of the Decapod Crustacea of the Meditteranean
1958   coast of Israel, with an appendix listing the Decapoda of the eastern Mediterranean.
        Bull.Res.Counc.Israel, (7B):126 p.

Holthuis, L.B. and H. Rosa, List of species of shrimps and prawns of economic value. FAO Fish.Tech.
1965   Pap., (52):21 p.

Ingle, R.W., A guide to the seashore. London, Paul Hamlyn, 1-159
1969

Irvine, F.R., Crustaceans, Turtles, Cetaceans, etc. In The fishes and fisheries of the Gold Coast,
1947   by F.R. Irvine. London, Crown Agents for Colonies, pp. 283-320

Ivanov, A.V.,   Commercially important aquatic invertebrates, pp. 1-355   (in Russian)
    1955

Ivanov, B.G.,   A world survey of the shrimping trade.   (Sovremennoe sostoyanie mirovogo promylsa
    1967   krevetok.) Jerusalem, Israel Program for Scientific Translations, IPST.Cat.No. 1837:
            106 p. and Springfield, Va., Clearinghouse for Federal Scientific and Technical Transla-
            tion, TT67-51268:106 p. (Transl.from Russian edition, 1964)

Iyigüngor, D.,   La pêche aux crevettes en Turquie. Proc.Tech.Pap.GFCM, 4:63-8
    1957

Jensen, A.S.,   Grønlands Fauna. Et Forsøg paa en Oversigt. Festskrift udgivet af Københavns Universitet;
    1928   Anledning af Hans Majestaet Kongens Fødseldag 26. Sept.1928. Copenhagen, Bianco Luno, 87 p.

Johnson, D.S.,   The Atyidae. Notes on the freshwater Crustacea of Malaya. 1. Bull.Raffles Mus.,
    1961   (26):120-53

_____,   A review of the brackish water prawns of Malaya. Bull.Natl.Mus.Singapore, 33(2):7-11
    1965

_____,   Edible crustaceans. Malay.Nat.J., 19(5):275-82
    1966

_____,   Biology of potentially valuable fresh-water prawns with special reference to the rice-
    1968   land prawn Cryphiops (Macrobrachium) lanchesteri (De Man). FAO Fish.Rep., (57) Vol. 2:
            233-41

Jones, S.,   The crustacean fishery resources of India. Symp.Ser.Mar.Biol.Assoc.India, (2)Pt.4:1328-40
    1967

_____,   The prawn fishery resources of India. FAO Fish.Rep., (57) Vol.3:735-47
    1969

Joyce, E.A.,   The commercial shrimps of the northeast coast of Florida. Prof.Pap.Fla.Board Conserv.,
    1965   (6):1-224

Joyce, E.A. and B. Eldred,   The shrimping industry. Educ.Ser.Fla.Board Conserv., (15):1-47
    1966

Kagwade, P.V.,   Prawn catches by mechanised vessels in the trawling grounds of Bombay and Saurashtra.
    1967   Symp.Ser.Mar.Biol.Assoc.India, (2)Pt.4:1348-81

Kamita, T.,   Freshwater shrimps from Tottori prefecture, Japan. Res.Rep.Tottori Fish.Exp.Stn., (24):
    1954   1-33

_____,   Studies on the fresh-water shrimps, prawns and crawfishes of Japan. Matsue, 186 p.
    1961

_____,   Some shrimps and prawns from New Caledonia. Bull.Osaka Mus.Nat.Hist., (20):1-10
    1967

Kemp, S.,   The Decapoda Natantia of the coasts of Ireland. Sci.Invest.Fish.Branch Irel., 1908(1):
    1910   3-190

_____,   Leander styliferus, Milne-Edwards, and related forms. Notes on Crustacea Decapoda in
    1917   the Indian Museum. 9. Rec.Indian Mus., 13:203-31

_____,   Decapod and stomatopod Crustacea. In Zoological results of a tour in the Far East, by
    1918   N. Annandale. Mem.Asiat.Soc.Bengal, 6:217-97

_____,   On various Caridea. Notes on Crustacea Decapoda in the Indian Museum. 17. Rec.
    1925   Indian Mus., 27:249-343

Kemp, S. and R.B.S. Sewell,   The species obtained by R.I.M.S.S. "Investigator" during the survey
1912   season 1910-11. Notes on Decapoda in the Indian Museum. 3. Rec.Indian Mus., 7:15-32

Kennedy, F.S., et al.,   Studies of the rock shrimp, *Sicyonia brevirostris*, a new fishery resource on
1977   Florida's Atlantic shelf. Fla.Mar.Res.Publ., (27):1-69

Kirkegaard, I. and R.H. Walker,   Synopsis of biological data on the tiger prawn *Penaeus esculentus*
1969   Haswell, 1879. Fish.Synop.CSIRO, (3):8 p.

_____, Synopsis of biological data on the eastern king prawn *Penaeus plebejus* Hess, 1865.
1970   Fish.Synop.CSIRO, (7):8 p.

_____, Synopsis of biological data on the greentail prawn *Metapenaeus bennettae* Racek and Dall,
1970   1965. Fish.Synop.CSIRO, (6):8 p.

_____, Synopsis of biological data on the rainbow prawn *Parapenaeopsis scultptilis* (Heller,
1970   1862). Fish.Synop.CSIRO, (4):8 p.

_____, Synopsis of biological data on the school prawn *Metapenaeus macleayi* (Haswell). Fish.
1970   Synop.CSIRO, (5):8 p.

Kirkegaard, I., D.J. Tuma and R.H. Walker,   Synopsis of biological data on the banana prawn *Penaeus*
1970   *merguiensis* De Man, 1888. Fish.Synop.CSIRO, (8):8 p.

Kishinouye, K.,   Note on Japanese *Penaeus* and its classification. Dobutsugaku Zasshi (Zool.Mag.)
1896   Tokyo, 8:372-74 (in Japanese)

_____, Japanese species of the genus *Penaeus*. J.Fish.Bur.Tokyo, 8:1-29,1-34
1900

_____, Notes on the Sergestidae. Proc.Imp.Acad.Tokyo, 4:125-7
1928

Klima, E.F.,   Length-weight relation and conversion of "whole" and "headless" weights of royal-red
1969   shrimp, *Hymenopenaeus robustus* (Smith). Spec.Sci.Rep.Fish.U.S.Fish Wildl.Serv., (585):
          5 p.

Kobjakova, Z.I.,   Order Decapoda. In Atlas of the invertebrates of the far eastern seas of the USSR,
1966   by E.N. Pavlovskii, pp.200-15. Jerusalem, Israel Program for Scientific Translations,
          IPST. Cat.No.1672. (Translated from the original 1955 Russian edition)

Kouki, M.,   Poissons méditerranéens. Cuisine et valeur nutritionnelle, pp. 1-253.
1963-1972   (Exact year of issue unknown)

Kubo, I.,   On the Japanese atyid shrimps. J.Imp.Fish.Inst.Tokyo, 33:67-100
1938

_____, Leander. Studies on Japanese palaemonoid shrimps. 3. J.Imp.Fish.Inst.Tokyo, 35:17-85
1942

_____, Studies on penaeids of Japanese and its adjacent waters. J.Tokyo Coll.Fish., 36:1-467
1949

_____, On two penaeids, *Metapenaeus affinis* (H. Milne-Edwards) and *M. burkenroadi*, nom.nov.,
1954   erected on the Japanese form known as *M. affinis*. Systematic studies on the Japanese
          macrurous decapod Crustacea. 2. J.Tokyo Univ.Fish., 41(1):89-93

Kunju, M.M.,   Preliminary studies on the biology of the pelaemonid prawn, *Leander styliferus*
1956   Milne-Edwards in West Bengal, India. Proc.IPFC, 6:404-18

_____, Observations on the prawn fishery of Maharashtra coast. Symp.Ser.Mar.Biol.Assoc.India,
1967   (2)Pt.4:1382-97

_____, Synopsis of biological data on the penaeid prawn *Solenocera indica* Nataraj, 1945.
1970   FAO Fish.Rep., (57) Vol. 4:1317-33

Kurian, C.V. and V.O. Sebastian, Prawns and prawn fisheries of India. Delhi, Hindustan Publishing
1976   Corporation, 280 p.

Lai-shing, A., An inventory of demersal fisheries in Hong Kong. Proc.IPFC, 13(3):270-97
1972

Lanchester, W.F., Brachyura, Stomatopoda, and Macrura. On the Crustacea collected during the "Skeat"
1902   expedition to the Malay Peninsula, together with a note òn the genus *Actaeopsis*. Part 1.
Proc.Zool.Soc.Lond., 1901(2):534-74

Leach, W.E., Malacostraca Podophthalmata Britanniae; or descriptions of such British species of the
1815-75 Linnean genus *Cancer* as have their eyes elevated on footstalks. London, J.Sowerby: 124 p.

Lebour, M.V., Notes on the Plymouth Processa (Crustacea). Proc.Zool.Soc.Lond., 1936:609-17
1936

Limbaugh, C., H. Pederson and F.A. Chace, Shrimps that clean fishes. Bull.Mar.Sci.Gulf Caribb.,
1961   11:237-57

Lindner, M.J., Survey of shrimp fisheries of Central and South America. Spec.Sci.Rep.U.S.Fish
1957   Wildl.Serv.(Fish.), (235):166 p.

Lindner, M.J. and H.L. Cook, Synopsis of biological data on the white shrimp *Penaeus setiferus*
1970   (Linnaeus) 1767. FAO Fish.Rep., (57) Vol. 4:1439-69

Ling, S.W., The general biology and development of *Macrobrachium rosenbergii* (De Man). FAO Fish.Rep.,
1969   (57) Vol. 3:589-606

Ling, S.W. and T.J. Costello, Review of culture of freshwater prawns. Paper presented to the FAO
1976   Technical Conference on Aquaculture, Kyoto, Japan, 26 May-2nd June, 1976. Rome, FAO
Doc. No. FIR:AQ/Conf./76

Liu, J.Y., Economic shrimps and prawns of North China, 73 p. (in Chinese)
1955

_____, Notes on two species of *Acetes* of the family Sergestidae (Crustacea, Decapoda) from the
1956   coasts of North China. Acta Zool.Sinica, 8(1):29-40

Loesch, H. and Q. Avila, Claves para identificación de camarones peneidos de interés comercial en
1964   El Ecuador. Identification keys for commercial Ecuadorian penaeid shrimp. Bol.Cient.
Tec.Inst.Nac.Pesca Ecuador, 1(2):1-29

Longhurst, A.R., Crustacean resources. FAO Fish.Tech.Pap., (97):252-305
1970

Louvel, M., L'exploitation des eaux douces de Madagascar (pêche et pisciculture). Tananarive, Gouverne-
1930   ment général de Madagascar et dépendanées, 52 p.

Luther, W. and K. Fiedler, Die Unterwasserfauna der Mittelmeerküsten: ein Taschenbuch für Biologen
1967   und Naturfreunde. Hamburg, Parey, ed.2, 260 p.

McCormick, R.N., *Macrobrachium ohionis*, the large freshwater shrimp. Proc.Indiana Acad.Sci., 43:
1933   213-24

MacGinitie, G.E. and N. MacGinitie, Natural history of marine animals. New York, McGraw-Hill,
1949   473 p.

Man, J.G. De, Decapoden des Indischen Archipels. In Zoologische Ergebnisse einer Reise in Nieder-
1892   ländisch Ost-Indien, von M. Weber, Vol. 2:265-527

_____, Note sur quelques espèces du genre *Alpheus* Fabr., appartenant à la section dont
1899   l'*Alpheus edwardsi* Aud. est le représentant. Mém.Soc.Zool.Fr., 11:309-25

Man, J.G., De, Decapod Crustacea, with an account of a small collection from brackish water near
  1908   Calcutta and in the Dacca District, Eastern Bengal. The fauna of brackish ponds at
          Port Canning, lower Bengal. Part 10. Rec.Indian Mus., 2:211-31

_____, Note sur quelques espèces du genre *Alpheus* Fabr., appartenant au groupe *brevirostris*
  1909   de M. Mém.Soc.Zool.Fr., 22:146-64

_____, Family Penaeidae. The Decapoda of the Siboga Expedition. Part 1. Siboga Exped.Mon.,
  1911   (39a):1-131

_____, Family Alpheidae. The Decapoda of the Siboga Expedition. Part 2. Siboga Exped.Mon.,
  1911   (39a):133-465

_____, Explanation of plates of Penaeidae. The Decapoda of the Siboga Expedition. Supplement
  1913   to Part 1. Family Penaeidae. Siboga Exped.Mon., (39a)(suppl.)

_____, On some European species of the genus *Leander* Desm., also a contribution to the fauna
  1915   of Dutch waters. Tijdschr.Ned.Dierkd.Ver.(2), 14:115-79

_____, Families Pasiphaeidae, Stylodactylidae, Hoplophoridae, Nematocarcinidae, Thalasso-
  1920   caridae, Pandalidae, Psalidopodidae, Gnathophyllidae, Processidae, Glyphocrangonidae and
          Crangonidae. The Decapoda of the Siboga Expedition. Part 4. Siboga Exped.Mon., (39a)
          Pt.3:1-318

_____, On a collection of macrurous Decapod Crustacea of the Siboga Expedition, chiefly
  1922   Penaeidae and Alpheidae. The Decapoda of the Siboga Expedition. Part 5. Siboga Exped.
          Mon., (39a) Pt. 4:1-51

_____, Contribution à l'étude des Décapodes macroures marins et fluviatiles du bassin du Congo
  1925   Belge. Ann.Mus.Congo Belge (Zool.), (3)(3)1(1):1-54

Massuti, M., Las gambas de interés comercial en España. FAO Fish.Rep., (57) Vol.2:303-7
  1968

Menon, M.K., On the paddy field prawn fishery of Travancore-Cochin and an experiment in prawn
  1955   culture. Proc.IPFC, 5:131-5

_____, Identification of marine and inshore prawns of commercial value in India. Proc.IPFC,
  1956   6:345-6

Miller, G.C., Commercial fishery and biology of the fresh-water shrimp, *Macrobrachium*, in the lower
  1971   St. Paul River, Liberia, 1952-53. Spec.Sci.Rep.U.S. Fish Wildl.Serv.(Fish.), (626):1-13

Mistakidis, M.N., Shrimp species and distribution of shrimp grounds in the Caribbean area and
  1972   adjacent regions. FAO Fish.Circ., (144):21 p.

Miya, Y., The Alpheidae (Crustacea, Decapoda) of Japan and its adjacent waters. Part 2. Publ.
  1974   Amakusa Mar.Biol.Lab.Kyushu Univ., 3(2):103-95

Miyake, S. and K.I. Hayashi, Two allied species, *Heptacarpus rectirostris* (Stimpson) and
  1968   *H. futilirostris* (Bate), from Japan. Studies on the hippolytid shrimps from Japan. 4.
          J.Fac.Agric.Kyushu Univ., 14:433-47

Mohamed, K.H., Penaeid prawns in the commercial shrimp fisheries of Bombay with notes on species and
  1967   size fluctuations. Symp.Ser.Mar.Biol.Assoc.India, (2)Pt.4:1408-18

_____, Synopsis of biological data on the jumbo tiger prawn *Penaeus monodon* Fabricius, 1798.
  1970   FAO Fish.Rep., (57) Vol. 4:1251-66

_____, Synopsis of biological data on the Indian prawn *Penaeus indicus* H. Milne Edwards, 1837.
  1970   FAO Fish.Rep., (57) Vol. 4:1267-88

Monod, T.,   Crustacea. 4. Decapoda (excl. Palaemonidae, Atyidae et Potamonidae). In Contribution
1927   à l'étude de la faune du Cameroun, Faune Colon.Fr., 1:593-624

_____, L'industrie des pêches au Cameroun. Mission Monod (1925-1926) Cameroun. 1. Paris, Société
1928   d'editions geographiques, maritimes et colonaise. 509 p.

_____, Crevettes et crabes de la côtes occidentale l'Afrique. Mém.Inst.Fondam.Afr.Noire,
1967   77:103-234

Motoh, H.,   An annotated list of scientific and English common names of commercially important penaeid
1977   prawns and shrimps. Tech.Rep.Aquacult.Dep.South East Asian Dev.Cent.Manila, (2):14 p.

Moulherat, J.L. and M. Vincke, Etude en vue du développement de la pêche au Pangalanes-Est (zone
1968   Tamatave-Andevoranto). Madagascar, Centre Technique Forestier Tropical, 195 p.

Munro, S.R., Prawns of tropical Australia. Austr.Fish.Newsl., 27(1):12-4
1968

Muthu, M.S., On some new records of penaeid prawns from the east coast of India. Indian.J.Fish.,
1971   15:145-54

Nataraj, S., On some species of Acetes (Crustacea, Sergestidae) from Travancore. Rec.Indian Mus.,
1949   45:139-47

Neiva, G. De S. and M.N. Mistakidis, Identificación de algunos camarones marinos del litoral centro-
1966   sur del Brasil. Doc.Tec.CARPAS, 4:1-6

Newman, W.A., On the introduction of an edible oriental shrimp (Caridea, Palaemonidae) to
1963   San Francisco Bay. Crustaceana, 5:119- 32

Nobre, A., Crustáceos Decápodes e Stomatópodes marinhos de Portugal. Fauna marinha de Portugal, ed.2.
1936   Vol. 4. Barcelos, Companhia Editora do Minho

Nouvel, H. and L.B. Holthuis, Les Processidae (Crustacea Decapoda Natantia) des eaux européennes.
1957   Zool.Verh.Leiden, 32:1-53

Obarrio, J.L., Investigación del camarón en Panamá. In Trabajos presentados al final del curso por
1954   los señores becados. Segundo Centro Latinoamericano de Capacitación Pesquera. Mexico,
Octubre-Diciembre de 1954. Rome, FAO, II CLACP/Tr.-41

Oliveira, L.P.H., de, Verificação da existência de Atya scabra Leach, camarão d'agua doce da familia
1945   Atyidae, Crustacea, no nordeste do Brasil. Mem.Inst.Oswaldo Cruz, 43:177-90

Omori, M.,   The biology of a sergestid shrimp Sergestes lucens Hansen. Bull.Ocean Res.Inst.Univ.Tokyo,
1969   (4):1-83

_____, The systematics, biogeography, and fishery of epipelagic shrimps of the genus Acetes
1975   (Crustacea, Decapoda, Sergestidae). Bull.Ocean Res.Inst.Univ.Tokyo, (7):91 p.

_____, The glass shrimp, Pasiphaea japonica sp.nov. (Caridea, Pasiphaeidae), a sibling species
1976   Pasiphaea sivado, with notes on its biology and fishery in Toyama Bay, Japan. Bull.Nat.
Sci.Mus.Tokyo, (A, Zool.), 2(4):249-66

Osbeck, P.,   Reise nach Ostindien und China. Rostock, Deutsche Übersetzung von J.G. Georgius, 552 p.
1765

Palombi, A. and M. Santarelli, Gli animali commestibili dei mari d'Italia; descrizione, biologia,
1961   pesca, valore economico e nomi italiani dialettali e stranieri dei pesci - tunicati-
echinodermi - molluschi - crostacei ad uso dei pescatori di professione, dilettanti e
subacquei. Milano, Heopli, 437 p. (2nd ed.)

Panikkar, N.K., The prawn industry of the Malabar coast. J.Bombay Nat.Hist.Soc., 39:343-53
1937

Panikkar, N.K. and M.K. Menon, Prawn fisheries of India. Proc.IPFC, 6:328-44
1956

Paolucci, C., I podoftalmi Decapodi del medio Adriatico Italiano. Riv.Mens.Pesca Idrobiol.,
1909   11:148-59, 219-56

Parisi, B., Natantia. I decapodi giapponesi del Museo di Milano. 7. Atti Soc.Ital.Sci.Nat.,
1919   58:59-99

Patwardhan, S.S., *Palaemon* (the Indian river-prawn). Indian Zool.Mem., (6):102 p.
1956

Pennak, R.W., Fresh-water invertebrates of the United States. New York, Ronald Press, 769 p.
1953

Pennant, T., Crustacea. Mollusca. Testacea. In British zoology, by T. Pennant, Warrington, printed
1777   printed by W. Eyres for B. White London, 4 Vols (4th ed.)

_____, Crustacea. Mollusca. Testacea. In British zoology, by T. Pennant, London, printed for
1812   Wilkie and Robinson, 4 Vols. (new ed.)

Pérez-Farfante, I., A new species and two new subspecies of shrimp of the genus *Penaeus* from the
1967   western Atlantic. Proc.Biol.Soc.Wash., 80:83-100

_____, Western Atlantic shrimps of the genus *Penaeus*. Fish.Bull.U.S.Fish.Wildl.Serv.,
1969   67(3):461-591

_____, Sinopsis de datos biológicos sobre el camarón blanco *Penaeus schmitti* Burkenroad, 1936.
1970   FAO Fish.Rep., (57) Vol. 4:1417-38

_____, A key to the American Pacific shrimps of the genus *Trachypenaeus* (Decapoda, Penaeidae),
1971   with the description of a new species. Fish.Bull.NOAA/NMFS, 69:635-46

_____, A redescription of *Penaeus (Melicertus) canaliculatus* (Olivier, 1811), a wide-ranging
1976   Indo-West Pacific shrimp (Crustacea, Decapoda, Penaeidae). Zool.Meded.Leiden, 50:23-37

_____, American solenocerid shrimps of the genera *Hymenopenaeus*, *Haliporoides*, *Pleoticus*,
1977   *Hadropenaeus* new genus, and *Mesopenaeus* new genus. Fish.Bull.NOAA/NMFS, 75:261-346

Pérez-Farfante, I. and H.R. Bullis, Western Atlantic shrimps of the genus *Solenocera* with description
1973   of a new species (Crustacea:Decapoda:Penaeidae). Smithsonian Contrib.Zool., (153):1-33

Pericchi Lopez, J.J., La industria del camarón en Venezuela. Explotación y procesamiento del camarón.
1965   Caracas, Corporación Venezolano de Fomento, 69 p.

Pesta, O., Die Decapodenfauna der Adria. Versuch einer Monographie. Leipzig und Wien, Franz Deuticke,
1918   500 p.

Ping, C., Preliminary notes on the fauna of Nanking. Contrib.Biol.Lab.Sci.Soc.China, (Zool.), (7):
1931   173-201

Purwito, Exploratory shrimp trawling with the R.I. "Jalanidhi". Proc.IPFC, 13(3):649-652
1972

Qureshi, M.R., Shrimp fisheries of Pakistan. Proc.IPFC, 6:359-362
1956

Qureshi, S. and T.A. Hashmi, Shrimp fisheries of West Pakistan. Abstr.Pap.Symp.Crust.Ernakulam: 73
1965

Racek, A.A., Littoral Penaeinae from New South Wales and adjacent Queensland waters. Austr.J.
1955   Mar.Freshwat.Res., 6(2):209-41

_____, Penaeid prawn fisheries of Australia with special reference to New South Wales.
1957   Res.Bull.State Fish.N.S.W., (3):1-19

Racek, A.A., Prawn investigations in eastern Australia. Res.Bull.State Fish.N.S.W., (6):1-57
1959

_____, Indo-West Pacific penaeid prawns of commercial importance. In Coastal aquaculture in
1973   the Indo-Pacific region, edited by T.V.R. Pillay. Papers presented at the Indo-Pacific
        Fisheries Council Symposium on Coastal Aquaculture, Bangkok, Thailand, 18-21 November 1970.
        West Byfleet, Fishing News (Books) Ltd. for FAO and IPFC, pp.152-72

Racek, A.A. and W. Dall, Littoral Penaeinae (Crustacea Decapoda) from northern Australia, New Guinea,
1965   and adjacent waters. Verh.K.Akad.Wet.(B Natuurk.), 56(3):1-119

Radhakrishnan, N., On the prawn resources of Karwar region. Symp.Ser.Mar.Biol.Assoc.India, (2)Pt.4:
1967   1421-3

Rai, H.S., The shell-fisheries of the Bombay Presidency. Part 2. J.Bombay Nat.Hist.Soc., 36:884-97
1933

Rajyalakshmi, T. and M. Ranadhir, The commercial prawn *Macrobrachium malcolmsonii* (H. Milne Edwards)
1969   of the River Godavary, a discussion on the trend and characteristics of the population
        during 1963-1966. FAO Fish.Rep., (57) Vol. 3:903-21

Ramamurthy, S., Studies on the prawn fishery of Kutch. Symp.Ser.Mar.Biol.Assoc.India, (2)Pt.4:
1967   1424-36

Raman, K., Observations on the fishery and biology of the giant freshwater prawn *Macrobrachium*
1967   *rosenbergii* De Man. Symp.Ser.Mar.Biol.Assoc.India, (2)Pt.2:649-69

Rao, P.V., Synopsis of biological data on the penaeid prawn *Parapenaeopsis stylifera* (H. Milne
1970   Edwards, 1837). FAO Fish.Rep., (57) Vol. 4:1575-1605

Rapson, A.M. and C.R. McIntosh, Prawn surveys in Papua and New Guinea. Fish.Bull.Dep.Agric.Stock
1971   Fish.Papua New Guinea, (3):126 p.

Rasalan, S.B., M.N. Delmendo and T.G. Reyes, Some observations on the biology of the freshwater
1969   prawn *Macrobrachium lanceifrons* (Dana), with notes on the fishery. FAO Fish.Rep.,
        (57) Vol. 3:923-33

Rathbun, M.J., The Brachyura and Macrura of Porto Rico. Bull.U.S.Fish Comm., 20(2):1-127
1901

_____, Decapod crustaceans of the northwest coast of North America. In Harriman Alaska
1904   Expedition, Vol. 10:1-190

_____, The Brachyura and Macrura of the Hawaiian Islands. Bull.U.S.Fish Comm., 23 (3):
1906   827-930

Rathbun, R., Crustaceans, worms, radiates, and sponges. Natural history of useful aquatic animals.
1884   Part 5. In The fisheries and fishery industries of the United States, by G.B. Goode.
        Washington, Vol. 1:759-850

Reeve, M.R., The suitability of the English prawn *Palaemon serratus* (Pennant) for cultivation - a
1969   preliminary assessment. FAO Fish.Rep., (57) Vol. 3:1067-73

Richardson, L.R. and J.C. Yaldwyn, A guide to the natant Decapod Crustacea (shrimps and prawns) of
1958   New Zealand. Tuatara, 7:17-41

Ricketts, E.F. and J. Calvin, Between Pacific tides. Rev. by J.W. Hedgpeth. Stanford, Calif.,
1968   Stanford University Press, 614 p.

Rioja, E., Contribución al estudio de los caracteres sexuales secundarios de dos especies de los
1942   generos *Trachypeneus* y *Xiphopeneus* de las costas mexicanas del Pacifico. Estudios carci-
        nologicos. 12. An.Inst.Biol.Mex., 13:675-84

Risso, A., Histoire naturelle des Crustacés des environs de Nice. Paris, Librairie Grecque-Latine-
    1816   Allemande, 175 p.

Rondelet, G., Libri de piscibus marinis, in quibus verae piscium effigies expressae sunt. Quae in
    1554   tota piscium historia contineantur, indicat elenchus pagina nona et decima. Lugduni
           (Lyons), 583 p.

Rosa, H., Note on FAO scientific meeting on the biology and culture of shrimps and prawns with a
    1964   preliminary list of their species of economic value and information on their distribution.
           FAO Fish.Circ., (14):26 p.

Roth-Woltereck, E., Untersuchungen an Atyiden (Decapoda) von Belgisch Kongo, mit besonderer
    1942   Berücksichtigung der Rassen- und Artbildungsfrage. Rev.Zool.Bot.Afr., 36:229-312

Roux, J., Crustacés décapodes d'eau douce de la Nouvelle-Calédonie. Nova Caledonia, 4(2):181-240
    1926

Sars, G.O., Account of the postembryonal development of Pandalus borealis Krøyer, with remarks on the
    1900   development of other Pandalis, and description of the adult Pandalus borealis. Rep.Norw.
           Fish.Mar.Invest., 1(3):1-45

Scheer, D., Biology and fishery of the Baltic shrimp (Leander adspersus var. fabricii) on the coast
    1967   of the German Democratic Republic. Symp.Ser.Mar.Biol.Assoc.India, (2)Pt.2:670-5

Schenkel, E., Beitrag zur Kenntnis der Dekapodenfauna von Celebes. Verh.Naturfosch.Ges.Basel.,
    1902   13:485-585

Schmitt, W.L., The marine decapod Crustacea of California with special reference to the decapod
    1921   Crustacea collected by the United States Bureau of Fisheries steamer "Albatross" in
           connection with the biological survey of San Francisco Bay during the years 1912-1913.
           Univ.Calif.Publ.Zool., (23):1-359

_____, Report on the Crustacea Macrura (families Peneidae, Campylonotidae and Pandalidae)
    1926   obtained by the F.I.S. "Endeavour" in Australian seas, with notes on the species of
           Penaeus described by Haswell and contained, in part, in the collections of the Macleay
           Museum, at the University of Sydney. Zool.Biol.Result.Fish.Exped.Endeavour, 5(6):311-81

_____, The macruran, anomuran, and stomatopod crustaceans collected by the American Museum
    1926   Congo Expedition, 1909-15, with field notes by Herbert Lang and James P. Chapin.
           Bull.Am.Mus.Nat.Hist., (53):1-67

Shen, C.J., On three new species of Caridina (Crustacea Macrura) from South-West China. Contrib.
    1948   Inst.Zool.Natl.Acad.Peiping, (4):119-26

Shigueno, K., Shrimp culture in Japan. Tokyo, AITP (Assoc.Int.Tech.Promotion), 153 p.
    1975

Simpson, A.C., B.R. Howell and P.J. Warren, Synopsis of biological data on the shrimp Pandalus
    1970   montagui Leach, 1814. FAO Fish.Rep., (57) Vol. 4:1225-49

Sivertsen, E. and L.B. Holthuis, Crustacea Decapoda (the Penaeidea and Stenopodidea excepted).
    1956   Rep.Sci.Result.Michael Sars N.Atl.Deep-Sea Exped., 5(12):1-54

Slack-Smith, R.J., The prawn fishery of Shark Bay, Western Australia. FAO Fish.Rep., (57) Vol. 3:
    1969   717-34

Smith, S.I., The Crustacea of the fresh waters of the United States. Rep.U.S.Fish Comm., 2:637-65
    1874

Sollaud, E., Sur deux nouveaux Palémonides, à développement condensé, vivant dans les eaux douces
    1914   du Tonkin: Leander mani n.sp. et Coutierella tonkinensis n.g. n.sp. Bull.Soc.Zool.Fr.,
           (39):314-24

_____, Sur un Palaemonetes éndemique, P. zariquieyi, n.sp., localisé dans la plaine littorale
    1938   du Golfe de Valence. Trav.Stn.Zool.Wimereux, 13:635-45

Sowerby, A., de C., A naturalist's note-book in China,
1925

Stalio, L., Catalogo metodico e descrittivo dei Crostacei dell'Adriatico. Atti Inst.Veneto Sci.
1877   Lett.Arti, 5(3):355-85, 499-539, 629-72, 773-807, 977-1008, 1111-27, 1344-420

Starobogatov, Y.I., Peneidy (sem.Peneidae - Crustacea Decapoda) Tonkinskogo Zaliva. Penaeidae
1972   (Crustacea Decapoda) of Tonking Gulf. Explor.Fauna Seas, 10(18):359-415 (in Russian)

Stebbing, T.R.R., South African Crustacea. Part 8 of S.A. Crustacea, for the Marine Investigations
1915   in South Africa. Ann.S.Afr.Mus., 15:57-104

Stephensen, K., Skjoldkrebs. Storkrebs. 1. Danmarks Fauna Handb., 9:1-193
1910

_____, Crustacea Decapoda. Zool.Iceland, 3(25):1-31
1939

Sund, O., The glass shrimps (Pasiphaea) in northern waters. Bergens Mus.Aarb., 1912(6):1-17
1913

_____, Skårungen. En bok for kystungdommen om sjø og sjødyr, fartøy og ferdsel. Oslo,
1942   Fabritius & Sønners Forlag, 249 p.

Suseelan, C., Observations on the deep-sea prawn fishery off the south-west coast of India with
1976   special reference to pandalids. J.Mar.Biol.Assoc.India, 16:491-511

Suseelan, C. and K.H. Mohamed, On the occurrence of Plesionika ensis (A. Milne Edwards) (Pandalidae,
1969   Crustacea) in the Arabian Sea with notes on its biology and fishery potentialities.
        J.Mar.Biol.Assoc.India, 10:88-94

Suvatti, C., Fauna of Thailand. Bangkok, Department of Fisheries, 1100 p.
1950

Tang, Y.A., The use of saponin to control predaceous fishes in shrimp ponds. Prog.Fish-Cult.,
1961   23:43-95

Tanikawa, E., Marine products in Japan: size, technology and research. Tokyo, Koseisha-Koseikaku,
1971   507 p.

Thallwitz, Decapoden-Studien, insbesondere basirt auf A.B. Meyer's Sammlungen im Ostindischen
1891   Archipel, nebst einer Aufzählung der Decapoden und Stomatopoden des Dresdener Museums.
        Abh.Ber.K.Zool.Anthropol.-Ethnogr.Mus.Dresden, 1890-1891 (3):1-55

Tham Ah Kow, Unit stocks of shrimps and prawns in the IPFC region and unit fisheries exploiting them.
1968   FAO Fish.Rep., (57) Vol. 2:205-17

Thomas, D., Prawn fishing in Nigerian waters. In, Proceedings of the Symposium on the oceanography
1969   and fisheries resources of the tropical Atlantic, organized by Unesco, FAO and OAU.
        Abidjan, Ivory Coast, 20-28 Oct. 1966. Review papers and contributions. Paris, Unesco,
        pp. 415-7

Thomas, M.M., Notes on some interesting penaeid prawns (Crustacea, Decapoda) from the southeast
1971   coast of India. Journ.Mar.Biol.Assoc.India, 11:191-7, fig.1

Tiews, K., Synopsis of biological data on the Common Shrimp Crangon crangon (Linnaeus, 1758).
1970   FAO Fisher.Rep., 57(4):1167-1224, figs.1-20

Tirmizi, N.M. and Q. Bashir, Shore and offshore penaeid prawns of northern Arabian Sea: i-vii,
1973   figs.1-46

Tiwari, K.K., On a new species of Palaemon from Banaras, with a note on Palaemon lanchesteri de Man.
1949   Rec.Indian Mus., 45:333-45, figs.1,2

_____, Distribution of the Indo-Burmese freshwater prawns of the genus Palaemon Fabr., and its
1955   bearing on the Satpura hypothesis. Bull.Nat.Inst.Sci.India, 7:230-9, figs.1-3

_____, Occurrence of the freshwater prawn Macrobrachium latimanus (Von Martens) in India and
1961   Ceylon. Crustaceana, 3:98-104, figs.1-3

_____, Alpheid shrimps (Crustacea: Decapoda: Alpheidae) of Vietnam. Ann.Fac.Sci.Saigon,
1963   1963:269-362

Turner, C.H. and J.C. Sexsmith, Marine baits of California. Sacramento, Department of Fish and Games,
1964   71 p.

Urita, T., Decapod Crustaceans from Saghalien, Japan. Bull.Biogeogr.Soc.Japan, (12):1-78
1942

Urita, T. and E. Nomura, Some observations on Pandalus kessleri Czerniavski. Sci.Rep.Tôhoku Imp.Univ.,
1938   4(13):235-52

U.S. Bureau Commercial Fisheries, Survey of the United States shrimp industry. Volume 1. Spec.Sci.
1958   Rep.U.S.Fish Wildl.Serv.(Fish.), (277):311 p.

Vidal J., J. and B. Rosetti B., Cruceros exploratorios para camarones y langostino de profundidad en
1971   la costa Pacifico de Panamá. R/V Orion, Diciembre 1970-Marzo 1971. Circ.Proy.Reg.Desarr.
        Pesq.Centro-Am.San Salvador, (71/4):43 p.

_____, Cruceros exploratorios para camarones y langostino de profundidad en el Pacifico de
1971a   Costa Rica. R/V Orion, R/V Tauro, Marzo-Agosto 1971. Circ.Proy.Reg.Desarr.Pesq.Centro-Am.
        San Salvador, (71/5):31 p.

Villalobos, A., Estudio morfologico de la Atya scabra (Crust.Decap.). Mexico, Universidad Nacional
1943   Autonoma de Mexico, 70 p.

Villegas, F., Informe preliminar sobre las posibilidades de cultivo de langostino Penaeus paulensis
1974   Pérez-Farfante en lagunas salobres del Uruguay. Paper presented to the FAO/CARPAS
        Symposium on aquaculture in Latin America. Montevideo, 26 Nov.-2 Dec. 1974. Rome, FAO,
        Doc.No. (6/74/SE 17):4 p.

Voss, G.L., A key to the commercial and potentially commercial shrimp of the family Penaeidae of the
1955   western North Atlantic and the Gulf of Mexico. Tech.Ser.Fla.Board Conserv., (14):23 p.

White, A., A popular history of British Crustacea; comprising a familiar account of their classifi-
1857   cation and habits. London, Lovell Reeve, 358 p.

Williams, A.B., Marine Decapod Crustaceans of the Carolinas. Fish.Bull.U.S.Fish Wildl.Serv., 65(1):
1965   298 p.

Wollebaek, A., Decapoda collected during fishing investigations directed by Dr. Hjort in 1897 and
1900   1898. Rep.Norw.Fish.Mar.Invest., 1(4):1-29

Worth, S.G., Fresh-water shrimps, a natural fish food. Bull.U.S.Bur.Fish., 28:853-8
1908

Yaldwyn, J.C., Crustacea Decapoda Natantia from the Chatham Rise: a deep water bottom fauna from
1960   New Zealand. Bull.N.Z.Dep.Sci.Ind.Res., 139(1):13-53

Yasuda, J., An biological note on the shrimp, Trachypenaeus curvirostris (Stimpson). Bull.Japan.Soc.
1949   Sci.Fish., 15:180-9

_____, Shrimps of the Seto Inland Sea of Japan. Proc.IPFC, 6:378-86
1956

_____, Species, distribution, movement and composition of shrimps. Study of rationalization
1957   of the shrimp fishery in Seto-Inland Sea. 2. Bull.Naikai Reg.Fish.Res.Lab., (10):28-36

Yokoya, Y.,   On the distribution of decapod crustaceans inhabiting the continental shelf around Japan,
   1933   chiefly based upon the materials collected by S.S. Sôyô-Maru, during the year 1923-1930.
           J.Coll.Agric.Tokyo, 12:1-226

Yonge, C.M.,   The sea shore.   The new naturalist; a survey of British natural history. London,
   1949   Collins, 311 p.

Yoshida, H.,   Important marine shrimps and lobsters of Tyôsen (Korea).   Bull.Fish.Exp.Stn.Tyôsen,
   1941   (7):1-36

Yoshida, H.O.,   Exploratory bottom trawling in Hawaiian waters.   Proc.IPFC, 13(3):255-61
   1972

Zariquiey Alvarez, R.,   Crustáceos Decápodos mediterráneos.   Manuel para la clasificación de las
   1946   especies que pueden capturarse en las costas mediterráneas españolas.   Publ.Biol.Mediterr.
           Inst.Esp.Estud.Mediterr., Barc., (2):181 p.

_____,   Una nueva especie del género *Plesionika* Bate.   Decápodos españoles. 8.   Publ.Inst.
   1955   Biol.Apl.Barc., 19:105-13

_____,   Crustáceos Decápodos ibéricos.   Invest.Pesq., Barc., 32:510 p.
   1968

INDEX

5. ALPHABETICAL INDEX OF FAMILY AND SPECIES NAMES

5.1 Scientific Names

INDEX

INDEX

INDEX

INDEX

INDEX

INDEX

INDEX

INDEX

INDEX

INDEX

INDEX

INDEX

INDEX

INDEX

INDEX

INDEX

INDEX

INDEX

INDEX

INDEX

INDEX

5.2 Vernacular Names (international and local)

INDEX

INDEX

INDEX

INDEX

INDEX

INDEX

INDEX

INDEX

INDEX

INDEX

INDEX

INDEX

INDEX

INDEX

INDEX

INDEX

Russian Names